CLINICAL MICROBIOLOGY REVIEW

Third Edition
Peter Q. Warinner, MD

WYSTERIA
Long Island, New York
www.wysteria.com

Library of Congress Cataloging-in-Publication Data

Warinner, Peter Q.
    Clinical microbiology review / Peter Q. Warinner.-- 3rd ed.
       p.;cm.
    Includes index
    ISBN 0-9677839-3-3
    1. Medical microbiology--Outlines, syllabi, etc. I. Title.
    [DNLM: 1. Microbiology--Handbooks. 2. Microbiology--Outlines. 3. Communicable Diseases--Handbooks. 4. Communicable Diseases--Outlines. QW 39 W277c2001]
QR46 .W28 2001
616'.01--dc21

                          2001026937

Printed in the U.S.A.
ISBN 0-9677839-3-3

TABLE OF CONTENTS:

COVER ART **by Joseph Lewy**

ACKNOWLEDGMENTS

For their inspiration, advice and support:

Doris J. Bucher, Ph.D.
Associate Professor of Microbiology & Immunology
New York Medical College, Valhalla, NY

Gary P. Wormser, M.D.
Professor of Medicine and Pharmacology
Chief, Division of Infectious Disease
New York Medical College
Westchester County Medical Center, Valhalla, NY

For use of their microorganism specimen collections:

Maria E. Aguero-Rosenfeld, M.D.
Associate Professor of Pathology
New York Medical College
Associate Director of Clinical Pathology
Westchester County Medical Center, Valhall, NY

Dr. Joseph S. Tatz
Assistant Clinical Professor
Department of Pathology
Westchester County Medical Center, Valhalla, NY

Chapter 1   BASIC TERMINOLOGY REVIEW

CELL WALL: contains peptidoglycan:

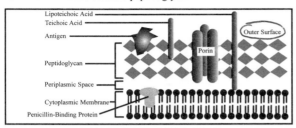 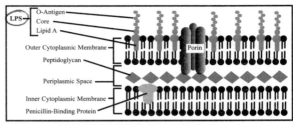

GRAM POSITIVE CELL WALL   GRAM NEGATIVE CELL WALL

OXYGEN REQUIREMENTS for the pathogen:

Obligate Aerobic:	Requires presence of oxygen.
Aerobic (facultative):	Prefers the presence of oxygen, but tolerates absence.
Microaerophilic:	Grows only in less than atmospheric level of oxygen.
Anaerobic (facultative):	Prefers absence of oxygen, but tolerates presence.
Obligate Anaerobic:	Requires absence of oxygen.

GROWTH ENVIRONMENT for the pathogen within the host:

Extracellular:	Prefer to exist outside of host cells, may adhere to, or move between, host cells.
Intracellular:	Prefer to exist inside of host cells, but can survive outside.
Obligate Intracellular:	Requires intracellular environment for survival, cannot survive outside.

Invasive: Indicates the ability of a pathogen to penetrate membranes and tissues of a host's body. For example, a non-invasive pathogen will remain in the intestinal lumen, but an invasive pathogen will penetrate the intestinal epithelium.
  Note: Invasive pathogens may be extracellular (moving between host cells) or intracellular (moving through host cells).

FEATURES of the pathogen:
  Microscopic characteristics:
    Morphology: coccus (spheres), coccobacillus, bacillus (rods), spirochete, "club," "boxcar," etc.
    Grouping: pairs, chains, clusters, filamentous, "coffee bean pairs," "Chinese-character clumps," etc.
  Culture characteristics:
    Media: blood agar, chocolate agar, special additives, etc.
    Conditions: aerobic, anaerobic.
    Cell culture (tissue culture): necessary for obligate intracellular pathogens.
    Colony characteristics: color, speed of growth, size, shape, "swarming," etc.

MOTILITY
  1. Non-motile
  2. Flagellated Motility:

        Monotrichous   Amphitrichous   Lophotrichous   Peritrichous

  3. Other Motility: tumble, corkscrew, darting, twitching, rotating, etc.

CAPSULES: Extra coat that tightly surrounds bacteria to enhance survival (promotes adhesion, resists antibiotics, resists phagocytosis).
    Composition varies: polysaccharide, polypeptide, lipid, protein, etc.
GLYCOCALYX: Also known as "slime layer" or exopolysaccharide: material that loosely coats bacteria to enhance survival.
    It helps promote adhesion, resist antibiotics, resist phagocytosis.
SPORES: Special dormancy state that enhances long-term survival in extremely harsh conditions. Special conditions are later required for germination back to normal metabolic state.

TOXINS (see treatment section below for explanation of toxoid and antitoxin):
    Exotoxin: A toxic substance produced and released by the pathogen into the surrounding environment.
        e.g. Enterotoxin: a type of exotoxin that has its effect on the GI tract.
        e.g. Neurotoxin: a type of exotoxin that has its effect on the nervous system.
    Food Poisoning in most cases, is caused by an exotoxin that is "pre-formed" by the pathogen in the food before the host eats the food.
        It is the toxin, not the pathogen, that causes the illness.
    Endotoxin: A species-specific lipopolysaccharide (LPS) molecule that is built into the outer membrane of all gram negative bacteria.
        Endotoxin is released upon disruption of membrane. Each LPS is made up of a polysaccharide "O" unit for antigenic variation, and a phospholipid "Lipid A" unit for toxicity.

BACTERIAL GENETICS

Plasmid: Circular, self-replicating, extra-chromosomal bacterial DNA which carries genes for the following: antibiotic resistance (R-plasmid); for conjugation (F-plasmid); for toxins, and other non-life-essential products.

Conjugation: "Males" possess "F-factor" on plasmid; male gives copy of plasmid to "female" via male sex pilus. "Female" gains possession of plasmid genetic material including the "F-factor;" thereby becomes "male."

High-Frequency Recombination (Hfr) conjugation: The "F-factor" is coded on the male chromosome, not on a plasmid. During conjugation, female gains possession of some male chromosomal genetic material along with F-factor.

Bacteriophage ("phage"): A virus that infects bacteria.

Lytic Transduction: Phage-infected bacteria ruptures; the phage picks up some bacterial DNA; the phage infects another bacteria and inserts the new DNA.

Lysogenic Transduction: Phage-infected bacteria gets pieces of its DNA excised; those pieces get incorporated into the phage as the phage reassembles and exits (without lysis of host bacteria); the same phage then infects a new bacteria and inserts DNA from the first bacteria.

SOURCE AND DEFINITION OF INFECTION

Pathogen: A disease-causing organism.

Host: A person who temporarily harbors organisms.

Reservoir: The place where a pathogen lives naturally: the soil, an animal's blood stream, a human colon, etc.

Colony: This occurs when organisms temporarily survive in a place outside their normal habitat, but cause no disease. Colonization may occur on inanimate objects (fomites), or within a human host.

Commensal organism: ("Normal Flora"): This is an organism that lives harmlessly at a specific site within a human host. Note: commensal organisms may become pathogens when they move to a different location within the host.

Carrier: A person who unnaturally harbors a pathogen, for a long period of time, but exhibits no symptoms of the disease. The carrier may be capable of transmitting the pathogen (and the disease) to another person.

Infection: The condition whereby colonization within a human host progresses to cause disease.

Transmissible: The ability of an infection to spread from one person to another.

Contagious: The concept that a disease can be transmissible.

Communicable: The concept that a disease can be transmissible.

ROUTES OF TRANSMISSION

Iatrogenic: Infection caused by health-care professional as result of some treatment or procedure, either directly or indirectly.

Nosocomial: Acquired within the hospital environment.

Community acquired: Acquired outside the hospital environment.

Horizontal: Transmission of infection from person to person:
May be through: Direct Contact; Respiratory droplets; Fecal-Oral route; Sexually Transmitted Disease (STD); etc.

Vertical: The infected mother transmits infection to her unborn/newborn child.
1. In-utero:
    Across placenta;
    Ascending to uterus from vagina.
2. At birth:
    Passage through vagina.
3. After birth:
    Breast-feeding.

Vector-borne: This is when an infection is introduced into the host by some insect which carries the pathogen. The insect is the vector, it bites the reservoir first then bites the host second. The reservoir for vector-borne pathogens is usually some animal. The human is the host.

Zoonotic: Zoonotic pathogens have animals as their reservoirs, infection is spread to human hosts by several methods:
    By direct contact with the animals.
    By animal bites or scratches.
    By drinking water that was exposed to animal urine or feces.
    By ingestion of food products made from the animals.
    Note: In some zoonotic infection cases, once a human is infected, some horizontal or vertical transmission may occur subsequently.

Exogenous: Infection comes from source outside the host's body.

Endogenous: Infection comes from a source within the host's own body, and spreads to another part of the body through various ways:
    Direct Extension: The infection spreads to adjacent tissues.
    Hematological spread: The infection spreads to other parts of the body via the blood stream.
    Lymphangytic spread: The infection spreads to other parts of the body via the lymphatic system
    Ascending: (e.g. Via urethra to Kidney, etc.) The infection rises through the body.
    Aspiration: The infection spreads into the respiratory tract from gastric regurgitation or orally from lack of cough response.
    Auto-inoculation: The infection gets transferred from one place on the host's body to another place on the host's body due to several possible methods: carried on hands after touching the infected site; via fecal-urinary route due to poor hygiene; etc.

TYPES OF INFECTION

Incubation period of infection: The time period between initial contact with the pathogen and the onset of symptoms.

Local infection: Infection confined to a specific site or organ.

Systemic infection: Infection spreading throughout the body via bloodstream or lymphatics.

Disseminated infection: Same as systemic.

Acute infection: Severe symptoms manifest over a short period of time (days - weeks).

Subacute infection: Mild symptoms manifest over a period of weeks - months.

Chronic infection: Symptoms manifest over a long period of time (month - years).

Persistent infection: An active infection which continues in spite of typically effective treatment.

Recrudescent: Symptoms relent for a brief period (days, weeks) then return. The infection is continuous.

Relapse: Symptoms relent for a long period (weeks, months) then return. The infection is continuous even though it appeared to go away.

Latency: This is when the infecting pathogen goes into a period of dormancy within the host, symptoms may subside for very long periods (months, years, decades). The infection is continuous. This is the period before reactivation.

Reactivation: The infecting pathogen remains dormant somewhere within the host for a long period of time (months, years, decades) then becomes active again to cause symptoms.

Reinfection: A new infection that occurs, after a previous infection with the same pathogen had fully resolved.

Or: A new infection of an organ after previous infection of same organ had fully resolved, regardless of pathogen.

Recurrent: Same as reinfection.

Mixed: Infection with many types of pathogens, often said of a combination of anaerobes and aerobes.

Co-infection: The requirement that two pathogens be present within a host at the same time in order to produce disease (the co-infecting one on its own will cause no disease).

Superinfection: The condition whereby a new pathogen is introduced at the same site where there is a pre-existing infection caused by a different pathogen. The first pathogen may alter the host in such a way as to permit the second one to thrive. The second pathogen may cause symptoms that differ from the pre-existing infection.

Opportunistic: The condition whereby a relatively non-virulent pathogen manages to cause disease in a host who is immunocompromised. The same pathogen would cause no disease in an immunocompetent host.

Endemic: A status within a particular geographic area or particular subset population whereby a pathogen infects a fixed percentage of persons. As one person heals, another becomes infected; percentage of infected remains approximately constant.

Epidemic (a.k.a. "outbreak"): A status within a particular geographic area or particular subset population whereby a pathogen infects an increasing percentage of persons over a relatively short period of time.

Pandemic: A status whereby an epidemic spreads across continents.

-emia: (bacteremia, viremia, spirochetemia, fungemia, parasitemia, etc.): Presence pathogen in host's bloodstream with no systemic symptoms.

Sepsis (a.k.a. septicemia): Presence of pathogens and/or their toxins in the host bloodstream with concurrent constitutional symptoms: fever, tachycardia, tachypnea, increased white cell count, low blood pressure, etc.

Pyogenic: Infection by pathogen that causes pus (inflammatory response).

Pyrogenic: Infection by pathogen that causes fever.

Suppurative: Infection by pathogen that causes pus (inflammatory response).

Post-infectious, non-suppurative sequelae: A type of affliction that arises within a host after an infection has fully resolved and after the infecting pathogen has been fully cleared from the host's body. This type of affliction may be caused by self-directed antibodies as a delayed and abnormal autoimmune response to the previously infecting pathogen.

TYPES OF HOSTS

Immunocompetent: A person with a normal functioning immune system.

Immunocompromised: A broad term which encompasses the following terms:

Immunodeficient: A person whose immune system is abnormal, due to an endogenous process (either congenital or acquired).

Immunoincompetent: Same as Immunodeficient.

Immunosuppressed: A person whose immune system is adversely affected by medications, radiation, or some other exogenous process.

Immunodepressed: Same as immunosupressed.

Examples of immunocompromised states:

1. AIDS (destroys T-cells).
2. Chemotherapy which disrupts hematopoiesis (suppresses bone marrow).
3. Radiation which disrupts hematopoiesis (suppresses bone marrow).
4. Long term immunosuppressive medication given due to organ transplantation.
5. Congenital immunodeficiency.
6. Splenectomy (allows infection by encapsulated organisms).
7. Trauma (disrupted anatomic barriers).
Etc.

VIRULENCE FACTORS

Features to enhance the pathogen's survival and promote invasion of the host:

Toxins: Weaken the host

Capsules: Enables the pathogen to resist the host immune response and to resist antimicrobial medications.

Enzymes: Breaks down various host tissues and allows infection to spread.

Motility: Allows the pathogen to move and spread infection or evade host defenses.

Rapid proliferation: Allows the pathogen to establish colonization and infection before the host defenses can act.

Drug resistance: Allows the pathogen to resist antimicrobial medications intended to destroy it.

Attachment ability: Gives the pathogen a physical advantage to cause colonization and infection.

Antigen variation: Allows the pathogen to evade the host defenses.

Etc.

TREATMENTS

<u>**Active Therapy:**</u> Exogenous agents or other treatments are used to directly combat the pathogens within the host:
   Examples: antimicrobial medications, surgery, etc.

<u>**Supportive Therapy:**</u> Providing life support and comfort measures such as respiratory ventilation; fluid resuscitation, anti-fever medications, anti-hypotensive medication, pain medication, etc. The goal is to optimize the body's own recuperative powers to fight off the pathogen.

<u>**Preventive:**</u> Any means by which pathogens are thwarted from infecting hosts, or by which hosts are able to avoid contact with pathogens.
   1. <u>**Acquired Immunity:**</u> Previous infection with the same pathogen confers long lasting immunity.
   2. <u>**Active Immunization:**</u> Exogenous agents are used to generate immunity, this process takes weeks or months to develop.
      Vaccines:
         <u>Live-Attenuated</u>: Living but inactive pathogens are injected into a host to stimulate host immunity but cause no disease.
         <u>Dead</u>: Parts of dead pathogens are injected into the host to stimulate host immunity.
      Toxoids:
         Inactivated exotoxin is injected into a host to stimulate host immunity against the toxin.
         The host will form antibodies to the toxin: "**Antitoxin**."
   3. <u>**Passive Immunization:**</u> A form immunity that is gained exogenously, and that is immediately effective:
      Donor Antibody Transfer: Pre-formed pathogen-specific antibody is removed from an immune donor and intravenously injected into a non-immune host after that host has been exposed to a deadly pathogen.
      Donor Antitoxin Transfer: Pre-formed exotoxin-specific antibody is removed from an immune donor (human or animal) and intravenously injected into a non-immune host after the host has been exposed to a deadly exotoxin.
   4. <u>**Herd Immunity:**</u> The concept that vaccination of most members of a community will decrease the likelihood that an individual non-immune person will come in contact with an infecting pathogen.
   5. <u>**Destruction of pathogen's Vector or Reservoir:**</u> e.g. Fight Yersinia pestis by using insecticides to kill the flea vectors, and by using rat poison to kill the rat reservoir.
   6. <u>**Destruction of pathogen's habitat:**</u> e.g. Fight Staphylococcus aureus by washing hospital surfaces with alcohol.
   7. <u>**Education of the individuals within a community:**</u> Teaching people about how infections occur can help them avoid infections.

HOST DEFENSE

<u>**Anatomic/Natural:**</u> Anatomical structures and physiological processes such as: Skin, mucous membranes, blood-brain barrier, secretions (tears, saliva, perspiration, stomach acid, and urine), normal flora colonization to crowd out pathogens, intestinal tract peristalsis, respiratory tract cilia, coughing, sneezing, expectorating, emesis, and diarrhea.

<u>**Humoral:**</u> Immune globulin antibodies: **IgM, IgG, IgA**
   <u>**Titer:**</u> to measure a host's level of a specific antibody, a sample of the host's serum is removed then put through a series of dilutions; the point of greatest dilution which still reacts in an antibody-antigen reaction is called the "titer." A high titer correlates to a strong host response, and can be used as an indication of infection by, or exposure to, a pathogen. A high IgM titer sometimes indicates recent /acute infection/exposure, and a high IgG titer sometimes indicates remote/chronic infection/exposure.
      <u>Note</u>: The greater the dilution that still reacts = "**higher titer**" = higher antibody level. Example: **1:360** is a high titer.
      The lesser the dilution necessary to cause a reaction = "**lower titer**" = lower antibody level. Example: **1:20** is a low titer.

<u>**Cell-mediated:**</u> **CD4** T-cells, **CD8** T-cells.

<u>**Opsonization:**</u> This is the act of a pathogen being labeled by immune structures which act as a flags to stimulate phagocytosis: Done by:
      IgG   C3b   IgM+C3b   IgG+C3b

<u>**Chemotaxis:**</u> Some substances get released or activated during an infection to act as a chemical signal to attract phagocytes, e.g. **C5a**.

<u>**Phagocytosis:**</u> This is the process whereby the pathogens are "injested" by certain immune cells for clearance from the host. Done by:
      Neutrophils [PMNs (Poly-Morpho-Nuclear leukocytes)]; **Macrophages** [MACROs]; **Monocytes** [Monos], and **Eosinophils**.

<u>**Cytokines:**</u> These are endogenous substances which get released by the host into the blood stream.
   They can be toxic or disruptive to pathogens, they can cause fever in order to disrupt pathogen metabolic pathways, etc.

<u>**Complement:**</u> These are circulating plasma proteins that can get "activated" during an infection to help fight the pathogens.
   <u>Classic pathway</u> (antibody dependent): Immune complexes activate complement.
   <u>Alternative pathway</u> (antibody independent): Bacterial products activate complement without the immune complexes present.

CLASSIC COMPLEMENT PATHWAY	ALTERNATIVE COMPLEMENT PATHWAY
Antigen-Antibody Immune Complex	**Bacterial Products**
\	/
C1 becomes "activated C1"	Circulating C3 becomes C3b, combines with Factor B
\	/
C4 and C2 are circulating	**C3b,Bb-complex forms**
\	/
C4, C2 combine due to action of activated C1	Combine C3bB with Properidin (P) and Factor D
\	/
C4b,2a-Activation Unit	**C3b,Bb,P-Activation Unit**
\	/
Combine with circulating C3	Combine with circulating C3

   C3a comes off   **C4a, 2a3b**   **C3b,P,Bb3b**   C3a comes off

         Combine with circulating C5

   C5a comes off   **C5b combines with circulating C6, C7, C8, C9
   to form "Membrane Attack Complex"**

The human immune system has some peculiar traits so that previous infection or exposure to a pathogen may or may not result in:

Type-specific-immunity: The host becomes immune to the specific strain of that particular pathogen species.

Cross-immunity: The host becomes immune to a particular pathogen species as well as to other similar species.

Auto-Immune Reaction (or Post-Infectious-Auto-Immune Reaction): The host antibodies attack "self" tissue mistaking the host's own tissue for an invading pathogen. Sometimes occurs long after an infection has resolved ('post-infectious").

DIAGNOSTIC TESTS

A. OBTAIN SPECIMENS:

Throat swabs; Sputum smear; Blood smear or culture; CSF analysis or culture; Tissue biopsy; Urine sample slide or culture; Urethral discharge slide or culture; Vaginal discharge slide or culture; Stool sample slide or culture; Joint tap synovial fluid slide or culture; Any Body Cavity fluid slide or culture.

Contamination of Specimen: Organisms, from the environment, can grow undesirably in culture along with the infecting pathogen. This can lead to misdiagnosis.

B. DIRECT DETECTION OF PATHOGENS WITHIN A SPECIMEN:

Staining Methods:

1. Histological Slides:

Gram Stain: for bacteria:

Organisms are G-POS (blue/purple) or G-NEG (red).

Giemsa Stain: for miscellaneous blood smears and for protozoa:

Organisms are pink/purple.

Silver Stain (GBS or Grocott-Gomori methenamine-silver nitrate): for fungi in tissue:

Fungi are brown against green background.

Wright Stain: for malarial parasites.

Ziehl-Neelsen and Kinyoun ("acid-fast"): for Mycobacteria:

"Modified" for Nocardia and Cryptosporidium.

Organisms are purple against blue background.

Etc.

2. Immunoassay Methods:

These methods depend on antigen-antibody reactions. Typically, the infecting pathogen has a specific antigen that an antibody can target. Commercially available antibody is designed in such a way that it carries a "label," or in such a way that it can be "labeled" at a later time. The label is what indicates that a positive reaction has occurred.

Radioactive Immunoassay (RIA): the "label" is a radioactive molecule.

Immunofluorescence Assay (IFA): the "label" is a fluorescent molecule.

Enzyme-Linked Immunoassay (EIA): e.g. ELISA, the "label" is an enzyme which can react in a colorometric reaction.

LA (Latex Particle Agglutination): the "label" is a large latex particle coated with antibody so that organisms which express the specific antigen will all attach to the particle.

3. DNA Probe with PCR amplification:

A "probe" DNA sequence is artificially constructed to exactly compliment the infecting pathogen's DNA. This artificial DNA probe carries a "label." The infecting pathogen's DNA is separated into single strands, then amplified by PCR. The artificial DNA probe is introduced; complimentary matching strands will bind with the probe ("Hybridize"). The label is what indicates a positive match.

C. INDIRECT DETECTION OF PATHOGENS IN A HOST:

1. Serological Methods:

When the host becomes infected, specific antibodies are produced. In general, the IgM Titer begins to rise within 1-2 weeks and peaks after about 4 weeks then drops to a low level. In general, the IgG Titer begins to rise within 4 weeks and peaks after about 6 weeks, but persists for many years. Serologic tests are used to detect a 4 fold rise in antibody titers within two blood samples drawn about 2 weeks apart near the beginning of an infection.

2. Culture Techniques:

The tissue or body fluid specimen is introduced to special nutritive medias and incubated under special conditions. In time, bacterial colonies may grow. The bacteria from these colonies are used to conduct a series of laboratory tests for exact identification of the infecting pathogen.

Cell Culture (also called Tissue Culture) techniques are similar to regular culture techniques except that the infecting pathogens require the presence of living cells or tissue in order to survive in culture.

D. LABORATORY TESTS:

Infecting pathogens that are grown in culture can be put through numerous tests for exact identification. Tests such as: Catalase, Oxidase, Urease, Lactase, Indole, Methyl Red, Hemolysis, CAMP test, Bile-solubility, Lancefield Group, antibiotic susceptibility, etc., etc. are sometimes necessary.

Chapter 2

GRAM POSITIVE COCCI

Staphylococcus aureus
Skin infections
Food poisoning
Toxic shock syndrome
Osteomyelitis
Infective arthritis
Acute endocarditis
Pneumonia
Sepsis
Parotitis

Staphylococcus epidermidis
Bacteremia
Sub-acute endocarditis
Neonatal bacteremia

Staphylococcus saprophyticus
UTI

Streptococcus Group A
Skin infections
Necrotizing fasciitis
Pharyngitis
Scarlet fever
Acute glomerular nephritis
Acute rheumatic fever

Streptococcus Group B
Neonate meningitis
Neonate pneumonia
Post-partum endometritis
Streptococcus pneumoniae
Lobar pneumonia
Meningitis
Sinusitis
Otitis media

Streptococcus pneumoniae
Lobar pneumonia
Meningitis
Sinusitis
Otitis media

Streptococcus Group D
(*S. bovis* and others)
Bacteremia
Sub acute endocarditis
Colon cancer

Streptococcus Viridans Group
(*S. mutans* and others)
Sub-acute endocarditis
Dental caries

Enterococcus spp
(*E. faecalis* and others)
UTI
Bacteremia
Sub-acute endocarditis

Peptostreptococcus spp
(Anaerobic)
See:
    Commensal Anaeroic Bacteria

Staphylococcus aureus

GRAM STAIN:
POS

AEROBIC

EXTRACELLULAR

FEATURES:
- **Morphology:**
  Cocci
- **Grouping:**
  Clusters
- **Colonies:**
  -White/yellow
  -Round
  -On blood-agar.

MOTILITY:
None

CAPSULE:
None

GLYCOCALYX:
None

EXOTOXINS:
- **Hemolysins:** (disrupt blood cells)
  - **Alpha toxin:** Causes septic shock and dermonecrosis, also causes some lysis of RBC's
  - **Beta toxin:** Sphingomyelinase activity. Causes lysis of RBC's in the cold after warm incubation. Basis of CAMP Test.
  - **Delta toxin:** Leukocidin activity
  - **Gamma toxin:** Causes tissue necrosis

- **Panton-Valentine Leukocidin:** (a.k.a. P-V Leukocidin)
  - Disrupts PMNs and Macros.
  - Causes influx of Ca++ then degranulation and lysis.

- **Enterotoxins:** (disrupts intestinal mucosa, causes emesis, diarrhea)
  - **Toxin A:** preformed in food, causes food poisoning.
  - **Toxin F:** similar to Toxic Shock Syndrome Toxin.

- **Toxic Shock Syndrome Toxin:** Superantigen.
  - Causes release of Il-2 from CD4+ T-cells and IL-1 from Macros

- **Exfoliatin:** (produced by "Phage Group II" strains) Epidermolytic.
  - Causes intraepidermal separation at stratum granulosum.

VIRULENCE FACTORS:
- **Exotoxins:** See above.
- **β-Lactamase:** Coded on Plasmid: for Penicillin resistance.
- **Mutant Penicillin-Binding-Proteins:** For Methicillin resistance.
- **Coagulase** (free or bound):
  Catalyzes the formation of thrombin which catalyzes the formation of fibrin which coats the bacteria.
- **Protein A:** Binds Fc portion of IgG to block complement binding and block opsonization.
- **Other Enzymes:**
  Lipase, Protease, Hyaluronidase, nuclease, fibrinolysin.

LAB TESTS:
- **Catalase:**   Pos
- **Coagulase:**   Pos
- **DNase:**   Pos
- **Mannitol:**   Pos
- **Hemolysis:**   Beta
- **6.5%NaCl:**   Growth

SOURCE AND TRANSMISSION:
- **Colonizes** human nose, sometimes skin; may also survive on contaminated fomites, and on contaminated food.
- **Horizontal transmission** occurs via human contact, sneezes, and contact with the contaminated environment.
- **Nosocomial transmission** is very common.

CLINICAL:
- **Skin Infections:**
  - **Furuncles, Boils, Carbuncles**.
  - **Scalded Skin Syndrome** in young children (Ritter's disease).
  - **Burn** and **wound** infections.

- **Food Poisoning:**
  - Due to ingestion of **Enterotoxin A** in food, not ingestion of bacteria.
  - Symptoms: nausea and vomiting.

- **Toxic Shock Syndrome:**
  - Mostly in women during use of tampons.

- **Osteomyelitis:** (*S. aureus* is # 1 causative organism)
  - In metaphysis of children, epiphysis of adults.
  - From trauma or hematogenous spread.

- **Infective Arthritis:** (*S. aureus* is # 1 causative organism in adults.)

- **Acute Endocarditis:** (*S. aureus* is # 1 causative organism.)
  - Infects normal, abnormal and prosthetic heart valves.

- **Post Viral Lobar Pneumonia:**
  - Especially following Influenza virus.

- **Bacteremia and Sepsis:** (*S. aureus* is # 1 causative organism.)
  - Community acquired.

- **Parotitis:**
  - Infection of the parotid gland and duct of Stensen.

HOST DEFENSE AND IMMUNITY:
- **Opsonization** by IgG, C3b, or IgM+C3b
- **Phagocytosis** by PMNs.
- **Cytokines** released by CD4+ T-cells.
- **Note**: No immunity gained by infection.

TREATMENT:
- **Nafcillin** or other penicillinase-resistant penicillin.
- **Vancomycin** especially in penicillin allergy and **MRSA**.
- **Cephalosporins** 1st Generation.
- **Bacitracin** Topical Ointment for wound prophylaxis.

VACCINE AND TOXOID:
None

Staphylococcus epidermidis

GRAM STAIN:
POS

AEROBIC

EXTRACELLULAR

FEATURES:
- **Morphology:**
  Cocci
- **Grouping:**
  Clusters, tetrads
- **Colonies:**
  -White/yellow
  -Round
  -On blood-agar.

MOTILITY:
None

CAPSULE:
None

GLYCOCALYX:
Exopolysaccharide

EXOTOXINS:
None

VIRULENCE FACTORS:
- **Glycocalyx:** the exopolysaccharide **"slime"** enables adhesion, resistance to phagocytosis, and resistance to antibiotics.
- **β-Lactamase:** Coded on Plasmid: for Penicillin resistance.
- **Mutant Penicillin-Binding-Proteins:** For Methicillin resistance.

SOURCE AND TRANSMISSION:
- **Normal flora** of skin and mucus membranes.
- **Skin trauma** causes spread to blood.

CLINICAL:
- **Bacteremia and Sepsis:**
  - **Nosocomial/ Iatrogenic:** Via catheters, IV lines, feeding tubes, prosthetics (heart valves, hip joints, pace makers, etc.), CSF shunts.
  - **Drug Abusers:** from IV injections.
  - **Immunocompromised** and neutropenic patients.

- **Subacute Endocarditis:**
  - Results from bacteremia.
  - Infects abnormal or prosthetic valves, sometimes healthy valves.

- **Neonatal Bacteremia:**
  - Nosocomial, especially in neonatal ICUs.

HOST DEFENSE AND IMMUNITY:
- **Opsonization** by IgG, C3b, or IgM+C3b.
- **Phagocytosis** by PMNs.
- **Cytokines** released by CD4+ T-cells.
- **Note**: No immunity gained by infection.

TREATMENT:
- **Vancomycin** especially in penicillin allergy

LAB TESTS:
- **Catalase:**   Pos
- **Coagulase:**   Neg
- **DNase:**   Neg
- **Mannitol:**   Neg
- **Hemolysis:**   None
- **Novobiocin:**   Susceptible

VACCINE AND TOXOID:
None

Staphylococcus saprophyticus

GRAM STAIN:
POS

AEROBIC

EXTRACELLULAR

FEATURES:
- **Morphology:**
  Cocci
- **Grouping:**
  Clusters
- **Colonies:**
  -White/yellow
  -Round
  -On blood-agar.

MOTILITY:
None

CAPSULE:
None

GLYCOCALYX:
None

EXOTOXINS:
None

VIRULENCE FACTORS:
- **Multiple drug resistance**.
- **Hemagglutinin proteins and surface proteins** may mediate attachment to urinary tract epithelial cells.
- **Urease** may mediate pathogenesis.

LAB TESTS:
- **Catalase:**   **Pos**
- **Coagulase:**   Neg
- **DNase:**   Neg
- **Mannitol:**   Neg
- **Hemolysis:**   None
- **Novobiocin:**   **Resistant**

SOURCE AND TRANSMISSION:
- **Normal flora** of genitourinary skin.
- **Poor hygiene** causes spreads to urinary tract, especially related to sexual activity.

CLINICAL:
- **UTI**:
  - Upper (**Pyelonephritis**) and lower (**Cystitis**) urinary tract infections.
  - Most cases show **Pyuria**.
  - Mostly in healthy, young, sexually-active women.

HOST DEFENSE AND IMMUNITY:
- **Opsonization** by IgG, C3b, or IgM+C3b.
- **Phagocytosis** by PMNs.
- **Cytokines** released by CD4+ T-cells.
- **Note**: No immunity gained by infection.

TREATMENT:
- **Trimethoprim-Sulfamethoxazole** (TMP-SMZ)
- **Levofloxacin** as an alternative.

VACCINE AND TOXOID:
None

Streptococcus Group A

Streptococcus pyogenes

GRAM STAIN:
POS

AEROBIC

EXTRACELLULAR

FEATURES:
- **Morphology:**
  Cocci
- **Grouping:**
  Chains
- **Colonies:**
  -Gray-white
  -Small
  -On blood-agar.

MOTILITY:
None

CAPSULE:
Hyaluronic acid

GLYCOCALYX:
None

EXOTOXINS:
- **Hemolysins:** (Disrupt blood cells)
  - **Streptolysin O:** Causes beta hemolysis.
    Inactivated by oxidation.
    Causes host immune system to produce antibody "**ASO.**"
  - **Streptolysin S:** Causes beta hemolysis on blood-agar plates.
    Resists inactivation by oxidation.
    Non-antigenic, but may have leukocidin activity.

- **Erythrogenic Toxin:** Produces an erythematous reaction.
  - Causes the Rash of Scarlet Fever.
  - Coded on viral DNA which integrates into bacteria by lysogeny
    (a process whereby a temperate bacteriophage infects bacterium).

VIRULENCE FACTORS:
- **Exotoxins:** See above.
- **Protein M** (of cell wall): Provides antigenic variation.
  - Blocks opsonization by complement alternate pathway,
    thus *Group A Streptococcus* evades phagocytosis.
- **Capsule:** Hyaluronic acid.
  - Resists phagocytosis.
- **Hyaluronidase:** Enzyme.
  - Degrades hyaluronic acid in connective tissue.
- **Peptidase:** Enzyme.
  - Destroys **C5a** complement as chemotactic signal to PMNs.
- **Streptokinase:** Enzyme.
  - Catalyzes activation of plasmin to lyse blood clots.
- **Streptodornase (DNase):** Enzyme.
  - Degrades DNA.
  - Provides antigenic variation.
- **Pili, Lipoteichoic acid, and F-Protein:**
  - All mediate attachment to epithelium.

LAB TESTS:
- **Catalase:** Neg
- **Hemolysis:** **Beta**
- **6.5%NaCl:** No growth
- **CAMP Test:** Neg
- **Bile Esculin:** Neg
- **Lancefield:** **Group A**
  (type of Carbohydrate C)
- **Bacitracin:** **Susceptible**

SOURCE AND TRANSMISSION:
- **Normal flora** of skin and oropharynx.
- **Skin trauma** results in infections upon penetration of tissues.

CLINICAL:
- **Skin Infections:**
  - **Impetigo** (Streptococcal Pyoderma): Purulent with crusting.
  - **Cellulitis:** (#1 causative organism) *Group A Step* infects wounds
    such as burns, trauma, and IV drug abuser injection sites.
  - **Erysipelas:** Mostly of the face, "**Slapped cheeks**" rash.

- **Necrotizing Fasciitis:** "**Flesh-Eating** Streptococcus Disease."
  - Rapidly spreading gangrene of skin and fascia.
  - Starts as trivial skin infection but is rapidly fatal.

- **Pharyngitis:**
  - **Exudate** on tonsils, mostly in **children** (5-15 yrs old).

- **Scarlet Fever (Scarlatina):**
  - **Red** maculopapular "**sandpaper**" rash on trunk, intense at skinfolds.
  - White and red "**Strawberry tongue.**"
  - Follows pharyngeal or other infections by strains which elaborate
    erythrogenic toxin.

- **Post-Streptococcal Acute Glomerular Nephritis (AGN):**
  - Non-suppurative sequelae. No *Group A Streptococcus* present.
  - Post-pharyngitis or post-skin infection (after infection resolves).
  - Symptoms: facial edema, blood in urine ("smoky" urine).

- **Post-Streptococcal Acute Rheumatic Fever (ARF):**
  - Non-suppurative sequelae. No *Group A Streptococcus* present.
  - Post-pharyngitis only (after infection resolves).
  - Symptoms: migratory arthritis, subcutaneous nodules, carditis, and
    erythema marginatum.
  - May proceed to **Sydenham's Chorea**.
  - May proceed (years or decades) to **Rheumatic Heart Disease (RHD).**

HOST DEFENSE AND IMMUNITY:
- **IgA, IgM, IgG antibodies** to M Protein offer resistance and
  type specific immunity.
- **PMNs.**
- **Autoimmunity** develops via cross reactionin ARF.
- **Immune complexes** involve C3 from complement alternate pathway
  deposited at glomerular BM in AGN.
- **Note:** Serum C3 levels will be low in AGN.
- **Note:** ASO titers are elevated in AGN and ARF.

TREATMENT:
- **Penicillin G**
- **Erythromycin** in Penicillin allergy.
- **Benzathine Penicillin** prophylaxis to
  prevent recurrence of ARF.
- **Sulfonamides prophylaxis** prophylaxis to
  prevent recurrence of ARF in Penicillin allergy.
- **Bacitracin** Topical Ointment for wound prophylaxis.

VACCINE AND TOXOID:
None

Streptococcus Group B

Streptococcus agalactiae

GRAM STAIN:
POS

AEROBIC

EXTRACELLULAR

FEATURES:
- **Morphology:**
  Cocci
- **rouping:**
  Pairs, short chains
- **Colonies:**
  -Gray-white
  -On blood-agar.

MOTILITY:
None

CAPSULE:
Polysaccharide

GLYCOCALYX:
None

EXOTOXINS:
None

VIRULENCE FACTORS:
- **Capsule:** Type-specific polysaccharide.
  Resists phagocytosis.
- **Sialic acid:** Capsular component.
  Inhibits alternate pathway of complement.
  Especially type III strain.

LAB TESTS:
- **Catalase:**   Neg
- **Hemolysis:**   **Beta**
- **6.5%NaCl:**   No growth
- **CAMP Test:**   **Pos**
- **Bile Esculin:**   Neg
- **Lancefield:**   **Group B**
       (type of Carbohydrate C)

SOURCE AND TRANSMISSION:
- **Normal flora** of vagina.
- **Vertical transmission** either at birth or via ascension in utero.

CLINICAL:
- **Neonate Meningitis:**
  - **Symptoms:** fever, lethargy, poor feeding. Seizures = poor prognosis.
  - Invades via mucus membranes, respiratory tract, sepsis; often fatal.
  - Meningitis must be diagnosed via lumbar puncture:
    CSF: ↑PMNs, ↓Glucose, Cloudy, Culture = *Group B Strep*.
  - **Early onset** (age 0-5 days):
    Vertical transmission in utero; ascending, due to ruptured amnionic sac.
  - **Late onset** (age 5-90 days):
    Vertical transmission at time of delivery; or can be nosocomial.

- **Neonate Pneumonia:**
  - **Symptoms:** cyanosis, tachypnea and respiratory distress, often fatal.
  - **Early onset** only; via ascending vertical transmission.

- **Post-Partum Endometritis:**
  - Especially following C-Section.

HOST DEFENSE AND IMMUNITY:
- **IgG Antibodies** to capsule.
- **PMNs.**
- **Classic pathway complement** C1 activated by capsule, antibody-dependent opsonization.
- **Alternate pathway complement** is involved in antibody-independent opsonization.
- **Note:** Neonate host defense is quickly defeated.

TREATMENT:
- **Ampicillin plus aminoglycoside** for neonates.
- **Penicillin G** for adults.
- **Vancomycin** in Penicillin allergy.

VACCINE AND TOXOID:
None

Streptococcus pneumoniae

GRAM STAIN:
POS

AEROBIC

EXTRACELLULAR

FEATURES:
- **Morphology:**
  Cocci
- **Grouping:**
  Pairs
- **Colonies:**
  -Gray-white
  -Variable
  -On blood-agar.

MOTILITY:
None

CAPSULE:
Polysaccharide
(more than 80 types)

GLYCOCALYX:
None

EXOTOXINS:
None

VIRULENCE FACTORS:
- **Capsule:** Polysaccharide.
  Enables *S. pneumoniae* to resist phagocytosis.
- **IgA protease:** Enzyme
  Prevents opsonization by IgA at mucus membranes.
- **Adhesins:**
  Mediates attachment of *S. pneumoniae* to epithelial cells.

LAB TESTS:
- **Catalase:**   Neg
- **emolysis:**   **Alpha (green)**
- **6.5%NaCl:**   No growth
- **CAMP Test:**   Neg
- **Bile Esculin:** Neg
- **Lancefield:**   **None**
     (type of Carbohydrate C)
- **Optochin**   +/- Sensitive
- **Bile Solubility** **Pos**

SOURCE AND TRANSMISSION:
- **Normal flora** of upper respiratory tract.
- **Horizontal transmission** occurs via respiratory droplets.
- **Pulmonary infections** occur when muccocilliary action fails. Alveoli get filled with bacteria which extend to entire lobe via pores of Kohn
- **Meningitis** occurs from extension of sinusitis or otitis media, or from choroid plexus seeding due to bacteremia.

CLINICAL:
- **Lobar Pneumonia:**
S. pneumoniae is #1 causative organism in adults and sickle cell disease
  - **Symptoms:** Fever, cough with sputum, dull chest percussion, X-ray shows segmental consolidation. Can be fatal. Abscess is rare.
  - **Diagnosis:** Presence of *S. pneumoniae* and PMNs in sputum.
  - **Note:** Pulmonary infection is often predisposed by viral infection, alcoholism, smoking, or any condition which suppresses cough reflex or disrupts cilia.

- **Meningitis:**
S. pneumoniae is #1 causative organism in adults and elderly.
  Symptoms: Fever, neck pain, headache, Brudzinski and Kernig signs
     Can be fatal.
  Diagnosis: Lumbar puncture prior to antibiotic treatment:
     CSF: ↑PMNs, ↓Glucose, Cloudy, Culture.
  Note: Meningitis often follows sinusitis and otitis media by direct extension of infection.
  Note: Meningitis often follows bacteremia via seeding of choroid plexus.

- **Sinusitis:** *S. pneumoniae* is #1 causative organism.
  - Sinus infection often follows allergy or viral induced edema which prevents sinus drainage.
- **Otitis Media:** *S. pneumoniae* is #1 causative organism.
  - Middle ear infection often follows allergy or viral induced edema which prevents eustachian tube drainage.

HOST DEFENSE AND IMMUNITY:
- **IgG Antibody** to capsule offers resistance; and type specific immunity.
- **Classic pathway complement** C1 activated by capsule; antibody-dependent opsonization.
- **Alternate pathway complement** is involved in antibody-independent opsonization.
- **C5a complement** chemotaxis attracts PMNs.
- **Vaccine** confers immunity for a few years.

TREATMENT:
- **Penicillin G**
- **Ceftriaxone** for meningitis.
- **Vancomycin** in Penicillin allergy.

VACCINE AND TOXOID:
- **Vaccine**
  Made up of multiple-strain capsular antigens.

Streptococcus Group D

Streptococcus bovis and others

GRAM STAIN:
POS

AEROBIC

EXTRACELLULAR

FEATURES:
- **Morphology:**
  Cocci
- **Grouping:**
  Pairs, chains
- **Colonies:**
  -Gray-white
  -Variable
  -On blood-agar.

MOTILITY:
None

CAPSULE:
None

GLYCOCALYX:
None

EXOTOXINS:
None

VIRULENCE FACTORS:
None

LAB TESTS:
- **Catalase:**   Neg
- **Hemolysis:**   **Alpha**, **Beta**, or **Gamma**
- **6.5%NaCl:**   No growth
- **CAMP Test:**   Neg
- **Bile Esculin:**   **Pos**
- **Lancefield:**   **Group D**
     (type of Carbohydrate C)

SOURCE AND TRANSMISSION:
- **Normal flora** of GI tract.
- **Bacteremia** results from disruption of GI tract epithelium.

CLINICAL:
- **Bacteremia:**
  - *S. bovis* enters the blood via gastrointestinal route.
- **Sub-Acute Endocarditis:**
  - Arises from bacteremia. Can be fatal if untreated.
- **Colon Cancer:**
  - Strong association between *S. bovis* bacteremia and colon cancer. It is unknown which is cause or effect.

HOST DEFENSE AND IMMUNITY:
- **IgA and IgG antibodies**
- **PMNs**

TREATMENT:
- **Penicillin G**
- **Vancomycin** in Penicillin allergy.

VACCINE AND TOXOID:
None

Streptococcus Viridans Group

Streptococcus mutans and others

GRAM STAIN:
POS

AEROBIC

EXTRACELLULAR

FEATURES:
- **Morphology:**
  Cocci
- **Grouping:**
  Pairs, chains
- **Colonies:**
  -Gray-white
  -Variable
  -On blood-agar.

MOTILITY:
None

CAPSULE:
None

GLYCOCALYX:
Dextran

EXOTOXINS:
None

VIRULENCE FACTORS:
- **Dextran exopolysaccharide glycocalyx:**
  - Provides means of adherence to defective heart valves.
  - May block the action of antibiotics.
- **Lipoteichoic Acid (LTA):** Mediates adhesion to fibronectin in clots on defective heart valves.
- **Glucans:** Polysaccharides made by *S. mutans* from sucrose in the mouth, they provide a means of attachment to tooth enamel.
- **Other Acids:** Made by *S. mutans* from fermentation of sugars in the mouth contribute to tooth decay.

LAB TESTS:
- **Catalase:**   Neg
- **Hemolysis:**   **Alpha (green)**
- **6.5%NaCl:**   No growth
- **CAMP Test:**   Neg
- **Bile Esculin:** Neg
- **Lancefield:**   **None**
     (type of Carbohydrate C)
- **Optochin**   Resistant
- **Bile Solubility** Neg

SOURCE AND TRANSMISSION:
- **Normal flora** of oropharynx.
- **Bacteremia** causes infection when enters blood stream after dental work or due to poor oral hygiene.

CLINICAL:
- **Bacteremia:**
  - *S. mutans* enters the blood via dental disruption.

- **Sub-Acute Endocarditis:** (Number 1 causative organism).
  - Results from bacteremia which follows recent dental work.
  - Infects abnormal valves or prosthetic valves, rarely normal valves.
  - Can be fatal if untreated.

- **Dental Caries**

HOST DEFENSE AND IMMUNITY:
- **Lysis** of bacteria by serum enzymes and lysosomal enzymes.

TREATMENT:
- **Penicillin G plus Aminoglycoside**
  Must be given prophylactically before dental work or oral surgery to people with defective heart valves.
- **Amoxicillin or Ampicillin, plus Gentamicin** in cases of Endocarditis.
- **Vancomycin** in Penicillin allergy.

VACCINE AND TOXOID:
None

Enterococcus spp

Enterococcus faecalis and others

GRAM STAIN:
POS

AEROBIC

EXTRACELLULAR

FEATURES:
- **Morphology:**
  Cocci
- **Grouping:**
  Single, pairs, chains
- **Colonies:**
  -Gray-white
  -Variable
  -On blood-agar.

MOTILITY:
None

CAPSULE:
None

GLYCOCALYX:
None

EXOTOXINS:
None

VIRULENCE FACTORS:
- **Antibiotics resistance**
- **Adhesion:**
  to defective heart valves and urinary tract epithelial cells.
- **Note:**
  The mechanisms of virulence are unknown.

LAB TESTS:
- **Catalase:** Neg
- **Hemolysis:** **Alpha, Beta,** or **Gamma**
- **6.5%NaCl:** **Growth**
- **CAMP Test:** Neg
- **Bile Esculin:** **Pos**
  (Hydrolyzed)
- **Lancefield:** **Group D**
  (type of Carbohydrate C)

SOURCE AND TRANSMISSION:
- **Normal flora** of GI tract.
- **Bacteremia** causes infection when enters blood stream, usually via ascending urinary route, intra-abdominal route or via in-dwelling catheters.
- **Nosocomial:** Exogenous acquisition of *Enterococcus* occurs often in hospitals.

CLINICAL:
- **UTI:**
  - Upper (**pyelonephritis**) and lower (**cystitis**) urinary tract infections.
  - Most often nosocomial.
- **Bacteremia:**
  - Via urinary tract infection, intra-abdominal infection, or nosocomial from various in-dwelling lines such as IV lines or hemodialysis.
  - Bacteremia may be predisposed by chronic illness or diabetes.
  - Often fatal.
- **Sub-Acute Endocarditis:**
  - Results from bacteremia.
  - *Enterococcus* usually infects abnormal valves or prosthetic valves but can infect normal valves. Fatal if untreated.

HOST DEFENSE AND IMMUNITY:
Unknown

TREATMENT:
- **Vancomycin or Ampicillin, plus Aminoglycoside** in cases of Endocarditis.
- **Ampicillin** in cases of UTI.

Note: Vancomycin-resistant strains of Enterococcus exist [**VRE**].
- **Streptogramin or Linezolid** in cases of **VRE**.

VACCINE AND TOXOID:
None

Chapter 3

GRAM POSITIVE RODS

Including Non-Commensal Anaerobic Gram Positive Rods

GRAM POSITIVE RODS:	ZOONOTIC GRAM POSITIVE RODS:	NON-COMMENSAL ANAEROBIC GRAM POSITIVE RODS:	OTHER GRAM POSITIVE RODS:

Bacillus cereus
Food poisoning
Eye infections
	Listeria monocytogenes
	      (Zoonotic)
	Abortion
	Meningitis
	Neonatal Granulomas
		Clostridium botulinum
		      (Anaerobic)
		Botulism food poisoning
		    (flaccid paralysis)
		Infant botulism
		Wound botulism
			Actinomyces israelii
			      (Anaerobic)
			(see Commensal Anaerobes)

Corynebacterium diphtheriae Diphtheria Wound infections			*Propionibacterium acnes* (Anaerobic) (see Commensal Anaerobes)

		Clostridium difficile
		      (Anaerobic)
		Pseudomembranous colitis
		    (post-antibiotic colitis)
			Mycobacterium spp
			      (Obligate Aerobic)
			(see Gram Positive Acid Fast)

		Clostridium perfringens (Anaerobic) Gas gangrene Food poisoning GI necrosis	*Nocardia asteroides* (see Gram Positive Acid Fast)

	Bacillus anthracis
	      (Zoonotic)
	(see Zoonotic bacteria)
		Clostridium tetani
		      (Anaerobic)
		Tetanus wound infection
		    (spastic paralysis)	

Bacillus cereus

GRAM STAIN:
POS

AEROBIC

EXTRACELLULAR

FEATURES:
- **Morphology:**
  Rods
- **Grouping:**
  Single, pairs, chains
- **Colonies:**
  -Granular
  -On nutrient agar,
  with amino acids added

MOTILITY:
Flagella

CAPSULE:
None

GLYCOCALYX:
None

SPORES:
Require Oxygen for
Germination

EXOTOXINS:
- **Enterotoxins:**
  - **Necrotic toxin:** Has vascular permeability action.
  - **Cereolysin:** A hemolysin which disrupts cholesterol of cell membranes.

VIRULENCE FACTORS:
- **Exotoxins:**
- **Spore Formation:** Enables survival in extreme harsh conditions.
- **Enzymes:** Lecithinase (phospholipase C) and others.

LAB TESTS:
Not usually done

SOURCE AND TRANSMISSION:
- **Spores and _B. cereus_ bacteria** are found in soil, dust, decaying organic matter, and contaminated food.
- **Ingestion of the bacteria** causes non-invasive GI infection.

CLINICAL:
- **Emetic Food Poisoning:**
  - Symptoms: upper GI disturbance with vomiting.
  - _B. cereus_ spores cool and germinate in reheated rice, especially in Chinese restaurant fried rice then grow rapidly before being ingested by host to cause symptoms.
  - Symptoms arise within 6 hours.
  - Infection is self-limiting and lasts for a few hours.
- **Diarrheal Food Poisoning:**
  - Symptoms: lower GI disturbance with watery diarrhea.
  - _B. cereus_ spores cool, germinate in reheated meats or vegetables, then grow rapidly before being ingested to cause symptoms.
  - Symptoms arise within 24 hours.
  - Infection is self-limiting and lasts for one or two days.
- **Eye infections:**
  - Post-traumatic endophthalmitis, edema and ring abscesses.
  - Occur especially among drug abusers. May cause blindness.

HOST DEFENSE AND IMMUNITY:
Unknown

TREATMENT:
- **Fluid and electrolyte replacement** if necessary, but medication is not needed for food poisoning.
- **Vancomycin** for other infections.

VACCINE AND TOXOID:
None

Corynebacterium diphtheriae

GRAM STAIN:
POS

AEROBIC

EXTRACELLULAR

FEATURES:
- **Morphology:**
Rods, Club-shaped
    with **Granules**
- **Grouping:**
"V, L" or **ChineseLetter** clumps.
- **Colonies:**
-Dark gray or black.
-Potassium **Tellurite** medium.

MOTILITY:
None

CAPSULE:
None

GLYCOCALYX:
None

EXOTOXINS:
- **Diphtheria Toxin:**
    - An **ADP-Ribosyltransferase.**
    Peptide B: binds to host cells to transport peptide A inside.
    Peptide A: has enzymatic activity.
    - Attaches ADP Ribose
    Prevents ribosome movement along mRNA.
    - Blocks host **EF2**
    (a protein synthesis elongation factor tRNA translocase).
    - **Blocks protein synthesis**.
    - Can kill host's NK cells (natural killer cells).
- Coded on viral DNA
    which gets integrated into the bacteria by **lysogeny**
    (process whereby temperate Bacteriophage infects bacterium).

VIRULENCE FACTORS:
- **Diphtheria exotoxin**: see above.
- **Storage granules:**
    - Contain phosphate polymers for high-energy reserve.
    - Stain with metachromatic dye (cell=blue, granules=red).

LAB TESTS:
- **Loeffler medium: Growth**
- **Metachromatic staining:**
    Cells=blue
    Storage granules=red
- **Tellurite medium:**
    Gray-black colonies

SOURCE AND TRANSMISSION:
- **Humans** are the only reservoir for *C. diphtheria* upper respiratory tract infections and skin lesions.
- **Horizontal transmission** occurs via respiratory droplets.

CLINICAL:
- **Diphtheria:** (Rare in USA)
    - Symptoms: Pseudomembrane formation in throat: exudate forms a tough gray membrane which can lead to stridor, respiratory distress, cyanosis, lymphadenopathy. Can be fatal.
    - **Intoxication** consequences of diphtheria toxin:
    Cardiac Toxicity: occurs weeks after initial infection: Myocarditis, arrhythmias, A-V block. Can be fatal.
    Neurologic Toxicity: occurs only following severe infection:
    Early (first few days): paralysis of soft palate and pharynx.
    Late (months later): peripheral motor neuropathy.
    - Diagnosis must be made fast, and is based solely on symptoms.
- **Skin infections:** (Rare.)
    - Infects open wounds.
    - Mostly in persons with poor hygiene.
    - Mostly in the tropics.
    - Presents with gray membrane on non-healing wound.
- **Schick skin test:** (rarely performed):
    - POS sign: red-brown spot appears at site of intradermal toxin injection after 36 hrs (therefore, patient is immune).

HOST DEFENSE AND IMMUNITY:
- **Antibodies** develop to the toxin,
    but it is usually too late to stop the toxic effects and death.
- **Diphtheria Toxoid** with boosters gives long-standing immunity.
- **Note:** *C. diphtheria* is non-invasive so there is no systemic infection.

TREATMENT:
- **Erythromycin** to kill the organism.
- **Diphtheria Antitoxin**
    Horse-derived antibodies to the toxin
    Must be administered immediately.

VACCINE AND TOXOID:
- **Diphtheria Toxoid:**
    Inactive toxin is given as part of **DPT**.

Listeria monocytogenes

GRAM STAIN:
POS

ZOONOTIC

AEROBIC

INTRACELLULAR

FEATURES:
- **Morphology:**
  Rods, small almost like cocci
- **Grouping:**
  "**Chinese character**" clumps
- **Colonies:**
  - Translucent
  - On Blood agar

MOTILITY:
Tumble

CAPSULE:
None
GLYCOCALYX:
None

EXOTOXINS:
- **Hemolysins:** (disrupt blood cells)
  - **Listeriolysin O:**
    Mediates escape from phagolysosome.
    Enhanced by low pH and low iron (as found in lysosome).
    Acts by disrupting membranes (especially of the lysosome).

VIRULENCE FACTORS:
- **Hemolysin Listeriolysin O:**
  Enables *L. monocytogenes* to survive inside macrophages.

SOURCE AND TRANSMISSION:
- **Animals are zoonotic reservoirs** for *L. monocytogenes*
- **Food products**, especially unpasteurized milk, are sources.
- **Vertical transmission** occurs in utero via transplacental infection or during birth due to passage through vagina.
- **Zoonotic transmission** occurs via contact with farm animals.

CLINICAL:
- **Abortion:**
  - Bacteremia can occur during pregnancy.
  - Symptoms of mild fever for the mother.
  - Prematurely induces labor which may be fatal for the fetus.

- **Meningitis:**
  - **Neonatal Meningitis:** Late onset (age 5-90 days after birth): Vertical transmission occurs at time of delivery.
  - **Immunocompromised Meningitis:** elderly, cancer patients, and renal transplant patients.
  - Diagnosis: Lumbar puncture prior to antibiotic treatment:
    CSF: ↑PMNs, ↓Glucose, Cloudy, Culture.

- **Granulomatosis Infantiseptica:**
  - Neonatal granulomas and abscesses:
    Locations: skin, conjunctiva, organs, brain.
  - Results from vertical transmission either transplacental in utero or during birth.
  - Can be fatal.

HOST DEFENSE AND IMMUNITY:
- **T-cell mediated** response plus Macros.

TREATMENT:
- **Penicillin G** or **Ampicillin**
- **TMP-SMZ** in Penicillin allergy.
- **Ampicillin plus Gentamicin** for neonatal meningitis.
- **3rd Generation Cephalosporin**.
  In penicillin and sulfa double allergy.

VACCINE AND TOXOID:
None

LAB TESTS:
- **Catalase:**   Pos
- **Hemolysis:**   Beta
- **Methyl Red**   Pos
- **Voges-Proskauer** Pos
- **Bile Esculin**   Pos
   (hydrolyzed)

Clostridium botulinum

GRAM STAIN:
POS

OBLIGATE ANAEROBE

EXTRACELLULAR

FEATURES:
- **Morphology:**
  Rods
- **Grouping:**
- **Colonies:**
  -Not usually done.

MOTILITY:
None

CAPSULE:
None

GLYCOCALYX:
None

SPORES:
Killed at 80°C, 10 mins

EXOTOXINS:
- **Botulinum Toxin:**
  - **Preformed in food.**
    8 different types but types A, B, E cause human illness.
    Heat labile at 121 C for 15 min.
  - **Neurotoxin:** one of the most potent toxins known.
    Blocks release of ACh (acetylcholine) from neurons.
    Causes **flaccid paralysis.**
  - Coded on viral DNA
    which gets integrated into the bacteria by **lysogeny**
    (process whereby temperate Bacteriophage infects bacterium).

VIRULENCE FACTORS:
- **Botulinum exotoxin:** see above.
- **Spore Formation:**
  Enables survival in extreme and harsh conditions.

LAB TESTS:
Not usually done

SOURCE AND TRANSMISSION:
- **Spores** occur in soil and in contaminated foods.
- **Vacuum-packed canning** enables the organism to grow from spores, and to produce toxin.
- **Food poisoning** occurs by ingesting **preformed toxin.**
- **In infant botulism and wound botulism**, the organism itself invades the host to cause colonization and infection.

CLINICAL:
- **Botulism Food Poisoning:** (intoxication)
  - **Caused by ingestion of preformed toxin** in contaminated food.
    Note: no C. botulinum bacteria need to be ingested.
  - Symptoms:
    Early: Nausea, vomit, diarrhea, with **NO fever.**
    Late: **Flaccid Paralysis:**
      Respiratory distress from diaphragm paralysis.
      Can be fatal or take months-years to heal.
  - Diagnosis is made on basis of symptoms and history.

- **Infant Botulism:**
  - C. botulinum colonizes neonate colon as "normal" flora.
  - Toxin is then produced to cause symptoms.
  - The source of C. botulinum in infant botulism is often **honey.**
  - Symptoms: feeble cry, weakness, paralysis, respiratory distress.
    May account for SIDS (Sudden Infant Death Syndrome).
    Infant may spontaneously recover.

- **Wound Botulism:**
  - Spores enter wound, organisms grow and produce toxin.

HOST DEFENSE AND IMMUNITY:
- **Antibodies** are ineffective.
- **Note:** No immunity is gained by infection or intoxication.

TREATMENT:
- **Botulinum Antitoxin**
  Horse-derived antibodies to the toxin.
- **Respiratory support.**
- **Prevention:** Avoid bulging cans, avoid uncooked or unboiled food, and avoid home-canning.
- **Surgical wound debridement** for wound infection.
- **Metronidazole** for wound infection.

VACCINE AND TOXOID:
None

Clostridium difficile

GRAM STAIN:
POS

OBLIGATE ANAEROBE

EXTRACELLULAR

FEATURES:
- **Morphology:**
  Rods
- **Grouping:**
- **Colonies:**
  -Not usually done.

MOTILITY:
Peritrichous
Flagella

CAPSULE:
None

GLYCOCALYX:
None

SPORES

EXOTOXINS:
- **Enterotoxin:**
  - **Toxin A:**
    Agent of diarrhea and colitis.

- **Cytotoxin:**
  - **Toxin B:**
    Causes lysis of host cells.
    Requires presence of Toxin A.

VIRULENCE FACTORS:
- **Exotoxins:** see above.
- **Antibiotic Resistence:**
  C. difficile has a great ability to resist many antibiotics.
- **Spore Formation:**
  Enables survival in extreme and harsh conditions.

LAB TESTS:
- **Stool Specimen Tests** to detect toxin A or B.
- **CCFA media** (cycloserine, cefoxitin, and fructose agar) can be used to isolate the organism from stool samples.

SOURCE AND TRANSMISSION:
- **Spores** can survive on fomites and on surfaces in hospitals.
- **Iatrogenic, and Nosocomial infections** by *C. difficile* arrise when *C. difficile* colonizes and outgrows commensal flora during the course of treatment with some antibiotics.

CLINICAL:
- **Antibiotic-Associate Colitis (AAC):**
(*C. difficile* is #1 causative organism.)
  - Disease is also known as "**Pseudomembranous colitis.**"
  - **Nosocomial and iatrogenic:** most often arises within a few days of starting antibiotic therapy (especially clindamycin), especially in a newly hospitalized patient.
  - Symptoms: explosive diarrhea may be bloody and foul-smelling, fever, and yellow pseudomembrane formation in colon.
  - Antibiotics suppress commensal bacteria and enable the highly resistant *C. difficile* to flourish and produce toxins in abundance.
  - Diagnosis by stool sampling to detect concentration of Toxins. Colonoscopy is rarely done to see pseudomembrane.
  - Recurrence is possible.
  - Can be fatal in some cases if left untreated.

HOST DEFENSE AND IMMUNITY:
- **Maintenance of normal colonic flora**
  may prevent *C. difficile* colonization.

TREATMENT:
- **Continue current antibiotic treatment**
  only if absolutely necessary.
- **IV or oral Metronidazole**.
- **Oral Vancomycin** may be used.
- **Electrolyte and fluid replacement**
  may be necessary.

VACCINE AND TOXOID:
None

Clostridium perfringens

GRAM STAIN:
POS

OBLIGATE ANAEROBE

EXTRACELLULAR

FEATURES:
- **Morphology:**
  Rods
- **Grouping:**
  Singly, pairs, chains
- **Colonies:**
  -Opaque, round.
  -Blood agar.
  -Anaerobic

MOTILITY:
None

CAPSULE:
None

GLYCOCALYX:
None

SPORES

EXOTOXINS:
- **Alpha Toxin:**
  - **Lecithinase:**
  - Hemolytic activity lyses membranes,
    including RBC and platelet membranes.
  - **Necrotizing.**

- **Beta Toxin, Epsilon toxin, Iota toxin:**
  All are similar to Alpha toxin.

- **Other minor toxins:**
  Many other toxins are expressed which have various enzymatic
  activities to promote necrosis of tissue.

- **Enterotoxin:** Heat-labile agent of food poisoning.

VIRULENCE FACTORS:
- **Exotoxins:** see above.
- **Spore Formation:**
  Enables survival in extreme and harsh conditions.
  Germination is enhanced by ischemic conditions.
- **Short generation time:**
  Generation time of 10-12 minutes enables very rapid proliferation
  of C. perfringens.

SOURCE AND TRANSMISSION:
- **Spores** occur in soil, dust, air.
- **Normal Flora:** C. perfringens rarely, may be normal intestinal flora.
- **Surgery/Trauma:** Disease occurs by entry of spores in wound site.

CLINICAL:
- **Gas Gangrene:**
  - *C. perfringens* wound infection occurs mostly as a complication of
    surgery or trauma.
  - **Spreads very rapidly** to cause local or spreading tissue necrosis as
    well as systemic intoxication.
  - Can be rapidly fatal.
  - **Settings:** puncture wounds, GI tract surgery, burns, ischemic injury
    to skin or fascia, "back-alley" style abortions, war wounds,
    traffic accidents, and agricultural accidents.
  - **Alpha Toxin** causes **myonecrosis** (necrosis of skeletal muscle),
    gas is produced by *C. perfringens* fermentation of carbohydrates.

- **Food Poisoning:**
  - **Spores** cool and germinate in previously heated food (mostly meats)
    then grow rapidly before being ingested by host to cause a very
    common but mild form of food poisoning and diarrhea.
  - **Enterotoxin** is released by *C. perfringens* in the small intestines to
    cause symptoms within **7-15 hours** of ingestion.
  - **Infection is self-limited.**

- **Enteritis Necroticans:**
  - Extremely rare Beta-Toxin induced GI-necrotizing infection.

HOST DEFENSE AND IMMUNITY:
- **Antibodies** are most likely involved, but all host defenses seem to be
  ineffective against *C. perfringens* gas gangrene.
- **Antitoxin** is no longer available because it was ineffective and caused
  allergic reactions. Passive immunity is not available.

TREATMENT:
- **Wound debridement or amputation**
  especially of muscle, on a daily basis until infection
  is under control.
- **Penicillin G** to kill the organism and for prophylaxis.
- **Metronidazole** in penicillin allergy
  to kill the organism and for prophylaxis
- **Hyperbaric Oxygen**.

LAB TESTS:
- **Blood agar colonies** surrounded by **double zone beta hemolysis**.
- **Milk media** growth shows **stormy fermentation**.
- **Egg yolk agar** growth shows **lecithinase production**
  and **precipitation of insoluble diglycerides**.

VACCINE AND TOXOID:
None

Clostridium tetani

GRAM STAIN:
POS

OBLIGATE ANAEROBE

EXTRACELLULAR

FEATURES:
- **Morphology**:
Rods
    "Tennis Racquet"
- **Grouping**:
Singly, pairs, chains.
- **Colonies**:
-Transparent, villous.
-Serum agar
-Anaerobic

MOTILITY:
Peritrichous
Flagella

CAPSULE:
None

GLYCOCALYX:
None

SPORES:
Killed at 121°C, 15 min
Carried on the rod

EXOTOXINS:
- **Tetanus Toxin (Tetanospasmin):**
  - Enters neuronal tissue by retrograde transport
then irreversibly binds to block neurotransmitter release,
especially in **GABA** and **GLY** pathways.
  - **B chain:** binds to host cells to transport A chain inside.
  - **A chain:** has enzymatic activity.
  - **Neurotoxin effect:**
    Blocks GABA and GLY inhibitory pathways,
thus leaving the excitatory motor neurons un-opposed
in a state of **tetany**: This leads to **Spastic paralysis**.
  - **Coded on a Plasmid**.

- **Hemolysin:**
  - Tetanolysin.

VIRULENCE FACTORS:
- **Tetanus Exotoxin:** see above.
- **Spore Formation:**
  Enables survival in extreme and harsh conditions.

LAB TESTS:
Not usually done

SOURCE AND TRANSMISSION:
- **Spores** occur in soil.
- **Surgery/Trauma:** Disease occurs by entry of spores in wound site.

CLINICAL:
- **Tetanus Wound Infection:** ("Lock-jaw"):
  - *C. tetani* spores enter host via deep puncture wounds and dirty
wounds, they germinate, grow and produce toxin.
  - Tetanus toxin blocks **GABA** and **GLY** inhibitory neural pathways,
this leaves the excitatory motor neurons un-opposed in a state
of tetany. This causes **Spastic Paralysis** characterized by
unremitting muscle contractions.
  - Symptoms:
    Note: Diagnosis must be made on basis of symptoms only.
    Trismus: Lock-jaw
    Opisthotonos: whole body spasm with arched back and neck.
    Facial grimace.
    Respiratory distress occurs during spasms, can be fatal.
    Risus sardonicus: tetany of orbicularis oris.
  - Transport of toxin through neurons can take weeks, recovery may
take months (if host survives), recurrence is possible.
  - **Effects may remain localized** to near the wound site.

- **Neonatal Tetanus:**
  - Due to infection of **umbilical stump**:
    (some human societies support using **mud** on umbilical stump).
  - Symptoms: weakness, fever, rigidity. Mortality can be up to 90%.

HOST DEFENSE AND IMMUNITY:
- **Antibodies** develop to the toxin,
  but usually too late to stop the toxic effects.
- **Tetanus Toxoid** with boosters gives long-standing immunity.

TREATMENT:
- **Tetanus Antitoxin:**
  Human-derived antibodies to the toxin.
- **Diazepam** as a GABA-agonist.
- **Muscle relaxant**
- **Pain reliever**
- **Respiratory support**
- **Nutritional support**
- **IV Fluids**
- **Surgical wound debridement**
- **Metronidazole** to kill the organism.

VACCINE AND TOXOID:
- **Tetanus Toxoid:**
  Inactive toxin is given as part of **DPT**.
  Boosters are required every 10 years.

Chapter 4

COMMENSAL ANAEROBIC BACTERIA

GRAM POSITIVE COCCI:	GRAM POSITIVE RODS:	GRAM NEGATIVE RODS:	

Peptostreptococcus spp
Soft-tissue abscess
	Actinomyces israelii
	Oral Actinomycosis
	Lung Actinomycosis
	Pelvic Actinomycosis
	
	Propionibacterium acnes
	Acne vulgaris
		Bacteroides fragilis
		Intra-abdominal abscess
		Peritonitis
		Bacteremia and Sepsis
		Female genital infections
		
		Fusobacterium spp
		Odontogenic-Oral-
		    Mandibular infections
		Chronic sinusitis
		Brain abscess
		Lung abscess
		Bacteremia and sepsis
		
		Prevotella melaninogenica
		Periodontal disease
		  (gingivitis, trench mouth)
		Human bite wound infections
		Chronic sinusitis
		Brain abscess
		Lung abscess
		Bacteremia and sepsis
		Female genital infections	

Peptostreptococcus spp

GRAM STAIN:
POS

OBLIGATE ANAEROBE

EXTRACELLULAR

FEATURES:
- **Morphology:**
  Cocci
- **Grouping:**
- **Colonies:**
  -Small, white
  -Blood agar
  -Chocolate agar
  -Anaerobic

MOTILITY:
None

CAPSULE:
  Polysaccharide

GLYCOCALYX:
  None

EXOTOXINS:
None

VIRULENCE FACTORS:
- **Capsule:**
  - Enables *Peptostreptococcus* to resist phagocytosis.
  - Enhances abscess formation.
- ***Peptostreptococcus* are low-virulent** organisms that cause opportunistic infections.

LAB TESTS:
- **Culture**

SOURCE AND TRANSMISSION:
- **Commensal bacteria** of normal human GI tract, oral cavity, urogenital tract, and skin.
- **Endogenous spread** due to surgery, immunocompromise, diabetic complications, etc., can lead to infection.
- **Mixed Infections** with *Peptostreptococcus* mixed with other anaerobes as well as aerobes results in a powerful synergy.

CLINICAL:
- **Soft-Tissue Abscess:**
  - Decubitus skin ulcers.
  - Diabetic foot ulcers.
  - Human bite wound infections.
  - Breast abscesses.

- **Bacteremia:**
  - May result from local infection.
  - May lead to infection of any organ of the body.

HOST DEFENSE AND IMMUNITY:
- **IgM and IgG antibodies** against capsule are important during sepsis.
- **Classic complement pathway** combined with antibody, and alternate complement pathway, on its own, are important for opsonization. **C5a** is generated as a chemoattractant.
- **T-Cell mediated** immunity is important to fight abscess.
- **PMN phagocytosis** is important to fight abscess.

TREATMENT:
- **Penicillin G**
- **Vancomycin** in penicillin allergy.

VACCINE AND TOXOID:
None

Actinomyces israelii

GRAM STAIN:
   POS

OBLIGATE ANAEROBE

EXTRACELLULAR

FEATURES:
- **Morphology:**
   Rods
- **Grouping:**
   Branching
   Filamentous
- **Colonies:**
-Form **Sulfur Granules in vivo**
-Grow slowly on many medias
-Anaerobic

MOTILITY:
None

CAPSULE:
None
GLYCOCALYX:
None

EXOTOXINS:
None

VIRULENCE FACTORS:
- **Polymicrobial Infection** is a necessary condition because *A. israelii* is not very virulent and relies on groups of other bacteria to help get an infection started.
- **"Sulfur granules"** are actually masses of the filamentous organism bound together with **calcium phosphate.**

LAB TESTS:
- **H&E stain of sulfur granule: Eosinophilic**
(which is a densely packed colony of *A. Israelii* found only in vivo)
- **Immunofluorescence** and other stains can aid in visualizing the branching chains of bacteria surrounding the granule.

SOURCE AND TRANSMISSION:
- **Normal dental flora,**
- **Normal vaginal flora** in some women.
- **Overgrowth** of the organism due to poor hygiene, trauma, oral surgery, foreign body or due to aspiration, leads to local infection.

CLINICAL:
- **Oral Actinomycosis (cervical-facial):**
   - Symptoms: Dental abscess or painless soft tissue mass along jaw.
   - Lesion arises from over growth of normal oral flora and may spread by direct extension to nearby structures. Lesion may open through skin to form a **sinus tract** which may contain purulent material mixed with yellow **"sulfur granules."**
   - **Presence of sulfur granules** is pathopneumonic for *A. israelii* infection and of diagnostic value when combined with symptoms.

- **Note: Do not confuse this disease with actinomycetoma** which is caused by several aerobic bacteria (especially *Nocardia spp*) which are in the actinomycetes family. *A. israelii* does not cause mycetoma.

- **Lung Actinomycosis (Farmer's Lung):**
   - Symptoms: Pneumonitis, chest pain, hemoptysis, empyema, fever. X-ray may show mass lesion.
   - Infection was thought to arise from inhalation of spores present in grain but now is shown to arise from aspiration of the organism from the oral cavity. May extend to nearby structures.

- **Pelvic Actinomycosis:** Rare, serious infection arising from long term use of IUD.

HOST DEFENSE AND IMMUNITY:
- **Acute inflammation** locally, with walled off abscess formation.

TREATMENT:
- **Surgical debridement.**
- **Penicillin G** initially then,
- **Amoxicillin** for one year to prevent recurrence.
- **Tetracycline** in penicillin allergy.
- **Erythromycin** in pregnancy and penicillin allergy.
- **Prevention:** good oral hygiene.

VACCINE AND TOXOID:
None

Propionibacterium acnes

GRAM STAIN:
POS

OBLIGATE ANAEROBE

EXTRACELLULAR

FEATURES:
- **Morphology:**
Rods
- **Grouping:**
Sometimes branching
- **Colonies:**
-Anaerobic

MOTILITY:
None

CAPSULE:
None

GLYCOCALYX:
None

EXOTOXINS:
None

VIRULENCE FACTORS:
- **Inflammation:** *P. acne* has a great ability to stimulate the host's immune system to produce strong acute inflammation.

SOURCE AND TRANSMISSION:
- **Normal flora** of skin, mouth, eyes.
- **Organism proliferates in acne lesions:** it is not known if the infection is a cause of, or an effect of, the acne lesion.
- **Bacteremia** results when *P. acnes* enters the blood via any puncture wound, needle stick, etc.

CLINICAL:
- **Acne Vulgaris (common acne):**
  - Chronic inflammatory infection of the pilosebaceous unit.
  - Papules, Comedones (blackheads), Pustules or Cysts.
  - Occurs mostly on the face, chest, shoulders, and back.

- **Bacteremia:** Rarely associated with serious consequences.

HOST DEFENSE AND IMMUNITY:
- **Chemotactic substances** are released by *P. acnes*.
- **PMN** phagocytosis.
- **Complement** activation.

TREATMENT:
- **Benzoyl peroxide:** oxidizes the area for topical bacteriostatic effect.
- **Trimethoprim** for systemic treatment.
- **Retinoids** for cystic acne.

LAB TESTS:
- **Indole   Pos**
- **Gas liquid chromatography**
  Reveals **propionic acid** as a metabolite of *P. acne*.
- **Note:** *P. acne* frequently contaminates blood cultures due to its presence on skin.

VACCINE AND TOXOID:
None

Bacteroides fragilis

GRAM STAIN:
NEG

OBLIGATE ANAEROBE

EXTRACELLULAR

FEATURES:
- **Morphology:**
Rods, pale
- **Grouping:**
- **Colonies:**
-Smooth, white-gray
-Selective blood agar
-Anaerobic

MOTILITY:
None

CAPSULE:
Polysaccharide

GLYCOCALYX:
None

EXOTOXINS:
None

ENDOTOXIN:
- **Note:** Endotoxin of *B. fragilis* lacks Lipid A, it is **inactive**.

VIRULENCE FACTORS:
- **Capsule:**
  - Enables *B. fragilis* to resist phagocytosis.
  - Enhances abscess formation.
- **Succinic Acid production:**
  Enables *B. fragilis* to resist phagocytosis.
- **Enzymes:** Promote tissue damage:
  Collagenase, DNase, fibrinolysin, heparinase, hyaluronidase, and neuraminidase.
- **Catalase and Superoxide dismutase** enable *B. fragilis* to tolerate some oxygen and to escape phagocytic oxidative bursts.
- **β-Lactamase** coded on plasmid for β-lactam resistance.
- **Pili: (Fimbria):** Mediates attachment to epithelial cells.
- **Defective LPS** is a poor chemoattractant.

LAB TESTS:
- Catalase   +/-
- Indole   +/-
- 20% Bile   Growth
- Colistin   Resistant
- Kanamycin   Resistant
- Vancomycin   Resistant

SOURCE AND TRANSMISSION:
- **B. fragilis is the #1 commensal bacteria of normal human colon** (concentration 1011/g feces), and sometimes vagina.
- **Endogenous spread** due to perforation of bowel or vagina for any reason can lead to infection.
- **Mixed Infections** with *B. fragilis* mixed with other anaerobes as well as aerobes results in a powerful synergy.

CLINICAL:
- **Intra-Abdominal Abscess:** (#1 causative organism.)
  - Due to disruption of the colonic mucosa for any reason: trauma, surgery, ruptured appendix, or any other perforation.
  - Most often found mixed with other anaerobes and aerobes; aerobes consume local oxygen and enhance anaerobic growth.

- **Peritonitis:** (#1 causative organism due to perforation.)
  - Due to perforation of intestinal wall for any reason.

- **Bacteremia and Sepsis:** (Common cause of bacteremia.)
  - *B. fragilis* often spreads from an initial intra-abdominal infection.
  - Can lead to focal infections such as endocarditis, brain abscesses.
  - **Symptoms:** fever, prostration, but without septic shock (no lipid A) Very often fatal, especially if not treated effectively.

- **Genital Infections in Females:**
  - *B. fragilis* is an occasional cause of pelvic abscesses and **PID**.

HOST DEFENSE AND IMMUNITY:
- **IgM and IgG antibodies** against capsule are important during sepsis.
- **Classic complement pathway** combined with antibody, and alternate pathway on its own are important for opsonization.
  C5a is generated as a chemoattractant.
- **T-Cell mediated immunity** is important to fight abscess.
- **PMN phagocytosis** is important to fight abscess.

TREATMENT:
- **Surgical drainage** of abscesses, with debridement.
- **Metronidazole** for *B. fragilis* plus
- **3rd Gen Cephalosporin** for mixed infections.
- **Hyperbaric Oxygen**

VACCINE AND TOXOID:
None

Fusobacterium spp

GRAM STAIN:
NEG

OBLIGATE ANAEROBE

EXTRACELLULAR

FEATURES:
- **Morphology:**
  Rods Long, thin, tapered ends.
- **Grouping:**
- **Colonies:**
- -Irregular
- -"Crumb-like"
- -Selective blood agar
- -Anaerobic

MOTILITY:
None

CAPSULE:
None
GLYCOCALYX:
None

EXOTOXINS:
None

ENDOTOXINS:
- Lipopolysaccharide (LPS)

VIRULENCE FACTORS:
- **Endotoxin:** Active.
- **Succinic Acid production:** Enables resistance to phagocytosis.
- **Enzymes:** Promote tissue damage:
  Collagenase, DNase, fibrinolysin, heparinase, hyaluronidase, neuraminidase, and phospholipase A.
- **Superoxide dismutase** Enables *Fusobacterium* to escape phagocytic oxidative bursts.
- **β-Lactamase** coded on plasmid for β-lactam resistance.

LAB TESTS:
- **Catalase**   Neg
- **Indole**   +/-
- **20% Bile**   +/-
- **Colistin**   Sensitive
- **Kanamycin**   Sensitive
- **Vancomycin   Resistant**

SOURCE AND TRANSMISSION:
- **Commensal bacteria** of normal human gingiva.
- **Endogenous overgrowth** within dental plaques due to poor oral hygiene can lead to infection. Aspiration can occur.
- **Mixed Infections** with *Fusobacterium* mixed with other anaerobes as well as aerobes results in a powerful synergy.

CLINICAL:
- **Odontogenic-Oral-Mandibular Infections:**
  - **Ludwigs Angina:** Severe sub-maxillary, sub mandibular cellulitis. Spreads from mandibular-molar infection. Subsequent tongue elevation may lead to strangulation.

- **Chronic Sinusitis** (more than three months):
  - Can directly extend to brain.

- **Brain Abscess:** Extension from sinusitis.

- **Lung Abscesses and Necrotizing Pneumonia:**
  - Infection usually arrises from **aspiration** of *Fusobacterium*.
  - Infection sometimes arises from **septic embolism** from jugular vein.
  - **Symptoms:** foul-smelling sputum, cavitation, empyema.

- **Bacteremia and Sepsis:**
  - Most often spreads from an initial periodontal or lung infection.
  - Can lead to focal infections such as endocarditis or brain abscesses.
  - **Symptoms:** Fever, prostration; can be fatal if not treated effectively.

HOST DEFENSE AND IMMUNITY:
- **IgM and IgG antibodies** against capsule are important during sepsis.
- **Classic complement pathway** combined with antibody, and alternate pathway on its own are important for opsonization.
  C5a is generated as a chemoattractant.
- **T-Cell mediated immunity** is important to fight abscess.
- **PMN phagocytosis** is important to fight abscess.

TREATMENT:
- **Metronidazole** for *Fusobacterium* plus
- **3rd Gen Cephalosporin** for mixed infections.
- **Prevention:** Good Oral Hygiene.

VACCINE AND TOXOID:
None

Prevotella melaninogenica

GRAM STAIN:
NEG

OBLIGATE ANAEROBE

EXTRACELLULAR

FEATURES:
- **Morphology:**
  Rods, pale
- **Grouping:**
- **Colonies:**
- -Brown
- -Rabbit laked blood agar
- -Anaerobic

MOTILITY:
None

CAPSULE:
Polysaccharide

GLYCOCALYX:
None

EXOTOXINS:
None

ENDOTOXINS:
- **Lipopolysaccharide (LPS)**

VIRULENCE FACTORS:
- **Endotoxin:** Active
- **Capsule:**
  - Enables *P. melaninogenica* to resist phagocytosis.
  - Enhances abscess formation.
- **Succinic Acid production:**
  Enables *P. melaninogenica* to resist phagocytosis.
- **Enzymes:** Promote tissue damage:
  Collagenase, DNase, fibrinolysin, heparinase, hyaluronidase, neuraminidase, and phospholipase A.
- **Superoxide dismutase:** Enables *P. melaninogenica* to escape phagocytic oxidative bursts.
- **β-Lactamase** coded on plasmid for β-lactam resistance.
- **Vitamin K** produced by other bacteria enhances growth.

LAB TESTS:
- **Catalase**   Neg
- **Indole**   +/-
- **20% Bile**   No Growth
- **Colistin**   +/-
- **Kanamycin**   +/-
- **Vancomycin**   +/-
- **Pigmentation:**   Brown
- **Red Fluorescence under UV**

SOURCE AND TRANSMISSION:
- **#1 commensal bacteria of normal human gingiva** (concentration 1011/ml); also common in vagina.
- **Endogenous overgrowth** within dental plaques and tonsils due to poor oral hygiene can lead to infection. Aspiration can occur.
- **Mixed Infections** with *Fusobacterium* mixed with other anaerobes as well as aerobes results in a powerful synergy.

CLINICAL:
- **Periodontal Disease:**
  - **Gingivitis:** Bleeding gums and abscess formation, halitosis, loose teeth, and bone erosion.
  - **"Trench Mouth":** Rare; acute necrotizing ulcerative gingivitis.
- **Human bite wound infection.**
- **Chronic Sinusitis:** (more than three months): Can directly extend to brain.
- **Brain Abscess:** Extension from sinusitis.
- **Lung Abscess and Necrotizing Pneumonia:**
  - Infection follows aspiration of *P. melaninogenica*.
  - **Symptoms:** foul-smelling sputum, cavitation, empyema.
- **Bacteremia and Sepsis:**
  - Most often spreads from an initial periodontal or lung infection.
  - Can lead to focal infections such as endocarditis, brain abscesses.
  - **Symptoms:** fever, prostration; can be fatal if not treated effectively.
- **Genital Infections in Females:**
  - Common cause of vaginosis with foul-smelling vaginal discharge.
  - Sometimes involved in **PID**.

HOST DEFENSE AND IMMUNITY:
- **IgM and IgG antibodies** against capsule are important during sepsis.
- **Classic complement pathway** combined with antibody, and alternate pathway on its own are important for opsonization.
  C5a is generated as a chemoattractant.
- **T-Cell mediated immunity** is important to fight abscess.
- **PMN phagocytosis** is important to fight abscess.

TREATMENT:
- **Metronidazole** for *P. melaninogenica* plus
- **3rd Gen Cephalosporin** for mixed infections.
- **Prevention:** Good Oral Hygiene.

VACCINE AND TOXOID:
None

Chapter 5

GRAM NEGATIVE COCCI

Neisseria gonorrhoeae	*Neisseria meningitidis*	*Moraxella catarrhalis*	

Sexually transmitted diseases
    Urethritis
    Endocervical infection
    PID
    Fitz-Hugh-Curtis
        Syndrome
Neonatal purulent
        conjunctivitis
Monarticular arthritis
	Epidemic meningitis
	Meningococcemia
	Waterhouse-Friderichsen
	        syndrome
		Otitis media	

Neisseria gonorrhoeae

GRAM STAIN:
NEG

AEROBIC

INTRACELLULAR

FEATURES:
- **Morphology:**
Cocci
- **Grouping:**
Diplococci (pairs)
"**Coffee bean**" appearance
- **Colonies:**
-Small, transparent or white
-**Chocolate agar**

MOTILITY:
None

CAPSULE:
Unknown material

GLYCOCALYX:
None

EXOTOXINS:
None

ENDOTOXIN:
- **Lipooligosaccharide (LOS):**
  - May be released as membranes fragments into the extracellular space and may mediate joint problems in gonococcal arthritis.

VIRULENCE FACTORS:
- **Endotoxin:** Provides antigenic variation.
- **Capsule:** Enables resistance to phagocytes, provides antigenic variation.
- **Pili:** Mediates attachment to epithelial cells, provides antigenic variation.
- **IgA protease:** Prevents opsonization by IgA on mucus membranes.
- **Surface Proteins** (provide serotype and antigenic variations):
  Protein I (porin): forms hydrophilic pores in outer membrane.
  Protein II (Opa): mediates adherence, found in opaque strains.
  Protein III (Rmp): provides protection from antibodies.
- **β-Lactamase** coded on plasmid for β-lactam resistance.
- **Iron-binding protein:** Binds iron needed by *N. gonorrhoeae* for its own metabolic processes.

LAB TESTS:
- **Catalase**   Pos
- **Oxidase**   Pos
- **Sugar utilization reaction:**   Glucose only.
- **PCR** or **LCR** tests may be used for identification in cases where culture is not possible.

SOURCE AND TRANSMISSION:
- **Humans** are the only reservoir of *N. gonorrhoeae*.
- **Horizontal transmission** occurs via sexual contact.
- **Autoinoculation** brings infection to other parts of the body.
- **Vertical transmission** from mother to neonate during birth, occurs due to passage through infected vagina.
- **Deficiency of complement C5-C8** predisposes to bacteremia.

CLINICAL:
- **Male STD:** Site of infection may be urethral, anorectal, pharyngeal depending on sexual practice, but urethral is most common.
  - **Urethritis:**
    Symptoms: Purulent discharge and dysuria begin within 7 days.
- **Female STD:** Site of infection may be endocervical, anorectal, urethral, or vaginal, but endocervical is most common.
  - **Endocervical infection:**
    Symptoms: Purulent vaginal discharge, dysuria, pain, bleeding, but is often asymptomatic in women.
  - **Salpingitis, Cervicitis, Endometritis and PID:**
    Result from an ascending infection and may cause sterility due to scarring of uterine tubes.
  - **Fitz-Hugh-Curtis Syndrome** (Perihepatitis):
    Direct extension of infection from pelvis to liver capsule.
    RUQ pain, laparoscopy will show "**violin-string**" adhesions.
- **Neonates: Ophthalmia neonatorum:** a purulent conjunctivitis acquired by newborn at birth during passage through birth canal.
- **Monoarticular Arthritis:**
N. gonorrhoeae is #1 causative organism of teen/young adult arthritis.
  - Mostly of the knee, mostly in females.
  - Arises from *N. gonorrhoeae* bacteremia.
  - Associated with HLA-B27 genotype.
- **Adult Conjunctivitis:** Purulent, ulcerating, due to autoinoculation.

HOST DEFENSE AND IMMUNITY:
- **Complement and Phagocytosis:**
Once the columnar or cuboidal cells are penetrated by *N. gonorrhoeae*, there is a local acute inflammatory response with pus formation, activation of complement and many PMNs.

TREATMENT:
- **Ceftriaxone**
- **Cefoxitin plus Doxycycline**
  During concurrent infection with Chlamydia.
- **Spectinomycin**
  For use in pregnancy with penicillin allergy.
  Not for pharyngeal infection.
- **Prevention:** Condoms, sex education, abstinence.

VACCINE AND TOXOID:
None

Neisseria meningitidis

GRAM STAIN:
NEG

AEROBIC

INTRACELLULAR

FEATURES:
- **Morphology:**
Cocci
- **Grouping:**
Tetrads (groups of four)
"Coffee bean" appearance
- **Colonies:**
-Small, transparent
-**Chocolate agar**

MOTILITY:
None

CAPSULE:
Polysaccharide

GLYCOCALYX:
None

EXOTOXINS:
None

ENDOTOXIN:
- **Lipooligosaccharide (LOS):**
  - *N. meningitidis* produces and sheds excessive amounts of LOS endotoxin as membrane fragments into the extracellular space.
  - LOS endotoxin stimulates the release of the cytokines TNFa and IL-1 this can then lead to hypotension and septic shock.

VIRULENCE FACTORS:
- **Endotoxin:** Provides antigenic variation, and mediates shock.
- **Capsule:** Enables resistance to phagocytes, provides antigenic variation.
- **Pili:** Mediates attachment to non-ciliated epithelial cells of host.
- **IgA protease:** Prevents opsonization by IgA on mucus membranes.
- **Surface Proteins:** Provide antigenic variations.
- **Iron-binding protein:** Scavenges iron from host stores (such as hemoglobin, transferrin, and lactoferrin of PMNs). Iron is needed by *N. meningitidis* for its own metabolic processes

LAB TESTS:
- **Catalase   Pos**
- **Oxidase   Pos**
- **Sugar utilization reaction: Glucose or Maltose**
- **Latex agglutination** of CSF for rapid diagnosis
- **PCR** or **LCR** tests may be used for identification in cases where culture is not possible.

SOURCE AND TRANSMISSION:
- **Humans** carriers are the only reservoir of *N. meningitidis*. The organism colonizes the nasopharynx.
- **Horizontal transmission** occurs via respiratory droplets.
- **Deficiency of complement C5-C8** predisposes to bacteremia.

CLINICAL:
- **Epidemic Meningitis:**
(especially in children, young adults, and military):
  - **Symptoms:** Fever, neck pain, headache, Brudzinski/Kernig signs. Can be rapidly fatal.
  - **Diagnosis:** Lumbar puncture prior to antibiotic treatment: **CSF:** ↑PMNs, ↓Glucose, Cloudy, Culture.
  - **Follows upper respiratory** infection or meningococcemia.

- **Meningococcemia** (Sepsis with *N. meningitidis*):
  - **Symptoms:** Skin, mucus membranes and conjunctival rashes (blue/red petechia), weakness, hypotension, vascular collapse shock. Can be **rapidly fatal** in many cases.
  - Follows upper respiratory infection.
  - **Deficiency of complement C5-C8** predisposes to infection.
  - Petechia will worsen as infection progresses to **DIC**.

- **Waterhouse-Friderichsen Syndrome:**
Is a very fulminant form of *N. meningitidis* infection with rapid onset of **DIC**, bilateral **adrenal hemorrhage**, and coma. **Rapidly fatal**.

HOST DEFENSE AND IMMUNITY:
- **Circulating antibodies** against capsule.
- **Note:** Antibodies can cross-react to other strains.
- **Activation of complement**
- **PMNs** abound in CSF.
- **Previous infection** confers long lasting immunity.
- **Vaccination** confers long lasting immunity.
- **Endotoxin stimulates cytokines:**
TNFa and IL-1which may mediate shock.

TREATMENT:
- **Penicillin G**
- **Ceftriaxone** in meningitis.
- **Chloramphenicol** in penicillin allergy.
- **Rifampin** prophylaxis for contacts Household, schools, military, etc. And for carriers.
- **Hospitalization in ICU isolation** for management of shock, DIC, and transmission of disease.

VACCINE AND TOXOID:
- **Polyvalent Vaccine** of capsular antigens.

Moraxella catarrhalis

GRAM STAIN:
NEG

AEROBIC

EXTRACELLULAR

FEATURES:
- **Morphology:**
Cocci
- **Grouping:**
Diplococci (pairs)
- **Colonies:**
-Gray
-**Chocolate agar**

MOTILITY:
None

CAPSULE:
Polysaccharide

GLYCOCALYX:
None

EXOTOXINS:
None

ENDOTOXIN:
- **Lipopolysaccharide (LPS)**

VIRULENCE FACTORS:
- **Endotoxin:** Provides antigenic variation, and mediates shock.
- **Capsule:** Enables resistance to phagocytes, provides antigenic variation.
- **Pili:** Mediates attachment to non-ciliated epithelial cells of host.
- **Enzymes**

LAB TESTS:
- **Catalase: Pos**
- **Oxidase: Pos**
- **DNAase agar: Pos**
- **Sugar utilization reaction:** **Sucrose** only.

SOURCE AND TRANSMISSION:
- **Humans upper respiratory tract** and sometimes **vagina** are reservoirs for *M. catarrhalis*.
- **Horizontal transmission** occurs via respiratory droplets.
- **Note:** Children, COPD, and immunocompromised patients are at high risk for infection with *M. catarrhalis*.

CLINICAL:
- **Otitis Media:**
  - *M. catarrhalis* commonly causes otitis media in children.
- **Sinusitis**
- **Laryngitis**
- **Tracheitis**
- **Bacteremia** in immunocompromised, especially AIDS.

HOST DEFENSE AND IMMUNITY:
- **IgM, IgG, and IgA antibodies** against capsule.

TREATMENT:
- **Amoxicillin**
- **TMP-SMZ** in penicillin allergy.

VACCINE AND TOXOID:
None

Chapter 6

GRAM NEGATIVE RODS
Respiratory Related

Bordetella pertussis
Whooping cough

Haemophilus influenzae
Pneumonia
Meningitis
Epiglottitis
Sinusitis
Otitis media
Purulent conjunctivitis

Klebsiella pneumoniae
Pneumonia
UTI
Bacteremia

Legionella pneumophila
Legionnaires' disease
     (atypical pneumonia)
Pontiac fever

Pseudomonas aeruginosa
Pneumonia
Burn wound infections
Endocarditis
     (in IVdrug abusers)
UTI
Bacteremia
Corneal Keratitis
External otitis
     ("swimmer's ear")

Bordetella pertussis

GRAM STAIN:
NEG

AEROBIC

EXTRACELLULAR

FEATURES:
- **Morphology:**
Rods: small like cocci.
- **Grouping:**
Singly, pairs, chains.
- **Colonies:**
-White
-Slow growth (4 days)
-Bordet-Gengou agar

MOTILITY:
None

CAPSULE:
Polysaccharide

GLYCOCALYX:
None

EXOTOXINS:
- **Pertussis Toxin:**
  - **Deactivates inhibitory G-protein:** (Turns off the off signal.)
  5B-unit: Binds to host cells to transport peptide A inside.
  A-unit: Causes addition of ADP-Ribose to Gi-protein:
      increase adenylate cyclase, causes increase cAMP
  - **Blocks PMN diapededis:** Binds fucosyl residue on PMNs to
    prevent binding to ELAM on endothelial cells.
  - Mediates binding to ciliated epithelial cells.
  - Activates pancreatic Islet cells.
- **Adenylate Cyclase Toxin:**
Adenylate cyclase activity causes increase cAMP:
  - Blocks chemotaxis, protects against phagocytosis, oxidative lysis.
  - Stimulated by host's intracellular calmodulin, causes local edema.
- **Dermonecrotic Toxin:**
Causes vascular smooth muscle contraction and ischemic necrosis.
- **Tracheal Toxin:**
Causes ciliastasis (blocks the protective movement of cilia).

ENDOTOXIN:
- **Lipopolysaccharide (LPS)**

VIRULENCE FACTORS:
- **Exotoxins:** see above
- **Endotoxin:**
- **Capsule:** Enables resistance to phagocytes.
- **Filamentous Hemagglutinin:** surface protein which mediates
  attachment to cilited epithelial cells.

LAB TESTS:
- **Oxidase:**   Pos
- **DFA test:** (direct fluorescent antibody test) to identify
  B. pertussis in smear.
- **Agglutination reaction** with antiserum.

SOURCE AND TRANSMISSION:
- **Humans** are the only reservoir of *B. pertussis*.
- **Horizontal transmission** is via respiratory droplets mostly among
  infants and children.
- **Highly contagious.**

CLINICAL:
- **Whooping cough:**
  - Symptoms: Acute tracheobronchitis with **paroxysmal cough**
    characterized by bouts of repetitive coughing with occasional
    inspiratory "whoop" sound due to the **narrowed glottis**; cough
    produces copious **mucus** which contains dead epithelial cells.
  - Symptoms last 1 week to 1 month.

- **Complications of *B. pertussis* infection:**
  - Pneumonia from aspiration, can be fatal.
  - Physical injury from coughing.
  - CNS abnormalities and seizures due to venous congestion and
    pressure from coughing.

- **Complications from vaccination:**
  - Whole-dead-cell vaccine can cause encephalopathy on rare occasion.

HOST DEFENSE AND IMMUNITY:
- **IgM, IgG, and IgA antibodies** against the various cell surface
  components, capsule and toxins.
- **Infection is non-invasive:** it remains localized to the lumen of the
  upper respiratory tract.
- **Vaccine and previous infection** confer long lasting immunity
  (boosters rarely necessary because *B. pertussis* rarely infects adults).

TREATMENT:
- **Erythromycin:** May prevent complications and
reduce infectivity, but disease will still run its course.
- **Oxygen therapy or suction of mucus:**
May be necessary in children.

VACCINE AND TOXOID:
- **Vaccine/Toxoid:**
  - **Killed *B. pertussis* bacteria** combined with Inactive toxin
  is given as part of **DPT** vaccine (also known as **DTwP**).
  - **Acellular *B. pertussis* toxoid** given as part of **DTaP** vaccine.

Haemophilus influenzae

Type b *H. influenzae* (Hib)
Non-Typeable *H. influenzae* (ntHi)

GRAM STAIN:
NEG
BIPOLAR STAINING

AEROBIC

EXTRACELLULAR

FEATURES:
- **Morphology:**
  Rods: small like cocci
- **Grouping:**
- **Colonies:**
  -Translucent
  -Small and round
  -**Factor X (heme)**
  -**Factor V (NAD)**

MOTILITY:
None

CAPSULE:
Polysaccharide

GLYCOCALYX:
None

EXOTOXINS:
None

ENDOTOXIN:
- **Lipopolysaccharide (LPS)**

VIRULENCE FACTORS:
- **Endotoxin:**
- **Capsule:** Enables *H. Influenzae* type b to withstand phagocytosis. This polysaccharide capsule contains ribose, ribitol, phosphate; referred to as polyribitol phosphate (PRP).
  Note: Nontypeable *H. Influenzae* strain ntHi, has no capsule.
- **IgA protease:**
  Prevents opsonization by IgA on mucus membranes.
- **β-Lactamase coded on plasmid:** for penicillin resistance.

LAB TESTS:
- **Blood Agar** may be used only when *S. aureus* is present:
  S. aureus provides factor V, and blood agar provides factor X.
- **Catalase   Pos**
- **Fermentation of glucose** only.

SOURCE AND TRANSMISSION:
- **Humans** are the only reservoirs of *H. influenzae*.
- **Horizontal transmission** of type b is via **respiratory droplets**.
- **Normal flora ntHi:** The non-encapsulated strain ntHi (nontypeable *H. influenzae*) is part of the normal flora of pharynx and conjunctiva.

CLINICAL:
- **Pneumonia:** (especially in **young children** and **elderly**):
  - Symptoms: fever, cough with purulent sputum. Can be **fatal**.
  - Due to type b and ntHi strains.
  - Often predisposed by alcoholism, smoking, or COPD.

- **Meningitis:**
  (*H. Influenzae* is #1 causative organism in **young children** 6 mos-6 yrs)
  - Symptoms: fever, neck pain, headache, weakness, **nuchal rigidity**. Can be **rapidly fatal**.
  - Diagnosis: Lumbar puncture prior to antibiotic treatment:
    CSF: ↑PMNs, ↓Glucose, Cloudy, Culture.
  - Follows **upper respiratory** infection by **type b** (rarely ntHi strain).

- **Epiglottitis:**
  (*H. Influenzae* is #1 causative organism, especially in young children.)
  - Symptoms: fever and sore throat rapidly progressing to dysphagia and drooling. **Rapidly fatal** (hrs) from airway obstruction.
  - Due to type b.

- **Sinusitis and Otitis Media:**
  - Mostly in children; due to ntHi strains.

- **Purulent Conjunctivitis:**
  - Can occur as an epidemic; due to ntHi strains; can be **fatal**.

HOST DEFENSE AND IMMUNITY:
- **IgM, IgG antibodies** to the PRP capsule,
- **Infants lose maternal IgG** within months.
- **Activation of both classic and alternatepathways of complement** is important.
- **PMNs and Macros respond**, but Macros (especially in spleen) are most important.
- **Vaccine confers immunity** for a few years, boosters may be helpful.

TREATMENT:
- **Cefotaxime** or **ceftriaxone** for pneumonia or meningitis.
- **Intubation** immediately for epiglottitis.
- **Chloramphenicol** for all serious *H. influenzae* infections in penicillin allergy.
- **Rifampin** prophylaxis for contacts.

VACCINE AND TOXOID:
- **Vaccine:**
  Polysaccharide conjugated to protein for type b.

Klebsiella pneumoniae

GRAM STAIN:
NEG

AEROBIC

EXTRACELLULAR

FEATURES:
- **Morphology:**
Rods: large and long
- **Grouping:**
- **Colonies:**
-White
-Large
-Slimy, mucoid
-Blood agar

MOTILITY:
None

CAPSULE:
Polysaccharide
Very large capsule

GLYCOCALYX:
None

EXOTOXINS:
None

ENDOTOXIN:
- **Lipopolysaccharide (LPS)**

VIRULENCE FACTORS:
- **Endotoxin:**
- **Capsule:** Enables resistance to phagocytes.
- **β-Lactamase:** coded on R-plasmid for β-lactam resistance and aminoglycoside resistance.
- **Urease:** may help mediate the development of UTIs.

LAB TESTS:
- **Oxidase**　　Neg
- **Lactose**　　Pos
　　(Pink colonies on MacConkey)
- **Indole**　　　　Neg
- **Methyl red**　　Neg
- **Voges-Proskauer**　Pos
- **Simmon's citrate**　Pos
- **TSI** (H_2S)　　Neg
- **Urease**　　Pos
- Fermentation of **glucose**, **sucrose** and **lactose**.

SOURCE AND TRANSMISSION:
- **Normal Flora** of human colon in some cases.
- **Nosocomial transmission** occurs via in-dwelling catheters and endotracheal tubes.

CLINICAL:
- **Pneumonia:**
  - Bronchopneumonia and **Lobar pneumonia**.
  - Symptoms: fever, cough, empyema and hemoptysis with the formation of **thick "currant jelly" sputum**.
  - **Abscess formation** is common. **Can be fatal**.
  - X-ray shows "bowed fissure" infiltrated lower lobe.
  - Nosocomial acquired or community acquired in patients with alcoholism, diabetes mellitus or COPD.

- **UTI:**
  - *K. pneumoniae* is a very common cause of nosocomially acquired urinary tract infections.

- **Bacteremia:**
  - *K. pneumoniae* is second only to *E. coli* as a cause of nosocomially acquired bacteremia.

HOST DEFENSE AND IMMUNITY:
- **IgM, IgG, and IgA antibodies** against capsule and LPS.

TREATMENT:
- **Multiple antibiotics**
  such as **Cefotaxime plus Gentamicin**
  (3rd generation cephalosporin plus aminoglycoside).
- **TMP-SMZ** in penicillin allergy.
- **Note:** treatment must be tailored to susceptibility of the particular isolated strain.

VACCINE AND TOXOID:
None

Legionella pneumophila

GRAM STAIN:
NEG

AEROBIC

INTRACELLULAR

FEATURES:
- **Morphology:**
  Rods: thin
- **Grouping:**
- **Colonies:**
- Slow growth (5 days)
- On buffered charcoal
  yeast extract (BCYE)
  with cysteine and iron.

MOTILITY:
Monotrichous
Flagella

CAPSULE:
None

GLYCOCALYX:
None

EXOTOXINS:
- *L. pneumophilia* releases some toxins which may mediate its
  ability to proliferate within alveolar macrophages.

ENDOTOXIN:
- **Lipopolysaccharide (LPS)**

VIRULENCE FACTORS:
- **Endotoxin:**
- **Prevention of fusion of the phagolysosome:** when ingested by
  alveolar macrophages or blood monocytes. This enables the
  L. pneumophilia to proliferate within these cells.
- **Proteolytic enzymes:** (proteases, esterases, phosphatases,
  endonucleases and peptidases) are produced to lyse the host
  macros and monos. This becomes a cycle of ingestion,
  proliferation, then escape by lysis.
- **β-Lactamase coded on plasmid:** for penicillin resistance.

LAB TESTS:
- Produces **brown** pigment.
- **Catalase**   Pos
- DFA test: Direct IFA stain of specimen.
- Urinary Antigen test.

SOURCE AND TRANSMISSION:
- **Air conditioners, whirlpool baths, humidifiers**, and
  contaminated water supply systems can be reservoirs for
  L. pneumophilia both in hospitals and in community settings.
- **Transmission occurs by inhalation** of aerosols, by **aspiration** of
  contaminated water, but **not from person to person**.

CLINICAL:
- **Legionnaires' Disease:**
  - **Atypical Pneumonia**.
  - Symptoms: non-productive cough and fever develops within 7 days.
  - X-ray usually shows unilateral, lower lobe involvement.
  - May be **fatal in the elderly and immunocompromised patients**,
    otherwise may resolve spontaneously.
  - Nosocomial or community acquired.
- **Pontiac Fever:**
  - Symptoms: fever, chills, headache and sometimes nausea develop
    within 48 hours and spontaneously resolve within 1 week.

HOST DEFENSE AND IMMUNITY:
- **T-cell mediated immunity** is the best host defense against
  L. pneumophilia.
- Antibodies and complement are ineffective to opsonize the organism.

TREATMENT:
- **Azithromycin** or other macrolide.
- **Levofloxacin** as an alternative.
- **Prevention:**
  Super-hot water flushing of water supply,
  and use of UV light is effective,
  but chlorination is not effective.

VACCINE AND TOXOID:
None

Pseudomonas aeruginosa

GRAM STAIN:
NEG

OBLIGATE AEROBE

EXTRACELLULAR

FEATURES:
- **Morphology:**
  Rods: long and thin
- **Grouping:**
  Singly, pairs, chains
- **Colonies:**
  - Large
  - Nutrient agar
  - **Blue-green color**
  - **Fuity odor**

MOTILITY:
Monotrichous
Flagella

CAPSULE:
None

GLYCOCALYX:
Exopolysaccharide

EXOTOXINS:
- **Exotoxin A (Diphtheria-like toxin): ADP-Ribosyltransferase.**
  Peptide B: binds to host cells to transport peptide A inside.
  Peptide A: has enzymatic activity.
  - Attaches ADP Ribose, prevents ribosome movement on mRNA.
  - Blocks host **EF2**:
    (a protein synthesis elongation factor tRNA translocase).
  - Blocks protein synthesis.
  - Mediates local necrosis and systemic spread of infection.
- **Exoenzyme S (similar to exotoxin A):**
  - May specifically mediate burn wound and lung infections.
  - Mediates attachment to host cells, suppresses immune response.
- **Hemolysins (disrupt membrane lipids):**
  - **Phospholipase C:** Degrades phosphatidylcholine of surfactant, causes atelectasis.
  - **Rhamnolipid:** inhibits mucociliary action in respiratory system.

ENDOTOXIN:
- Lipopolysaccharide (LPS) mediates septic shock.

VIRULENCE FACTORS:
- **Exotoxin:**
- **Endotoxin:**
- **Glycocalyx:** Enables adherence to each other and to host epithelial cells. Enables resistance to opsonization and phagocytosis.
- **Proteolytic enzymes (elastase, protease, and others):**
  - **Elastase:** cleaves IgA and IgG, cleaves complement, causes inactivation of TNFa and IFNg, causes necrosis, disrupts the respiratory epithelium and inactivates the mucociliary action.
- **Pyocyanin:** a blue pigment which also mediates the formation of hydroxyl radicals and stimulates PMNs to damage host cells.
- **Multiple drug resistance:**
  - **β-Lactamase** coded on plasmid for β-lactam resistance.
  - **Acetylating enzymes** for aminoglycoside resistance.
  - **Mutant DNA gyrase** for fluoroquinolone resistance.
  - **Acetyltransferase** to break down chloramphenicol.

LAB TESTS:
- **Oxidase**   Pos
- **TSI (H_2S)**   Neg
- **Simmon's citrate** Pos
- *P. aeruginosa* colonies produce pigments which blend into the culture medium:
  blue (pyocyanin)
  green (pyoverdin)
- *P. aeruginosa* colonies produce a **fruity odor.**

SOURCE AND TRANSMISSION:
- *P. aeruginosa* **is everywhere**, especially in moist areas such as hospital sinks and respiratory equipment, swimming pools, whirlpool baths, raw vegetables, and human skin or mucosa.
- **Initial colonization of skin or mucosal surfaces is required** before the organism can spread to cause disease.

CLINICAL:
- **Pneumonia (necrotizing bronchopneumonia):**
  - Symptoms: fever, cough, purulent sputum, cyanosis, lung abscesses.
  - X-ray may show bilateral nodularity and cavitation in lower lobes.
  - Infection arises either from aspiration after pharyngeal colonization, or secondarily from seeding of lung tissue during bacteremia.
  - Occurs in **immunocompromised**, COPD or **cystic fibrosis** patients.
  - **Mostly nosocomially acquired.** Mostly fulminant and rapidly fatal.

- **Burn Wound Infection:**
  - Black or **blue-green discoloration** of wound; strong **fruity odor**.
  - May rapidly progress to cause necrosis of adjacent healthy tissue and to cause serious systemic infection. Can be **fatal**.
  - **Mostly nosocomially acquired**; especially in burn treatment units.

- **Endocarditis (acute or subacute) in IV drug users:**
  - Mostly effects the right heart, especially the tricuspid valve.

- **UTI:** nosocomially acquired; often iatrogenic from catheters.

- **Bacteremia:** most often in immunocompromised; can lead to septic shock; can be fatal. *P. aeruginosa* bacteremia can give rise to infection almost anywhere in the body.

- **Corneal Keratitis:** especially from contact lens use; can cause blindness.

- **Otitis Externa ("Swimmer's ear"):** may be benign or serious; often recurrent.

HOST DEFENSE AND IMMUNITY:
- **Natural immunity**, such as intact skin and mucus membranes, is very important.
- **Fully functioning IgM and IgG antibodies, classic and alternate complement, and PMNs** are all necessary to fight and clear systemic infections of *P. aeruginosa*.
- Immune-competent people have no trouble fighting *P. aeruginosa*.

TREATMENT:
- **Multiple antibiotics:**
  First choice may be gentamicin plus ticarcillin.
- **Aztreonam** in penicillin allergy.
- **Treatment must be tailored** to the specific strain of *P. aeruginosa*.
- **Prevention of burn wound infection** requires daily wound debridement and use of topical silver sulfadiazine (avoid hydrotherapy in bad burns).

VACCINE AND TOXOID:
None

Chapter 7

GRAM NEGATIVE RODS
Urinary Tract Related

Proteus mirabilis
UTI
Urolithiasis
 	
Proteus vulgaris
Morganella morganii
Providencia rettgeri
UTI
Urolithiasis
 	
Providencia stuartii
UTI
Bacteremia in nursing homes
	Enterobacter cloacae
	UTI
	Bacteremia
	Opportunistic pneumonia
	
	Serratia marcescens
	UTI
	Bacteremia
	Opportunistic Pneumonia
	Endocarditis in IV drug
	abusers
	Infective arthritis
	
	Klebsiella pneumoniae
	(see Gram Negative Rods
	        Respiratory Related)
	
	Pseudomonas aeruginosa
	(see Gram Negative Rods
	        Respiratory Related)
		Uropathogenic Escherichia coli
		UTI
		Bacteremia
		Sepsis
		Opportunistic pneumonia
		Neonatal meningitis	

Proteus mirabilis

GRAM STAIN:
NEG

AEROBIC

EXTRACELLULAR

FEATURES:
- **Morphology:**
Rods:
- **Grouping:**
Singly, pairs, chains.
- **Colonies:**
-**Swarming**
-Putrid odor
-Blood agar

MOTILITY:
Peritrichous
Flagella

CAPSULE:
None

GLYCOCALYX:
None

EXOTOXINS:
None

ENDOTOXIN:
- **Lipopolysaccharide (LPS)**

VIRULENCE FACTORS:
- **Endotoxin:**
- **Urease:**
  - Splits urea to ammonium hydroxide; this creates alkaline urine.
  - **Alkaline urine** promotes precipitation of salts to form stones.
  - These **"struvite" stones** obstruct urine flow and promote epithelial cell destruction and persistent infection.
- **Strong motility:**

LAB TESTS:
- **Oxidase**   Neg
- **Lactose**   Neg
- **Indole**   Neg
- **Methyl Red**   Pos
- **Voges-Proskauer**   Neg
- **Simmon's citrate**   Pos
- **Urease**   Pos
- **TSI (H$_2$S)**   Pos

SOURCE AND TRANSMISSION:
- **Normal flora** of colon in some cases, but also found in soil, water.
- **Autoinoculation** occurs via fecal contamination of the urethra.
- **Nosocomial, Iatrogenic** transmission occurs due to urinary catheters.
- **Horizontal transmission** is common due to lack of hand washing.

CLINICAL:
- **UTI:**
  - Upper (**pyelonephritis**) and lower (**cystitis**) urinary tract infections.
  - Symptoms:
    Pyelonephritis: flank pain, **fever**, dysuria, +/-cystitis symptoms.
    Cystitis: dysuria, pyuria, ↑frequency, ↑urgency, +/-hematuria.
  - Diagnosis: urine culture: **>105 bacteria/ml**.
  - *P. mirabilis* is a very common causative organism of UTI.
  - Mostly **community acquired**, but may be nosocomial.
  - Infections may be **acute** or **chronic**.

- **Nephrolithiasis** (a.k.a. Urolithiasis or Kidney stone formation):
  - **"Struvite stones"** a.k.a. **"Staghorn calculus"** are large stones formed in the renal pelvis due to the precipitation of **magnesium-ammonium phosphate salts** "triple phosphate salts." *Proteus* secretes urease which splits urea to generate alkaline urine which enables the precipitation of these salts.
  - The stones **obstruct urine flow** and promote persistence of UTI.
  - Urine sediment microscopy shows:
    characteristic **"Coffin Lid" Crystal:**

HOST DEFENSE AND IMMUNITY:
- **IgM, IgG, and IgA antibodies** against various cell surface components.
- **PMNs** respond in acute infections.
- **Macros and Lymphocytes** respond in chronic infections.

TREATMENT:
- **Ampicillin** for cystitis.
- **TMP-SMZ** for pyelonephritis, or for cystitis in penicillin allergy.
- **Levofloxacin** as an alternative.

VACCINE AND TOXOID:
None

Proteus vulgaris
Morganella morganii
Providencia rettgeri

GRAM STAIN:
NEG

AEROBIC

EXTRACELLULAR

FEATURES:
- **Morphology:**
Rods:
- **Grouping:**
Singly, pairs, chains.
- **Colonies:**
-**Swarming**
-Putrid odor
-Blood agar

MOTILITY:
Peritrichous
Flagella

CAPSULE:
None

GLYCOCALYX:
None

EXOTOXINS:
None

ENDOTOXIN:
- **Lipopolysaccharide (LPS)**

VIRULENCE FACTORS:
- **Endotoxin:**
- **Urease:**
  - Splits urea to ammonium hydroxide; this creates alkaline urine.
  - **Alkaline urine** promotes precipitation of salts to form stones.
  - These **"struvite" stones** obstruct urine flow and promote epithelial cell destruction and persistent infection.
- **Strong motility:**
- **Multiple antibiotic resistance:**

LAB TESTS:
- **Oxidase**   Neg
- **Lactose**   Neg
- **Indole**   **Pos**
- **Methyl Red**   **Pos**
- **Voges-Proskauer** Neg
- **Simmon's citrate** +/-
- **Urease**   **Pos**
- **TSI (H$_2$S)**   +/-

SOURCE AND TRANSMISSION:
- **Normal flora** of colon in some cases, but also found in soil, water.
- **Nosocomial, Iatrogenic** transmission occurs due to urinary catheters.
- **Opportunistic infection** is common in immunocompromised or otherwise debilitated patients.
- **Horizontal transmission** is common due to lack of hand washing.

CLINICAL:
- **UTI:**
  - Upper (**pyelonephritis**) and lower (**cystitis**) urinary tract infections.
  - **Symptoms:**
    Pyelonephritis: flank pain, **fever**, dysuria, +/-cystitis symptoms.
    Cystitis: dysuria, pyuria, ↑frequency, ↑urgency, +/-hematuria.
  - **Diagnosis:** urine culture: **>105 bacteria/ml.**
  - Mostly **nosocomially acquired.**
  - These are **opportunistic** infections in the **immunocompromised.**
  - Infections may be **acute** or **chronic.**

- **Nephrolithiasis** (a.k.a. Urolithiasis or Kidney stone formation):
  - **"Struvite stones"** a.k.a. **"Staghorn calculus"** are large stones formed in the renal pelvis due to the precipitation of **magnesium-ammonium phosphate salts** "triple phosphate salts." *Proteus* secretes urease which splits urea to generate alkaline urine which enables the precipitation of these salts.
  - The stones **obstruct urine flow** and promote persistence of UTI.
  - Urine sediment microscopy shows:
    characteristic **"Coffin Lid" Crystal:**

HOST DEFENSE AND IMMUNITY:
- **IgM, IgG, and IgA antibodies** against various cell surface components.
- **PMNs** respond in acute infections.
- **Macros and Lymphocytes** respond in chronic infections.
- Immune-competent people have no trouble fighting these bacteria.

TREATMENT:
- **Ampicillin** for cystitis.
- **TMP-SMZ** for pyelonephritis, or for cystitis in penicillin allergy.
- **Amikacin** for resistant strains.
- **Levofloxacin** as an alternative.

VACCINE AND TOXOID:
None

Providencia stuartii

GRAM STAIN:
NEG

AEROBIC

EXTRACELLULAR

FEATURES:
- **Morphology:**
Rods:
- **Grouping:**
Singly, pairs, chains.
- **Colonies:**
-Blood agar

MOTILITY:
Peritrichous
Flagella

CAPSULE:
None

GLYCOCALYX:
None

EXOTOXINS:
None

ENDOTOXIN:
- **Lipopolysaccharide (LPS)**

VIRULENCE FACTORS:
- **Endotoxin:**
- **Strong motility:**
- **Multiple antibiotic resistance:**

SOURCE AND TRANSMISSION:
- **Normal flora** of colon in some cases, but also found in soil, water.
- **Nosocomial, Iatrogenic** transmission occurs due to urinary catheters.
- **Opportunistic infection** is common in immunocompromised or otherwise debilitated patients.
- **Horizontal transmission** is common due to lack of hand washing.

CLINICAL:
- **UTI:**
  - Upper (**pyelonephritis**) and lower (**cystitis**) urinary tract infections.
  - Symptoms:
    Pyelonephritis: flank pain, **fever**, dysuria, +/-cystitis symptoms.
    Cystitis: dysuria, pyuria, ↑frequency, ↑urgency, +/-hematuria.
  - Diagnosis: urine culture: **>105 bacteria/ml**.
  - Mostly **nosocomially acquired**.
  - These are **opportunistic** infections in the **immunocompromised**.
  - Infections may be **acute** or **chronic**.

- **Bacteremia:**
  - *P. stuartii* is a very common causative organism of nosocomial bacteremia in **nursing home** patients with chronic urinary **catheterization**.

HOST DEFENSE AND IMMUNITY:
- **IgM, IgG, and IgA antibodies** against various cell surface components.
- **PMNs** respond in acute infections.
- **Macros and Lymphocytes** respond in chronic infections.
- Immune-competent people have no trouble fighting *P. stuartii*.

TREATMENT:
- **Ampicillin** for cystitis.
- **TMP-SMZ** for pyelonephritis, or for cystitis in penicillin allergy.
- **Amikacin** for resistant strains.
- **Levofloxacin** as an alternative.

VACCINE AND TOXOID:
None

LAB TESTS:
Oxidase	Neg
Lactose	Neg
Indole	**Pos**
Methyl Red	**Pos**
Voges-Proskauer	Neg
Simmon's citrate	+/-
Urease	Neg
TSI (H$_2$S)	+/-

Enterobacter cloacae

GRAM STAIN:
NEG

AEROBIC

EXTRACELLULAR

FEATURES:
- **Morphology:**
Rods:
- **Grouping:**
Singly
- **Colonies:**
-White
  - May be mucoid
-Blood agar

MOTILITY:
Flagella

CAPSULE:
  Polysaccharide
  small or absent

GLYCOCALYX:
None

EXOTOXINS:
None

ENDOTOXIN:
- **Lipopolysaccharide (LPS)**

VIRULENCE FACTORS:
- **Endotoxin:**
- **Multiple antibiotic resistance:**

LAB TESTS:
- **Oxidase**   Neg
- **Lactose**   **Pos**
  (Pink colonies on MacConkey)
- **Indole**   Neg
- **Methyl Red**   Neg
- **Voges-Proskauer** Pos
- **Simmon's citrate** Pos
- **Urease**   +/-
- **TSI (H$_2$S)**   Neg

SOURCE AND TRANSMISSION:
- **Normal flora** of colon in some cases.
- **Nosocomial, Iatrogenic** transmission occurs due to urinary catheters, or due to respiratory equipment.
- **Opportunistic infection** is common in immunocompromised or otherwise debilitated patients.
- **Horizontal transmission** is common due to lack of hand washing.

CLINICAL:
- **UTI:**
  - Upper (**pyelonephritis**) and lower (**cystitis**) urinary tract infections.
  - Symptoms:
    Pyelonephritis: flank pain, **fever**, dysuria, +/-cystitis symptoms.
    Cystitis: dysuria, pyuria, ↑frequency, ↑urgency, +/-hematuria.
  - Diagnosis: urine culture: **>105 bacteria/ml**.
  - Mostly **nosocomially acquired**.
  - These are **opportunistic** infections in the **immunocompromised**.
  - Infections may be **acute** or **chronic**.

- **Bacteremia:**
  - As a complication of UTI, pneumonia, IV lines, or IV injections.

- **Pneumonia:**
  - Mostly **nosocomially acquired**.
  - These are **opportunistic** infections in the **immunocompromised**.

HOST DEFENSE AND IMMUNITY:
- **IgM, IgG, and IgA antibodies** against various cell surface components.
- **PMNs** respond in acute infections.
- **Macros and Lymphocytes** respond in chronic infections.
- Immune-competent people have no trouble fighting *E.cloacae*.

TREATMENT:
- **Ampicillin** for cystitis.
- **TMP-SMZ** for pyelonephritis, or for cystitis in penicillin allergy.
- **Amikacin** for resistant strains.
- **Levofloxacin** as an alternative.

VACCINE AND TOXOID:
None

Serratia marcescens

GRAM STAIN:
NEG

AEROBIC

EXTRACELLULAR

FEATURES:
- **Morphology:**
Rods:
- **Grouping:**
Singly
- **Colonies:**
-White or red
-Large
-DNA agar

MOTILITY:
Flagella

CAPSULE:
None

GLYCOCALYX:
None

EXOTOXINS:
None

ENDOTOXIN:
- **Lipopolysaccharide (LPS)**

VIRULENCE FACTORS:
- **Endotoxin:**
- **Multiple antibiotic resistance:**
- **Note:** pigmented strains may be less virulent than non-pigmented strains.

LAB TESTS:
- Produces **red pigment**.
- **Oxidase**   Neg
- **Lactose**   Neg
- **Indole**   Neg
- **Methyl Red**   Neg
- **Voges-Proskauer** Pos
- **Simmon's citrate** Pos
- **Urease**   +/-
- **TSI (H_2S)**   Neg

SOURCE AND TRANSMISSION:
- **Normal flora** of colon in some cases.
- **Nosocomial, Iatrogenic** transmission occurs due to urinary catheters, or due to respiratory equipment, via IV lines, or via IV injections.
- **Opportunistic infection** is common in immunocompromised or otherwise debilitated patients.
- **Horizontal transmission** is common due to lack of hand washing.

CLINICAL:
- **UTI:**
  - Upper (**pyelonephritis**) and lower (**cystitis**) urinary tract infections.
  - Symptoms:
    Pyelonephritis: flank pain, **fever**, dysuria, +/-cystitis symptoms.
    Cystitis: dysuria, pyuria, ↑frequency, ↑urgency, +/-hematuria.
  - Diagnosis: urine culture: **>105 bacteria/ml**.
  - Mostly **nosocomially acquired**.
  - These are **opportunistic** infections in the **immunocompromised**.
  - Infections may be **acute** or **chronic**.
- **Bacteremia:**
  - As a complication of UTI, pneumonia, IV lines, or IV injections.
- **Pneumonia:**
  - Mostly **nosocomially acquired**.
  - These are **opportunistic** infections in the **immunocompromised**.
- **Endocarditis in IV drug users (heroin):**
  - Mostly effects the **right heart**, especially the **tricuspid valve**.
- **Infective Arthritis:**
  - Iatrogenic; occurs in patients who get intra-articular injections.

HOST DEFENSE AND IMMUNITY:
- **IgM, IgG, and IgA antibodies** against various cell surface components.
- **PMNs** respond in acute infections.
- **Macros and Lymphocytes** respond in chronic infections.
- Immune-competent people have no trouble fighting *S. marsescens*.

TREATMENT
- **Ampicillin** for cystitis.
- **TMP-SMZ** for pyelonephritis, or for cystitis in penicillin allergy.
- **Amikacin** for resistant strains.
- **Levofloxacin** as an alternative.

VACCINE AND TOXOID:
None

Uropathogenic Escherichia coli

GRAM STAIN:
NEG

AEROBIC

EXTRACELLULAR

FEATURES:
- **Morphology:**
Rods:
- **Grouping:**
Singly, pairs, chains
- **Colonies:**
-Gray
-May be mucoid
-Blood agar

MOTILITY:
Flagella

CAPSULE:
Polysaccharide
sometimes absent

GLYCOCALYX:
None

EXOTOXINS:
- **Hemolysins:** (disrupt blood cell membranes.)
  - Some hemolysins disrupt RBCs to release iron which is required
    by *E. coli* for its own metabolic processes.
  - α-hemolysin: secreted; disrupts lymphocytes.
  - β-hemolysin: membrane-bound; inhibits PMNs.

ENDOTOXIN:
- Lipopolysaccharide (LPS)

VIRULENCE FACTORS:
- **Exotoxins:**
- **Endotoxin:** (O-antigens): provides **antigenic variation**.
  - Most infections are due to strains O-4, O-6, O-75.
- **Capsule:** (K-antigens): provides antigenic variation.
  - K-antigen-expressing strains are associated with **pyelonephritis**.
  - **K-1** strains are associated with **meningitis** and **bacteremia**.
- **Flagella:** (H-antigens): provides **antigenic variation** and motility.
- **Pili:** (**P-Fimbria** in UTI; **S-Fimbria** in neonatal meningitis):
  - Mediates attachment to epithelial cells of the urinary tract.
- **Siderophores:** substance to chelate host iron:
  - Enhances iron uptake into *E. coli*.
- **Ability to resist opsonization** by complement.

LAB TESTS:
- **Oxidase**   Neg
- **Lactose**   Pos
  (Pink colonies on MacConkey)
- **Indole**   Pos
- **Methyl Red**   Pos
- **Voges-Proskauer** Neg
- **Simmon's citrate** Neg
- **Urease**   Neg
- **TSI (H$_2$S)**   Neg

SOURCE AND TRANSMISSION:
- **Normal flora** of colon in some cases.
- **Autoinoculation** occurs via fecal contamination of the urethra.
- **Nosocomial, Iatrogenic** transmission occurs due to urinary catheters.
- **Vertical transmission** either at birth due to passage through vagina,
  or in utero via ascending infection.
- **Horizontal transmission** is common due to lack of hand washing.

CLINICAL:
- **UTI:** (*E. coli* is #1 causative organism.)
  - Upper (**pyelonephritis**) and lower (**cystitis**) urinary tract infections.
  - Symptoms:
    Pyelonephritis: flank pain, **fever**, dysuria, +/-cystitis symptoms.
    Cystitis: dysuria, pyuria, ↑frequency, ↑urgency, +/-hematuria.
  - Diagnosis: urine culture: **>105 bacteria/ml**.
  - Most **community** acquired infections are uncomplicated;
    present as **cystitis**; and are found in **women** due to **short urethra**.
  - Most **nosocomial** infections are complicated; present as
    pyelonephritis; and are found in **immunocompromised** patients
    due to in-dwelling catheters, urolithiasis, or other **obstruction**.
    Infections may progress to bacteremia or sepsis.
  - Infections may be **acute** or **chronic**.

- **Bacteremia - Sepsis:** (*E. coli* is #1 causative nosocomial organism.)
  - Often as complication of pyelonephritis or iatrogenic from IV lines;
    may lead to **pneumonia** or **septic shock**; can be **fatal**.

- **Neonate Meningitis:** (*E. coli* is #2 causative organism.)
  - Symptoms: fever, lethargy, poor feeding. Seizures = poor prognosis.
  - Invades via mucus membranes, respiratory tract, **sepsis**; often **fatal**.
  - Meningitis must be diagnosed via lumbar puncture:
    CSF: ↑PMNs, ↓Glucose, Cloudy, Culture.
  - **Early onset** (age 0-5 days): Vertical transmission in utero
    Ascending infection, due to ruptured amnionic sac.
  - **Late onset** (age 5-90 days): Vertical transmission at delivery;
    Due to passage through vagina.
    Can be nosocomial.

HOST DEFENSE AND IMMUNITY:
- **IgM, IgG, and IgA antibodies** against various cell surface
  components.
- **PMNs** respond in acute infections.
- **Macros and Lymphocytes** respond in chronic infections.
- **Iron Sequestration** by host blood transferrin and by
  host PMN lactoferrin (iron is required by E. coli).

TREATMENT:
- **Ampicillin** for cystitis.
- **TMP-SMZ** for pyelonephritis,
  or for cystitis in penicillin allergy.
- **Ampicillin plus Gentamicin**
  for neonatal meningitis.
- **Levofloxacin** as an alternative.

VACCINE AND TOXOID:
None

Chapter 8

GRAM NEGATIVE RODS
Gastro-Intestinal Tract Related

STOMACH	SMALL INTESTINES	SMALL AND LARGE INTESTINES	LARGE INTESTINES

Helicobacter pylori
(Lumenal)
    Chronic gastritis
    Duodenal peptic ulcer
    Gastric peptic ulcer
    Gastric carcinoma
	Vibrio cholera
	(Lumenal)
	(Toxin)
	    Cholera diarrhea
	
	EnteroToxigenic
	    Escherichia coli
	(Lumenal)
	(Toxin)
	    Traveler's diarrhea
	
	EnteroPathogenic
	    Escherichia coli
	(aka EnteroAdherant *E. coli*)
	(Lumenal)
	    Childhood diarrhea
	
	EnteroAggregative
	    Escherichia coli
	(Lumenal)
	    Childhood diarrhea
		Campylobacter jejuni
		(Invasive)
		(Zoonotic)
		    Enterocolitis diarrhea
		    Reiter syndrome
		
		Yersinia enterocolitica
		(Invasive)
		(Zoonotic)
		    Enterocolitis diarrhea
		    Sepsis
		    Reiter syndrome
		
		Salmonella enteritidis
		Salmonella typhimurium
		(Invasive)
		(Zoonotic)
		    Enterocolitis
		    Bacteremia
		    Osteomyelitis
		    Reiter syndrome
		
		Salmonella typhi
		Salmonella paratyphoid
		(Invasive)
		    Enteric fever:Typhoid fever
		
		Vibrio parahaemolyticus
		(Invasive)
		    Food poisoning diarrhea
			EnteroHemorrhagic
			    Escherichia coli
			(O157:H7)
			(Lumenal)
			(Toxin)
			Hemorrhagic colitis
			Hemolytic-Uremic syndrome
			
			Shigella spp
			(Invasive)
			(Toxin)
			Bacillary dysentery
			Hemolytic-Uremic syndrome
			Reiter syndrome
			
			EnteroInvasive
			    Escherichia coli
			(Invasive)
			    Inflammatory dysentery

Helicobacter pylori

GRAM STAIN:
NEG

MICROAEROPHILIC

EXTRACELLULAR

FEATURES:
- **Morphology:**
Rods:
   S-shaped
   comma shaped
- **Grouping:**
- **Colonies:**
-Selective media

MOTILITY:
Amphitrichous
Flagella:
"Cork-Screw"
   movement

CAPSULE:
None

GLYCOCALYX:
None

EXOTOXINS:
None

ENDOTOXIN:
- **Lipopolysaccharide (LPS)**

VIRULENCE FACTORS:
- **Endotoxin:**
- **Endotoxin:** (O-antigens): provides antigenic variation.
- **Acid resistance:** *H. pylori* has a great ability to resist destruction by stomach acid.
- **Flagella with corkscrew motility:** enables movement into and within the protective mucus layer of the stomach.
- **Enzymes:**
  - **Urease** generates ammonium ions to buffer gastric acid; this enables survival within the hostile acidic environment.
  - **Mucinase** helps to break through the protective mucus layer.
- **Microaerophilism:** enables survival within stomach mucus layer.
- **Adhesion factors:**
  - Mediate attachment to epithelial cells of the **stomach**.

LAB TESTS:

• **Oxidase**	**Pos**
• **Catalase**	**Pos**
• **Urease**	**Pos**
• **Nitrate reduction**	Neg
• **Hippurate hydrolysis**	Neg
• **Cephalothin**	Susceptible
• **Nalidixic acid**	**Resistant**
• **TSI (H$_2$S)**	Neg

SOURCE AND TRANSMISSION:
- **Human GI tracts** are the only reservoirs for *H. pylori*.
- **Horizontal transmission** occurs via the fecal-oral route; especially in crowded living conditions.
- There is a direct relationship between increased age and increased likelihood of *H. pylori* infection in developed countries.

CLINICAL:
- **Chronic Gastritis (Type B)** (*H. pylori* is #1 associated organism):
  - Chronic infection follows acute infection.
  - *H. pylori* causes **superficial** mucosal inflammation of the **antrum** and **body** of the **stomach**; it is **non-invasive**.
  - Symptoms: this causes some nausea or upper abdominal discomfort, but, in many cases, the patient is **asymptomatic**.
  - 100% of chronic gastritis patients have *H. pylori* infection.

- **Duodenal Peptic Ulcer** (*H. pylori* is #1 associated organism):
  - Occurs in the **setting of *H. pylori* chronic gastritis**.
  - Symptoms: burning upper abdominal pain; 1-3 hrs **after meals**; pain is worse at night but **relieved by eating or use of antacids**.
  - Diagnosis:
    -Endoscopy with biopsy of gastric antrum.
    -Serological tests helpful but not reliable to follow eradication.
    -Breath test: *H. pylori* hydrolyzes carbon-labeled urea which can be detected in a sample of the patient's breath.
  - This ulceration is most often **chronic** and **recurrent**, and may lead to complications such as bleeding, anemia and perforation.
  - 90%-100% duodenal peptic ulcer patients have *H. pylori* infection.

- **Gastric Peptic Ulcer** (*H. pylori* is #1 associated organism):
  Similar to duodenal, except only 50%-80% of gastric peptic ulcers are associated with *H. pylori*.

- **Gastric Carcinoma:** occurs in setting of *H. pylori* chronic gastritis.

- **Note:** *H. pylori is* also associated with **MALT** (mucosa associated lymphoid tissue type lymphoma). Treatment of *H. pylori* casuses degradation of the tumor.

HOST DEFENSE AND IMMUNITY:
- **Strong chronic inflammatory response** with Monos, Macros and Lymphos in the gastric mucosa (mostly the antrum).
- **_H. pylori_ remains in the gastric lumen**; it is non-invasive.

TREATMENT:
- **Combination of the following**:
  Proton Pump Inhibitor
  plus **Clarithromycin**
  plus **Metronidazole**.

VACCINE AND TOXOID:
None

Vibrio cholera

GRAM STAIN:
NEG

AEROBIC

EXTRACELLULAR

FEATURES:
- **Morphology:**
Rods:
    S-shaped
    comma shaped
- **Grouping:**
- **Colonies:**
-Blood agar
-Yellow on TCBS agar

MOTILITY:
Polar
Monotrichous
Flagella

CAPSULE:
None

GLYCOCALYX:
None

EXOTOXINS:
- **Enterotoxin:**
  - **LT** (Heat Labile Toxin) **Cholera Toxin:**
  Coded on **chromosome**.
  Functions in the **small intestines**.
  Activates stimulatory G-protein: (turns **on** the **on signal**)
  Five B-subunits:
      Bind to GM1 ganglioside of mucosal cell membranes;
      mediates entry of the A-unit.
  One A-subunit: causes addition of ADP-Ribose to Gs-protein:
      ↑**adenylate cyclase** , causes ↑**cAMP**;
      mucosal cells secrete Cl- into lumen, water follows.

ENDOTOXIN:
- Lipopolysaccharide (LPS)

VIRULENCE FACTORS:
- **Exotoxin:**
- **Endotoxin:** (O-antigens): provides antigenic variation.
  - **O1 strains** can cause epidemics
  - **Non-O1 strains** cause sporadic infections but not epidemics.
- **Flagellum (H-antigens) and curved shape:**
  - Provides strong motility; enables penetration into mucus layer.
  - Provides antigenic variation.
- **Adhesion factors:**
  - Mediate attachment to epithelial cells of the **small intestines**.

LAB TESTS:

● **Oxidase**	**Pos**
● **Lactose**	**Pos**
(Pink colonies on MacConkey)	
● **Indole**	**Pos**
● **Methyl Red**	**Pos**
● **Urease**	Neg
● **TCBS agar**	**yellow colonies**
	(ferments sucrose)
● **7% NaCl**	No growth
● **Alkaline**	**Growth**

SOURCE AND TRANSMISSION:
- **Human GI tract** is reservoir for V. Cholera.
- *V. Cholera* **may exist free-living in fresh water**.
- **Horizontal transmission** occurs via fecal-oral route, especially from drinking contaminated water.
- **Epidemics** can occur anywhere.

CLINICAL:
- **Cholera:**
  - *V. cholera* remains in **lumen** of **small intestines**, mostly duodenum; it is **non-invasive**.
  - Symptoms: painless, voluminous, odorless **"rice-water" diarrhea** (the "rice" is mucus), **no fever**. The symptoms rapidly progress to include hypotension, dehydration, hypovolemia and shock. Can be **rapidly fatal** (hrs).
  - Diagnosis is made based on symptoms, history, and stool culture; treatment must be administered immediately.
  - Complications: electrolyte losses/imbalances, metabolic acidosis, hypoglycemia (especially in children), abortion (in pregnancy).
  - Infection requires a **very large infective dose** (10^7 organisms) because *V. cholera* is easily destroyed by stomach acid.

HOST DEFENSE AND IMMUNITY:
- **Stomach acid kills *V. cholera***, therefore, only a very large dose can cause infection.
- **Sectreted IgA, and exudate IgG antibodies** to various components and to cholera toxin.
- **Previous infection** confers long lasting type-specific immunity.
- **Non-Invasive:** *V. cholera* remains in the intestinal lumen.
- **Commensal anaerobic bacteria** of the large intestine compete and prevent *V. cholera* from colonizing there.

TREATMENT:
- **Oral or IV replacement of fluids and electrolytes**
  Immediate and continuous is absolutely essential.
- **Solution of table salt plus cooked rice** together in water can substitute as oral home-treatment alternative.
- **Tetracycline** to speed-up recovery.
- **Prevention:** good hygiene, avoid antacids, good waste water treatment.

VACCINE AND TOXOID:
Vaccine:
Ineffective, killed bacteria.

EnteroToxigenic Escherichia coli

GRAM STAIN:
NEG

AEROBIC

EXTRACELLULAR

FEATURES:
- **Morphology:**
Rods:
- **Grouping:**
Singly, pairs, chains
- **Colonies:**
-Gray
-May be mucoid
-Blood agar

MOTILITY:
Sometimes
Flagella

CAPSULE:
  Polysaccharide
  sometimes absent

GLYCOCALYX:
  None

EXOTOXINS:
- **Enterotoxin:** (coded on **plasmids**)
  - **LT** (Heat Labile Toxin) **"Cholera-Like" Toxin:**
    Functions in the **small intestines**.
    Activates stimulatory G-protein: (turns **on** the **on signal**)
    Five B-subunits:
      Bind to GM1 ganglioside of mucosal cell membranes;
      mediates entry of the A-unit.
    One A-subunit: causes addition of ADP-Ribose to Gs-protein:
      ↑**adenylate cyclase**, causes ↑**cAMP**;
      mucosal cells secrete Cl⁻ into lumen, water follows.

  - **ST** (Heat stable Toxin):
    Activates **guanylate cyclase**; ↑**cGMP**;
      blocks ion transport from lumen into cells;
      so water then flows into lumen.

ENDOTOXIN:
- **Lipopolysaccharide (LPS)**

VIRULENCE FACTORS:
- **Exotoxin:**
- **Endotoxin:** (O-antigens): provides antigenic variation.
- **Capsule:** (K-antigens): provides antigenic variation.
- **Flagella:** (H-antigens): provides antigenic variation and motility.
- **Pili: (Fimbria):** aka **Colonization factor Antigen (CFA)**:
  - Coded on a **plasmid**.
  - Provides antigenic variation.
  - Mediates attachment to epithelial cells of the **small intestines.**

LAB TESTS:

● **Oxidase**	Neg
● **Lactose**	**Pos**
(Pink colonies on MacConkey)	
● **Indole**	**Pos**
● **Methyl Red**	**Pos**
● **Voges-Proskauer**	Neg
● **Simmon's citrate**	Neg
● **Urease**	Neg
● **TSI (H₂S)**	Neg

SOURCE AND TRANSMISSION:
- **Normal intestinal flora** of some people in the endemic area.
- **Horizontal transmission** occurs via fecal-oral route when travelers ingest fecal-contaminated food or water, especially raw vegetables.

CLINICAL:
- **Traveler's Diarrhea: (Enteritis):**
  - *ETEC* remains in **lumen** of **small intestines**, it is **non-invasive**.
  - Symptoms: mild or explosive **watery diarrhea**, nausea, vomiting. Symptoms arise within 2-3 days of ingestion of the bacteria. Symptoms last about 4 days.
  - Infection occurs mostly in **adults** from industrialized countries who travel to the tropics (Mexico, Africa, Asia, developing countries).

HOST DEFENSE AND IMMUNITY:
- **Secreted IgA antibodies** to fimbriae.
- **Previous infection** confers long lasting type-specific immunity.
- **Non-Invasive:** *ETEC* remains in the intestinal lumen.

TREATMENT:
- **Self-limited** without treatment.
- **Fluid and electrolyte replacement** is necessary.
- **Prophylaxis is not recommended.**
- **Prevention** eat only cooked foods and drink only bottled water while traveling.

VACCINE AND TOXOID:
None

EnteroPathogenic Escherichia coli

GRAM STAIN:
NEG

AEROBIC

EXTRACELLULAR

FEATURES:
- **Morphology:**
Rods:
- **Grouping:**
Singly, pairs, chains
- **Colonies:**
-Gray
-May be mucoid
-Blood agar

MOTILITY:
Sometimes
Flagella

CAPSULE:
Polysaccharide
sometimes absent

GLYCOCALYX:
None

EXOTOXINS:
- **Enterotoxin:**

ENDOTOXIN:
- **Lipopolysaccharide (LPS)**

VIRULENCE FACTORS:
- **Exotoxin:**
- **Endotoxin:** (O-antigens): provides antigenic variation.
- **Capsule:** (K-antigens): provides antigenic variation.
- **Flagella:** (H-antigens): provides antigenic variation and motility.
- **Pili: (Fimbria):** a.k.a. *EPEC* **Adhesion Factor**:
  - Two kinds: one on plasmid, one on chromosome (**eae gene**).
  - Provides antigenic variation.
  - Mediates **focal attachment** to specific epithelial cells of the **small intestines**.

LAB TESTS:
Oxidase	Neg
Lactose	**Pos**
(Pink colonies on MacConkey)	
Indole	**Pos**
Methyl Red	**Pos**
Voges-Proskauer	Neg
Simmon's citrate	Neg
Urease	Neg
TSI (H$_2$S)	Neg

SOURCE AND TRANSMISSION:
- **Normal intestinal flora** of some people.
- **Horizontal transmission** occurs via fecal-oral route from child to child, when children are living, eating or playing together.
- **Horizontal transmission** also occurs via fecal-oral route from drinking contaminated water.

CLINICAL:
- **Childhood Diarrhea: (Enteritis):**
  - *EPEC* remains in **lumen** of **small intestines**. It is **non-invasive**, but **can disrupt the mucus layer**, and **destroy microvilli**.
  - Symptoms: diarrhea, nausea, vomiting, and **mucus in the stools**.
  - Infection occurs mostly in **young children**, especially in day-care centers or nursery schools; mostly in developing countries.

Note:
EPEC strains are sometimes called "Enteroadherent *E. coli*" or *EAEC*.

HOST DEFENSE AND IMMUNITY:
- **Secreted IgA antibodies** to fimbriae.
- **Previous infection** confers long lasting type-specific immunity.
- **Non-Invasive:** *EPEC* remains in the intestinal lumen.

TREATMENT:
- **Self-limited** without treatment.
- **Fluid and electrolyte replacement** is necessary.

VACCINE AND TOXOID:
None

465444756544465444

EnteroAggregative Escherichia coli

GRAM STAIN:
NEG

AEROBIC

EXTRACELLULAR

FEATURES:
- **Morphology:** Rods:
- **Grouping:** Singly, pairs, chains
- **Colonies:**
  - Gray
  - May be mucoid
  - Blood agar

MOTILITY:
Sometimes Flagella

CAPSULE:
Polysaccharide sometimes absent

GLYCOCALYX:
None

EXOTOXINS:
- **Enterotoxin:**

ENDOTOXIN:
- **Lipopolysaccharide (LPS)**

VIRULENCE FACTORS:
- **Exotoxin:**
- **Endotoxin:** (O-antigens): provides antigenic variation.
- **Capsule:** (K-antigens): provides antigenic variation.
- **Flagella:** (H-antigens): provides antigenic variation and motility.
- **Pili: (Fimbria):**
  - Coded on a **plasmid**.
  - Provides antigenic variation.
  - Mediates **aggressive attachment** to **specific epithelial cells** of the **small intestines**.

LAB TESTS:
- **Oxidase** Neg
- **Lactose** Pos
(Pink colonies on MacConkey)
- **Indole** Pos
- **Methyl Red** Pos
- **Voges-Proskauer** Neg
- **Simmon's citrate** Neg
- **Urease** Neg
- **TSI (H$_2$S)** Neg

SOURCE AND TRANSMISSION:
- **Normal intestinal flora** of some people.
- **Horizontal transmission** occurs via fecal-oral route from child to child, when children are living, eating or playing together.
- **Horizontal transmission** also occurs via fecal-oral route from drinking contaminated water.

CLINICAL:
- **Childhood Diarrhea: (Enteritis):**
  - *EAggEC* remains in **lumen** of **small intestines**. It is **non-invasive**, but **can disrupt the mucus layer**, and **destroy microvilli**.
  - They differ from *EPEC* because of their ability to aggressively, and specifically attach to certain mucosal cells.
  - Symptoms: **persistent diarrhea**, nausea, vomiting. Mucus and sometimes blood can be found in the stools.
  - Infection occurs mostly in **young children**, especially in day-care centers or nursery schools; mostly in developing countries.

HOST DEFENSE AND IMMUNITY:
- **Secreted IgA antibodies** to fimbriae.
- **Previous infection** confers long lasting type-specific immunity.
- **Non-Invasive:** *EAggEC* remains in the intestinal lumen.

TREATMENT:
- **Self-limited** without treatment.
- **Fluid and electrolyte replacement** is necessary.

VACCINE AND TOXOID:
None

Campylobacter jejuni

GRAM STAIN: NEG

ZOONOTIC

MICROAEROPHILIC

EXTRACELLULAR

FEATURES:
- **Morphology:**
  Rods:
  - S-Shape
  - Comma Shape
  - "Seagull-like" pairs
- **Grouping:**
- **Colonies:**
  - Slow growing
  - Selective media

MOTILITY:
Monotrichous
Flagella
Daring Movement

CAPSULE:
None

GLYCOCALYX:
None

EXOTOXINS:
- **Enterotoxin:**
  Enterotoxin and cytotoxin produced, but without significance.

ENDOTOXIN:
- **Lipopolysaccharide (LPS)**

VIRULENCE FACTORS:
- **Endotoxin:** (O-antigens): provides antigenic variation.
- **Capsule:** (K-antigens): provides antigenic variation.
- **Flagella:** (H-antigens):
  - Provides antigenic variation.
  - Flagella antigen undergoes **variation** by **gene rearrangement**.
  - Provides characteristic **darting motility**.
- **Human bile** provides a triving environment for *C. jejuni*.

LAB TESTS:
- **Oxidase**   **Pos**
- **Catalase**   Pos
- **Urease**   Neg
- **Nitrate reduction** Neg
- **Hippurate hydrolysis** **Pos**
- **Cephalothin**   **Resistant**
- **Nalidixic acid**   Susceptible

SOURCE AND TRANSMISSION:
- **Animals** are reservoirs for *C. Jejuni*, so **Zoonotic transmission** occurs via contact with animals: dogs, cats, farm animals, and fowl, especially chicken and turkey.
- **Zoonotic Transmission** also occurs via ingesting food products from the infected animals due to contamination during slaughtering; via raw milk; or by ingesting water contaminated by animal feces (e.g. while backpacking).
- **Horizontal transmission** occurs via fecal-oral route from child to child, when children are living, eating or playing together.

CLINICAL:
- **Enterocolitis:**
  - *C. jejuni* **invades** the mucosal cells of the **jejunum**, **ileum** and **large intestines**. *C. jejuni* thrives in **bile** secretions. The invasion does not progress to become a systemic invasion.
  - Symptoms: **fever**, nausea, abdominal pain and **watery diarrhea** or **bloody diarrhea** with **inflammation** and **pus in stool**. Symptoms arise within 48 hrs of ingesting the bacteria. Symptoms last about 5 days.
  - Symptoms can **mimic appendicitis**.
  - Infections by *C. jejuni* are **very common**, especially in **children** and **young adults**.

- Post-Campylobacter **Reiter Syndrome - Arthritis**:
  - Arthritic disease associated with HLA-B27 genotype.

- **Guillan-Barre Syndrome:**
  Associated with Post-Campylobacter infection.

HOST DEFENSE AND IMMUNITY:
- **Strong acute inflammatory response with PMNs.**
- **T-Cell mediated** immunity is important.
- **Secreted IgA and IgG exudate antibodies** against various bacterial components.
- **Previous infection** confers long lasting immunity.

TREATMENT:
- **Self-limited** without treatment.
- **Fluid and electrolyte replacement** is necessary.
- **Erythromycin** in severe cases.
- **Levofloxacin** as an alternative.
- **Prevention:** good hygiene, especially after handling animals, and avoidance of contaminated water especially when back-packing.

VACCINE AND TOXOID:
None

Yersinia enterocolitica

GRAM STAIN:
NEG

ZOONOTIC

AEROBIC

EXTRACELLULAR

FEATURES:
- **Morphology:**
Rods:
    Coccobacilli
- **Grouping:**
- **Colonies:**
-Blood agar

MOTILITY:
Flagella
Non-motile in host

CAPSULE:
None

GLYCOCALYX:
None

EXOTOXINS:
- **Enterotoxin:**
    Enterotoxin is produced but without significance.

ENDOTOXIN:
- **Lipopolysaccharide (LPS)**

VIRULENCE FACTORS:
- **Endotoxin:** (O-antigens): provides antigenic variation.
- **Flagella:** (H-antigens):
  - Provides antigenic variation.
  - Motility is observed in culture at 25EC but not in host at 37EC.
- **Special Requirements:**
  - **Iron** Y. enterocolitica do not have siderophores and therefore require presence of other organisms to supply them with iron.
  - **Calcium**
- **Ability to resist serum complement** (coded on plasmid).
- **Ability to grow in cold** conditions such as refrigeration.

LAB TESTS:
- **Oxidase**   Neg
- **Catalase**   **Pos**
- **Lactose**   Neg
- **Indole**   +/-
- **Methyl Red**   **Pos**
- **Voges-Proskauer** Neg
- **Simmon's citrate** +/-
- **Urease**   **Pos**
- **TSI (H$_2$S)**   Neg

SOURCE AND TRANSMISSION:
- **Animals** are reservoirs for Y. enterocolitica, **Zoonotic transmission** occurs via contact with animals: **dogs**, cats, farm animals and rodents, especially in **Scandinavia**.
- **ZoonoticTransmission** also occurs via ingesting **food products** from the infected animals due to contamination during slaughtering; via **raw milk**; via cold meat; or by ingesting **water** contaminated by animal **feces**.

CLINICAL:
- **Enterocolitis:**
  - Y. enterocolitica **invades** the mucosal cells of the **ileum and large intestines**. The invasion may progress to **Peyer's patches**.
  - Symptoms: **fever**, nausea, abdominal pain and **watery diarrhea or bloody diarrhea** with **inflammation** and **pus in stool**. Perforation of the ileum may occur in severe cases. Symptoms arise within 1 week of ingesting the bacteria. Symptoms last about 2 weeks.
  - Symptoms can **mimic appendicitis**.
  - Infection requires a **very large infective dose** (10^9 organisms) because Y. enterocolitica are easily destroyed by stomach acid.
  - Y. enterocolitica, although **uncommon**, infect mostly children.
- **Bacteremia - Sepsis:**
  - Mostly in **iron-overload** patients after multiple blood transfusions.
  - Very often **fatal**.
- Post-Yersinia **Reiter Syndrome - Arthritis**:
  - Arthritic disease associated with HLA-B27 genotype.

HOST DEFENSE AND IMMUNITY:
- **Strong acute inflammatory response** with PMNs.
- **Secreted IgA and IgG exudate antibodies** against various bacterial components.
- **Previous infection** confers long lasting immunity.
- **Complement is ineffective**.

TREATMENT:
- **Self-limited** without treatment.
- **Fluid and electrolyte replacement** is necessary.
- **Gentamicin** in sepsis cases.
- **Prevention:** good hygiene, especially after handling animals. Incubation of blood in blood banks before storage.

VACCINE AND TOXOID:
None

Salmonella enteritidis
Salmonella typhimurium

GRAM STAIN:
NEG

Non-Typhoidal *Salmonella*

ZOONOTIC

AEROBIC

INTRACELLULAR

FEATURES:
- **Morphology:**
Rods:
- **Grouping:**
Singly, pairs, chains.
- **Colonies:**
-Gray
-Blood agar

MOTILITY:
Flagella

CAPSULE:
Polysaccharide

GLYCOCALYX:
None

EXOTOXINS:
None

ENDOTOXIN:
- **Lipopolysaccharide (LPS)**

VIRULENCE FACTORS:
- **Endotoxin:** (O-antigens): provides antigenic variation.
- **Capsule:** (K-antigens): provides antigenic variation.
- **Flagella:** (H-antigens): provides antigenic variation and motility.
- **Ability to survive within Macros** (but not PMNs).
- **Invasion factor:**
  - Coded on a chromosome.
  - Mediates **invasion** of mucus layer and invasion of epithelial cells of the ileum and large intestine.
- **Multiple Drug Resistance Enzymes** (coded on **plasmid**):
  - **β-Lactamase:** for penicillin resistance.
  - **Acetlytransferase** to break down chloramphenicol.

LAB TESTS:

- **Oxidase**	Neg
- **Lactose**	Neg
- **Indole**	Neg
- **Methyl Red**	Pos
- **Voges-Proskauer**	Neg
- **Simmon's citrate**	+/-
- **Urease**	Neg
- **TSI (H_2S)**	Pos

SOURCE AND TRANSMISSION:
- **Animals** are reservoirs; **Zoonotic transmission** occurs mostly via ingestion of infected food products such as **eggs**, **milk**, and **chicken**.
- **Zoonotic transmission** may also occur via contact with animals.
- **Horizontal transmission** may occur via fecal-oral route from child to child, when children are living, eating or playing together.
- **Chronic Carrier status** is possible.

CLINICAL:
- **Enterocolitis:**
  - *S. enteritidis* and *S. Typhimurium* **invade** the mucosal cells of the **ileum** and **large intestines**. The invasion may progress to become a **systemic invasion**.
  - Symptoms: **fever**, nausea, vomiting and **watery diarrhea** with **inflammation** and **pus in stool**.
    Symptoms arise within 48 hrs of ingesting the bacteria.
    Symptoms last about 7 days but the *Salmonella* organisms may be carried in the stool for more than a month.
  - Symptoms can **mimic appendicitis**.
  - Infection requires a **very large infective dose** (10^5 organisms) because *Salmonella* are easily destroyed by stomach acid.

- **Bacteremia** (results from spread of enteric infection to blood stream):
  - May lead to infections elsewhere: arterial infections, **endocarditis**, billiary tract infections, **septic arthritis**, and others.
  - Recurrent *Salmonella* bacteremia occurs in **AIDS** patients.

- **Osteomyelitis:** *Salmonella* bone infection arises from hematogenous spread; especially in children with **sickle cell disease**.

- **Post-Salmonellosis Reiter Syndrome - Arthritis:**
  - Arthritic disease associated with HLA-B27 genotype.

HOST DEFENSE AND IMMUNITY:
- **Strong acute inflammatory response** with PMNs.
- **Secreted IgA and IgG exudate antibodies** against various bacterial components.
- **T-Cell mediated immunity** is important.
- **Stomach acid** kills *Salmonella* therefore, only a very large dose can cause infection.

TREATMENT:
- **Self-limited** without treatment.
- **Fluid and electrolyte replacement** is necessary.
- **Ciprofloxacin** or **TMP-SMZ** for systemic infections.
- **Ciprofloxacin** for chronic carriers.
- **Prevention:**
  Avoid raw eggs (Caesar salads).
  Avoid under-cooked chicken.
  Wash your hands always before eating.
  Avoid antacids.

VACCINE AND TOXOID:
None

Salmonella typhi
Salmonella paratyphi

GRAM STAIN:
NEG

Typhoidal *Salmonella*

SOURCE AND TRANSMISSION:
- **Human GI tract** is reservoir for *S. typhi* and *S. paratyphi*. Especially S.E. Asia, Africa, and Latin America.
- **Horizontal transmission** occurs via fecal-oral route, especially from drinking contaminated water.
- **Chronic Carrier status** is possible.

AEROBIC
INTRACELLULAR

FEATURES:
- **Morphology:**
Rods:
- **Grouping:**
Singly, pairs, chains.
- **Colonies:**
-Gray
-Blood agar

MOTILITY:
Flagella

CAPSULE:
Polysaccharide

GLYCOCALYX:
None

EXOTOXINS:
None

ENDOTOXIN:
- **Lipopolysaccharide (LPS)**

VIRULENCE FACTORS:
- **Endotoxin:** (O-antigens): provides antigenic variation.
- **Capsule: Vi-antigens:**
Aids in resistance to antibodies and complement.
- **Flagella:** (H-antigens):
  - Provides antigenic variation and motility.
  - Flagella antigen undergoes variation by **gene rearrangement**.
- **Ability to survive within Macros** (but not PMNs).
- **Invasion factor:**
  - Coded on a chromosome.
  - Mediates **invasion** of mucus layer and invasion of epithelial cells of the ileum and large intestine.
- **Multiple Drug Resistance Enzymes** (coded on **plasmid**):
  - β-Lactamase: for penicillin resistance.
  - **Acetlytransferase** to break down chloramphenicol.

CLINICAL:
- **Enteric Fever** (**Typhoid Fever** and **Paratyphoid Fever**):
  - *S. typhi* and *S. paratyphi* **invade** the **Peyer's Patches** of the **ileum** and **large intestines**. The invasion progresses via **thoracic duct** to become a **systemic invasion**.
  - Symptoms: **fever**, enterocolitis with **diarrhea** and abdominal pain, hepatosplenomegaly, **bradycardia**, and **rose spots on trunk**. **Late symptoms** (4 wks): intestinal hemorrhage and delirium. Symptoms arise within 7+ days of ingesting the bacteria. Symptoms last about 1 month if untreated, or 1 week if treated. Enteric Fever can be **fatal** or relapsing.
  - Infection requires a **very large infective dose** (10^5 organisms) because *Salmonella* are easily destroyed by stomach acid.
- **Abortion:**
Most pregnancies will end in abortion during Enteric fever.
- **Bacteremia**

HOST DEFENSE AND IMMUNITY:
- **Strong acute inflammatory response** with PMNs.
- **Secreted IgA and IgG exudate antibodies** against various bacterial components.
- **T-Cell mediated immunity** is important.
- **Stomach acid** kills *Salmonella* therefore, only a very large dose can cause infection.
- **Previous infection** confers long lasting immunity.

TREATMENT:
- **Ciprofloxacin** or **TMP-SMZ** for systemic infections.
- **Ciprofloxacin** for chronic carriers.
- **Prevention:**
Observe good hygiene while traveling.
Avoid antacids.

LAB TESTS:
- **Oxidase** — Neg
- **Lactose** — Neg
- **Indole** — Neg
- **Methyl Red** — **Pos**
- **Voges-Proskauer** — Neg
- **Simmon's citrate** — +/-
- **Urease** — Neg
- **TSI (H$_2$S)** — **Pos**

VACCINE AND TOXOID:
Vaccine:
Ineffective killed bacteria.

Vibrio parahaemolyticus

GRAM STAIN:
NEG

AEROBIC

EXTRACELLULAR

FEATURES:
- **Morphology:**
Rods:
   S-shaped
   comma shaped
- **Grouping:**
- **Colonies:**
-Green
-TCBS agar

MOTILITY:
Polar
Monotrichous
Flagella

CAPSULE:
None

GLYCOCALYX:
None

EXOTOXINS:
- **Enterotoxin:**
   An agent of food poisoning.
- **Cytotoxin:**

ENDOTOXIN:
- **Lipopolysaccharide (LPS)**

VIRULENCE FACTORS:
- **Exotoxin:**
- **Endotoxin:** (O-antigens): provides antigenic variation.
- **Flagellum (H-antigens) and curved shape:**
   - Provides strong motility; enables penetration into mucus layer.
   - Provides antigenic variation.
- **Halophilic:**
   - Can thrive in **salt water** or on salt media.

LAB TESTS:
- **Oxidase**   Pos
- **Lactose**   **Pos**
(Pink colonies on MacConkey)
- **Indole**   Pos
- **Methyl Red**   Pos
- **Urease**   Neg
- **TCBS agar**   **Green colonies**
            (Does not ferment sucrose)
- **7% NaCl**   **Growth**
- **Alkaline**   **Growth**

SOURCE AND TRANSMISSION:
- *V. parahaemolyticus* **exists free-living in salt water**.
- **Disease arises from ingesting raw or under-cooked seafood**;
   or from ingesting food contaminated by sea water.

CLINICAL:
- **Food Poisoning:**
   - **Enterotoxin**, preformed when *V. parahaemolyticus* colonizes food,
     is toxic to the mucosal cells of the **small intestines**.
   - *V. parahaemolyticus* **invades** mucosal cells of the **large intestine**,
     but invasion does **not** progress to become systemic.
   - Symptoms: abdominal pain with **explosive watery diarrhea**.
     Symptoms arise within 24 hrs of ingestion of contaminated food.
     Symptoms are self-limited and last about 3 days.
   - Infection requires a **very large infective dose**.

HOST DEFENSE AND IMMUNITY:
- **Strong acute inflammatory response** in reaction to enterotoxin.
- **Secreted IgA and exudate IgG antibodies** against various bacterial
   components.
- **Stomach acid** kills *V. parahaemolyticus* therefore, only a very large
   dose can cause infection.

TREATMENT:
- **Self-limited** without treatment.
- **Fluid and electrolyte replacement** is necessary.
- **Prevention:** cook all seafood well.

VACCINE AND TOXOID:
None

EnteroHemorrhagic Escherichia coli

GRAM STAIN:
NEG

Strain *O157:H7*

AEROBIC

EXTRACELLULAR

FEATURES:
- **Morphology:**
Rods:
- **Grouping:**
Singly, pairs, chains
- **Colonies:**
-Gray
-May be mucoid
-Blood agar

MOTILITY:
Sometimes
Flagella

CAPSULE:
Polysaccharide
sometimes absent

GLYCOCALYX:
None

EXOTOXINS:
- **Enterotoxins:** (coded by lysogeny from temperate bacteriophage)
  - **Shiga-like Toxin I (SLT I):**
    Functions in the **large intestines**.
    Five B-subunits:
    Bind to glycoproteins of mucosal cell membranes;
    mediates entry of the A-unit.
    One A-subunit:
    Inactivates the 28s rRNA subunit within the 60s subunit
    of host mucosal cells to **stop protein synthesis**.
    This **kills mucosal cells** to cause bloody stools.
    This also prevents nutrient absorption.
  - **Shiga-like Toxin II (SLT II):**
    Function is similar to SLT I.
  - **Note:** these toxins were formerly called Vero Toxins due to their
    toxicity to the cells of Vero monkeys.

ENDOTOXIN:
- **Lipopolysaccharide (LPS)**

VIRULENCE FACTORS:
- **Exotoxin:**
- **Endotoxin:** (O-antigens): provides antigenic variation.
- **Capsule:** (K-antigens): provides antigenic variation.
- **Flagella:** (H-antigens): provides antigenic variation and motility.
- **Pili: (Fimbria):**
  - Coded on a **plasmid**.
  - Provides antigenic variation.
  - Mediates attachment to epithelial cells of the **large intestines**.

LAB TESTS:
- **Oxidase**　　　　Neg
- **Lactose**　　　　**Pos**
(Pink colonies on MacConkey)
- **Sorbitol**　　　　Neg
(Colorless on Sorbitol-MacConkey)
- **Indole**　　　　Pos
- **Methyl Red**　　　Pos
- **Voges-Proskauer**　Neg
- **Simmon's citrate**　Neg
- **Urease**　　　　Neg
- **TSI (H$_2$S)**　　　Neg

SOURCE AND TRANSMISSION:
- **Human GI tract** is reservoir for *EHEC*.
- **Horizontal transmission** occurs via fecal-oral route, especially from drinking contaminated water.
- **Horizontal Transmission** is known to occur via fecal-oral route from eating undercooked hamburger in fast-food restaurants.

CLINICAL:
- **Hemorrhagic Colitis (non-inflammatory dysentery):**
  - *EHEC* remains in **lumen** of **large intestines**. It is **non-invasive**, but its toxins can destroy mucosal cells.
  - Symptoms: nausea with watery diarrhea that progresses to **bloody diarrhea** with **no fever** and **no inflammation**.
  - Infection mostly found in **children**, but can be **fatal** in the **elderly**.
- **Hemolytic-Uremic Syndrome:**
  - Symptoms:
    Acute renal failure, hemolytic anemia, thrombocytopenia.
  - Infection occurs mostly in children.
- **Note:** most *EHEC* infections are caused by one strain: *O157:H7*.

HOST DEFENSE AND IMMUNITY:
- **Lack of inflammation**.
- **Secreted IgA and exudate IgG antibodies** against various bacterial components.
- **Previous infection** confers long lasting type-specific immunity.
- **Non-Invasive:** *EHEC* remains in the intestinal lumen.

TREATMENT:
- **Self-limited** without treatment.
- **Fluid and electrolyte replacement** is necessary.
- **Note:** antibiotic use increases risk of Hemolytic-Uremic syndrome in children.

VACCINE AND TOXOID:
None

Shigella spp

Shigella dysenteriae (group A)
Shigella flexneri (group B)
Shigella boydii (group C)
Shigella sonnei (group D)

GRAM STAIN:
NEG

AEROBIC

INTRACELLULAR

FEATURES:
- **Morphology:**
  Rods:
- **Grouping:**
  Singly, pairs
- **Colonies:**
  -Colorless
  -EMB agar

MOTILITY:
None

CAPSULE:
None

GLYCOCALYX:
None

EXOTOXINS:
- **Enterotoxin:**
  - **Shiga Toxin:**
    Functions in the **large intestines**.
    Five B-subunits:
      Bind to glycoproteins of mucosal cell membranes;
      mediates entry of the A-unit.
    One A-subunit:
      Inactivates the 28s rRNA subunit within the 60s subunit
      of host mucosal cells to **stop protein synthesis**.
      This **kills mucosal cells** to cause bloody stools.
      This also prevents nutrient absorption.

ENDOTOXIN:
- **Lipopolysaccharide (LPS)**

VIRULENCE FACTORS:
- **Endotoxin:** (O-antigens): provides antigenic variation.
- **Ability to resist destruction by stomach acid**: this enhances
  Shigella's ability to cause infection with only a few organisms.
- **Invasion factor (similar to *EIEC*):**
  - Coded on **plasmid.**
  - Mediates **invasion and destruction** of **colonic epithelium.**
- **Few organisms are necessary for infection.**

LAB TESTS:
Oxidase	Neg
Lactose	Neg
Indole	+/-
Methyl Red	**Pos**
Voges-Proskauer	Neg
Simmon's citrate	Neg
Urease	Neg
Sereny test	**Pos**
TSI (H$_2$S)	Neg

SOURCE AND TRANSMISSION:
- **Human GI tract** is reservoir for *Shigella*.
- **Horizontal transmission** occurs via **fecal-oral route** from **child to
  child**, when children are living, eating or playing together.
- **Horizontal Transmission** is common among homosexual men.
- **Bacillary dysentery (Shigellosis) is extremely contagious**.
- **Epidemics can occur** especially among troops during war.

CLINICAL:
- **Bacillary Dysentery (Shigellosis):**
  - *Shigella* **invades** the mucosal cells of the **large intestine**, but the
    invasion does **not** progress to become a systemic invasion.
  - Symptoms: **fever** and nausea with watery diarrhea progresses to
    bloody diarrhea with **inflammation** and **pus in stool**.
  - Symptoms arise within 1-3 days of infection as the bacteria descend
    through the small intestines to settle in the large intestines.
    Symptoms last about 7 days.
  - Infection requires a **very small infective dose**:
    as few as **50-300 organisms** can cause disease.
  - Infection occurs mostly in **young children**, especially in day-care
    centers or nursery schools; in the USA and other countries.
    Infections can be **fatal**, especially in elderly or in epidemics.
  - **Note:** currently, *S. sonnei* is the most prevalent agent of Shigellosis;
  however, the dominant species changes from generation to generation.

- **Hemolytic-Uremic Syndrome:**
  - Symptoms:
    Acute renal failure, hemolytic anemia, thrombocytopenia.
  - Infection is mostly found in children.

- Post-Shigellosis **Reiter Syndrome - Arthritis:**
  - Arthritic disease associated with HLA-B27 genotype.

HOST DEFENSE AND IMMUNITY:
- **Strong acute inflammatory response** with PMNs.
- **Secreted IgA and exudate IgG antibodies** against various bacterial
  components.
- **Previous infection** confers long lasting type-specific immunity.
- **Limited-Invasion:** *Shigella* invades only the intestinal mucosa;
  it does not progress to cause systemic infection.

TREATMENT:
- **Self-limited** without treatment.
- **Fluid and electrolyte replacement** is necessary.
- **TMP-SMZ** in serious cases or during epidemics to
  stop transmission. It has little effect on symptoms.

VACCINE AND TOXOID:
None

EnteroInvasive Escherichia coli

GRAM STAIN:
NEG

AEROBIC

EXTRACELLULAR

FEATURES:
- **Morphology:**
Rods:
- **Grouping:**
Singly, pairs, chains
- **Colonies:**
-Gray
-May be mucoid
-Blood agar

MOTILITY:
Sometimes
Flagella

CAPSULE:
Polysaccharide
sometimes absent

GLYCOCALYX:
None

EXOTOXINS:
None

ENDOTOXIN:
- **Lipopolysaccharide (LPS)**

VIRULENCE FACTORS:
- **Endotoxin:** (O-antigens): provides antigenic variation.
- **Capsule:** (K-antigens): provides antigenic variation.
- **Flagella:** (H-antigens): provides antigenic variation and motility.
- **Pili: (Fimbria):**
  - Coded on a **plasmid.**
  - Provides antigenic variation.
  - Mediates attachment to epithelial cells of the **large intestines.**
- **Invasion factor (similar to Shigella):**
  - Coded on **plasmid.**
  - Mediates **invasion and destruction** of **colonic epithelium.**

LAB TESTS:
- **Oxidase**   Neg
- **Lactose**   **Pos**
(Pink colonies on MacConkey)
- **Indole**   **Pos**
- **Methyl Red**   **Pos**
- **Voges-Proskauer** Neg
- **Simmon's citrate** Neg
- **Urease**   Neg
- **TSI (H$_2$S)**   Neg

SOURCE AND TRANSMISSION:
- **Human GI tract** is reservoir for *EIEC.*
- **Horizontal transmission** occurs via fecal-oral route, especially from drinking contaminated water.

CLINICAL:
- **Enterocolitis** and Inflammatory Dysentery:
  - *EIEC* **invades** the mucosal cells of the **large intestine,** but invasion does **not** progress to become a systemic invasion.
  - Symptoms: fever and nausea with watery diarrhea progresses to **bloody diarrhea** with **inflammation** and **pus in stool**.
  - **Note:** these are shigella-like symptoms. Do not confuse *EIEC* with *EHEC* which produces a shigella-like toxin.
  - Infection caused by *EIEC* is **rare,** especially in the USA.

HOST DEFENSE AND IMMUNITY:
- **Strong acute inflammatory response** with PMNs.
- **Secreted IgA and exudate IgG antibodies** against various bacterial components.
- **Previous infection** confers long lasting type-specific immunity.
- **Limited-Invasion:** *EIEC* invades only the intestinal mucosa; it does not progress to cause systemic infection.

TREATMENT:
- **Self-limited** without treatment.
- **Fluid and electrolyte replacement** is necessary.

VACCINE AND TOXOID:
None

Chapter 9

ZOONOTIC BACTERIA

ZOONOTIC TRANSMISSION:
- Direct Contact
- Bites or Scratches
- Ingestion of Animal Food Products
- Inhalation of Animal Bodily Fluids
- Subsequent Horizontal or Vertical Transmission is Possible in some cases

MISCELLANEOUS	ENTERIC-RELATED	FEVER-RELATED	CAT-RELATED

Bacillus anthracis
    Cutaneous Anthrax
    Respiratory Anthrax
		Brucella spp
		    Brucellosis enteric fever
		    Undulant fever
			Bartonella henselae
			    Cat-Scratch disease
			    Bacillary angiomatosis
			    Sepsis

		Coxiella burnetii
		    (some **Vector** transmission)
		Q Fever acute febrile illness
		Q Fever pneumonia
		Q Fever Hepatitis
		Chronic Q Fever endocarditis
			Pasteurella multocida
			    Acute cellulitis
			    Sepsis

		Francisella tularensis
		    (some **Vector** transmission)
		Tularemia
		    ascending lymphadenitis	

Listeria monocytogenes (some **Vertical** transmission) (see Gram Positive Rods)	*Campylobacter jejuni* (some **Horizontal** transmission) (see Gram Negative Rods Gastro-Intestinal Tract)		

Mycobacterium bovis
(some **Horizontal** transmission)
(see Gram Positive Rods:
            Acid-Fast)
	Yersinia enterocolitica
	(some **Horizontal** transmission)
	(see Gram Negative Rods
	        Gastro-Intestinal Tract)		

Leptospira interrogans (see Spirochetes) *Chlamydia psittaci* (see Chlamydia)	*Salmonella enteritidis* *Salmonella typhimurium* (some **Horizontal** transmission) (see Gram Negative Rods Gastro-Intestinal Tract)		

Bacillus anthracis

GRAM STAIN:
POS

ZOONOTIC
▪Vector
Transmission is Possible in some cases

AEROBIC

EXTRACELLULAR

FEATURES:
Morphology:
Rods
  "Boxcar shaped"
Grouping:
Colonies:
-Gray-white
-Blood agar

MOTILITY:
None

CAPSULE:
Polypeptide
D-glutamate

GLYCOCALYX:
None

SPORES:
Require Oxygen for
Germination.

EXOTOXINS:
●**Anthrax Toxin (coded on a plasmid):**
  ▪**Edema Factor (EF):** an adenylate cyclase, causes ↑cAMP.
  ▪**Lethal Factor (LF):** effects unknown.
  ▪**Protective Antigen (PA):** mediates binding to epithelium and
    mediates entry of EF and LF into cells.

VIRULENCE FACTORS:
●**Exotoxins:**
●**Spore Formation:** Enables survival in extreme harsh conditions.
●**Unique Polypeptide Capsule:**
  Enables *B. anthracis* to escape phagocytosis.

LAB TESTS:
●**Catalase**   Pos
●**Hemolysis**   None
●**Polychrome methylene blue**
    is used to stain the peptide capsule.

SOURCE AND TRANSMISSION:
●**Reservoirs for spores:** grazing herbivores, contaminated animal
  skins, wool, goat hair and soil. Textile mills can be a source.
●**Zoonotic transmission** occurs when host contacts an infected animal
  or when host inhales spores.

CLINICAL:
●**Cutaneous Anthrax:**
  ▪**Symptoms:** **round black ulcer** (dime to quarter size) on the skin of
    extremities or face which develops over a few days and lasts
    weeks and heals with a permanent scar. Lymphadenopathy
    may be present but the ulcer is **painless**.
  ▪**Spores** enter wound, germinate, organism grows and releases toxin.
  ▪Can be **fatal** if untreated.

●**Respiratory Anthrax (Woolsorters Disease):**
  ▪Rare but **rapidly fatal**.
  ▪Host inhales spores (often found in wool), they germinate in
    oxygen-rich lungs, grow and release toxin.
  ▪There can be systemic consequences.

HOST DEFENSE AND IMMUNITY:
●**Antibodies** to the peptide capsule.
●**Vaccine** confers long lasting immunity.

TREATMENT:
●**Ciprofloxacin** drug of choice.
●**No Surgery:** The lesion does **not** get excised.

VACCINE AND TOXOID:
●**Vaccine**
  Killed bacteria toxin components.

Brucella spp

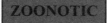

GRAM STAIN:
NEG

ZOONOTIC

AEROBIC

INTRACELLULAR

FEATURES:
- **Morphology:**
Rods:
   Coccobacilli
- **Grouping:**
- **Colonies:**
-Slow growth (4 weeks)
-Blood agar

MOTILITY:
None

CAPSULE:
None

GLYCOCALYX:
None

EXOTOXINS:
None

ENDOTOXIN:
- **Lipopolysaccharide (LPS)**

VIRULENCE FACTORS:
- **Endotoxin:** (O-antigens): provides antigenic variation.
- **Superoxide dismutase:** enzyme and other factors enable Brucella to survive within phagocytes.

LAB TESTS:
- **Oxidase**   +/-
- **Catalase**   **Pos**
- **Urease**   +/-
- **TSI (H$_2$S)**   +/-

SOURCE AND TRANSMISSION:
- **Animals** are reservoirs for *Brucella*, so **Zoonotic transmission** occurs via contact with farm animals such as cattle, goats, sheep and pigs.
- **Abattoir workers**, veterinarians and farmers are at risk.
- **Zoonotic transmission** may also occur via ingesting raw milk.
- **Iatrogenic Zoonotic transmission** may occur via accidental auto-inoculation by veterinarians attempting to inject vaccine into farm animals.

CLINICAL:
- **Brucellosis:**
  - <u>Symptoms</u>: **"Enteric fever"** like symptoms similar to typhoid fever. **Systemic infection** with multiple organ manifestation such as **GI tract** disturbances, **hepatosplenomegaly**, endocarditis, and **pulmonary** involvement. **Granuloma** formation is common, especially in the liver and other organs of the RES.
  - Symptoms begin about 1 to 2 months after infection.
  - Symptoms, with treatment, last about 2 weeks to several months.
  - Relapses are possible.
  - Can be **fatal**, especially from "culture negative" **endocarditis**.

- **Undulant Fever:**
  - <u>Symptoms</u>: **chronic** condition with **"flu-like"** symptoms, fever and **severe depression** results when Brucellosis remains untreated (symptoms resemble "chronic fatigue syndrome").

HOST DEFENSE AND IMMUNITY:
- **IgM and eventually IgG antibodies** are used to fight the infection.
- **T-cell mediated immunity and cytokines** are important to activate phagocytes and promote intracellular killing.
- **Delayed hypersensitivity** causes granuloma formation.

TREATMENT:
- **Doxycycline** (oral) plus **Gentamicin** (IV).
- **TMP-SMZ plus Gentamicin**
   For children or during pregnancy.
- **Prevention:**
   Pasteurization of milk.
   Vaccination of farm animals.

VACCINE AND TOXOID:
- **Vaccine** for animals only.

Coxiella burnetii

GRAM STAIN:
NEG

ZOONOTIC

AEROBIC

INTRACELLULAR

FEATURES:
- **Morphology:**
Rods:
    Coccobacilli
- **Grouping:**
- **Colonies:**
-Requires **cell culture**
    or embryonated eggs
    or test animals

CAPSULE:
None

GLYCOCALYX:
None

MOTILITY:
None

- **SPORES:**

EXOTOXINS:
None

ENDOTOXIN:
- **Lipopolysaccharide (LPS)**

VIRULENCE FACTORS:
- **Endotoxin:** (O-antigens): provides antigenic variation.
- **Superoxide dismutase:** enzyme and other factors enable Brucella to survive within phagocytes.
- **Spores:** Enable survival in extreme conditions or on fomites or in soil for long periods of time.

LAB TESTS:
- **Weil-Felix Reaction:**
    (Types of Rickettsial-infected serum can agglutinate strains of *Proteus vulgaris*)
    ox-19   Neg
    ox-2   Neg
    ox-K   Neg

SOURCE AND TRANSMISSION:
- **Animals** are reservoirs for *Coxiella*, so **Zoonotic transmission** occurs via contact with farm animals such as cattle, goats, sheep pigs, rabbits, birds, and many other animals.
- **Zoonotic Transmission** occurs mostly via inhalation of contaminated aerosols. *C. burnetii* is found in the urine, feces, milk, and placenta of animals, as well as in the nearby soil and dust.
- **Zoonotic Transmission** may occur via ingesting raw milk.
- **Abattoir workers**, veterinarians, and farmers are at risk.
- **VectorTransmission** may occur via **tick**, **mosquito** and **fly** vectors.

CLINICAL:
- **Q Fever: Acute Febrile Illness:**
    - Symptoms: **"flu-like"** with **fever**, chills, headache, photophobia and chest pain.
    - Symptoms begin about 3 weeks after infection.
    - Symptoms are self-limited and last about 2 weeks.
    - **Note:** very small dose, **less than 10 organisms can cause disease**.

- **Q Fever: Pneumonia: Atypical Pneumonia.**
    - Symptoms: interstitial pneumonia with **non-productive cough** and inspiratory crackles, fever, chills, headache, and chest pain.
    - Symptoms begin about 3 weeks after infection.
    - Symptoms last about 1 month

- **Q Fever Hepatitis:**
    - Fever and **"doughnut granuloma"** liver biopsy (lipid with fibrin ring).

- **Chronic Q Fever: Acute or Subacute Endocarditis:**
    - Symptoms: "culture-negative" endocarditis with nodular valve vegetations, hepatosplenomegaly, finger clubbing.
    - Rare but may be incurable or **fatal**.

HOST DEFENSE AND IMMUNITY:
- **IgM and eventually IgG antibodies** are used to fight the infection.
- **T-cell mediated immunity and cytokines** are important to activate phagocytes and promote intracellular killing.
- **Delayed hypersensitivity** causes granuloma formation.

TREATMENT:
- **Tetracycline** for pneumonia.
- **Doxycycline plus TMP-SMZ** (or plus Rifampin) for minimum of 2 yrs, and surgical valve replacement for endocarditis.
- **Prevention:** pasteurization of milk, destruction of animal placentas.

VACCINE AND TOXOID:
None

Francisella tularensis

GRAM STAIN:
NEG
BIPOLAR STAINING

ZOONOTIC

AEROBIC

INTRACELLULAR

FEATURES:
- **Morphology:**
Rods:
  Coccobacilli
  Bipolar Staining
- **Grouping:**
- **Colonies:**
- **Not** usually cultured
- Cysteine media
- **Dangerous**

MOTILITY:
None

CAPSULE:
Lipid

GLYCOCALYX:
None

EXOTOXINS:
None

ENDOTOXIN:
- **Lipopolysaccharide (LPS)**

VIRULENCE FACTORS:
- **Endotoxin:** (O-antigens): provides antigenic variation.
- **Lipid Capsule:**
  - Provides resistance to phagocytosis
  - Provides resistance to opsonization.

LAB TESTS:
- **Catalase**   Pos

SOURCE AND TRANSMISSION:
- **Animals** are reservoirs for *Francisella*, **Zoonotic transmission** occurs via contact with many **wild animals** such as beaver, muskrat, rabbit, squirrel, and sometimes deer.
- **Zoonotic Transmission** may occur via contact with contaminated water, or while handling cultures in the laboratory.
- **Hunters and trappers** are at risk.
- **VectorTransmission** may occur via **tick**, **mosquito** and **fly** vectors.

CLINICAL:
- **Tularemia: Febrile illness:**
  - Symptoms: fever, chills, headache, local or ascending lymphadenitis (with **tender, swollen lymph nodes**), and **local skin ulceration** at the point of entry. Can be **fatal** without proper treatment.
  - Symptoms begin about 5 days after animal contact.
  - Symptoms may last for months.

HOST DEFENSE AND IMMUNITY:
- **Antibodies are ineffective**.
- **T-cell mediated immunity and cytokines** are important to activate phagocytes and promote intracellular killing.
- **Delayed hypersensitivity** causes granuloma formation.
- **Previous infection** confers long lasting immunity.
- **Vaccination** confers immunity.

TREATMENT:
- **Streptomycin**

VACCINE AND TOXOID:
- **Vaccine**
Live-attenuated:
  only for people who are in contact
  with animal as occupation (trappers, etc.).

Bartonella henselae

formerly *Rochalimaea henselae*

GRAM STAIN:
NEG

ZOONOTIC

AEROBIC

INTRACELLULAR

FEATURES:
- **Morphology:**
Rods:
    Small, curved
- **Grouping:**
- **Colonies:**
-White mixed with tan
-Rough, circular
-Slow growth (1 month)
-Selective media

MOTILITY:
"Twitching"

CAPSULE:
None

GLYCOCALYX:
None

EXOTOXINS:
None

ENDOTOXIN:
- **Lipopolysaccharide (LPS)**

VIRULENCE FACTORS:
- **Endotoxin:**

LAB TESTS:
- **Oxidase**   Neg
- **Catalase**   Neg

SOURCE AND TRANSMISSION:
- **Cats** are reservoirs for *B. henselae*, usually in their blood.
- **Zoonotic transmission** occurs via bite or scratch from the infected cat (usually a Kitten).

CLINICAL:
- **Cat-Scratch Disease:**
    - Symptoms: local **lymphadenopathy** consisting of tender, swollen lymph nodes (most times just one node); pustules at the scratch site, and sometimes fever.
    - Symptoms begin about two weeks after the scratch.
    - Symptoms may last for months or years.
    - **Note:** CSD skin test is unsafe and no longer used.

- **Bacillary (Epithelioid) Angiomatosis:**
    - Symptoms: proliferative, neovascular **cutaneous** or visceral lesions especially in **immunocompromised** patients (AIDS).
    The lesions may be papular and may resemble Kaposi's sarcoma.

- **Bacteremia - Sepsis:**
    - Especially in **immunocompromised** patients.

HOST DEFENSE AND IMMUNITY:
- **T-cell mediated immunity** is important.
- **Previous infection** confers long lasting immunity.
- **Delayed hypersensitivity** causes granuloma formation.

TREATMENT:
- **Needle aspiration** but no antibiotics for cat-scratch disease.
- **Erythromycin** for bacillary angiomatosis and sepsis.
- **Prevention:** avoid cats in the case of HIV infection.

VACCINE AND TOXOID:
None

Pasteurella multocida

GRAM STAIN:
NEG
BIPOLAR STAINING

ZOONOTIC

AEROBIC

INTRACELLULAR

FEATURES:
- **Morphology:**
Rods:
    Coccobacilli
    Bipolar Staining
- **Grouping:**
- **Colonies:**
-Gray-yellow
-Musty odor
-Blood agar

MOTILITY:
None

CAPSULE:
Polysaccharide
Large capsule

GLYCOCALYX:
None

EXOTOXINS:
None

ENDOTOXIN:
- **Lipopolysaccharide (LPS)**

VIRULENCE FACTORS:
- **Endotoxin:** (O-antigens): provides antigenic variation.
- **Capsule:** provides resistance to phagocytosis

LAB TESTS:
- **Oxidase** +/-
- **Catalase** Pos
- **Indole** Pos
- **Methyl Red** Neg

SOURCE AND TRANSMISSION:
- **Animals** are reservoirs for *P. multocida*, usually in their **upper respiratory tract and saliva**.
- **Zoonotic transmission** occurs via bite or scratch by infected animal, especially cat or dog.
- **Zoonotic transmission** may also occur via open wounds which get licked by an infected dog or cat.

CLINICAL:
- **Acute Cellulitis:**
  - Symptoms: **rapid** development of local **erythema**, edema and pain following animal bite or scratch, usually on arm, leg or face.
  - Complications: tendonitis, osteomyelitis, and **abscess formation**.
- **Sepsis:**
  - Caused by spread of local infection through the blood, especially in **immunocompromised** patients (AIDS).
- **Respiratory Diseases:**
  - Usually as a complication of underlying chronic respiratory disease.

HOST DEFENSE AND IMMUNITY:
- **Strong acute inflammatory response** with PMNs.
- **IgM and eventually IgG antibodies** against bacterial components.

TREATMENT:
- **Penicillin G** or **ampicillin**.
- **Doxycycline** in penicillin allergy.
- **Prevention:**
    Avoid cats in the case of HIV infection.

VACCINE AND TOXOID:
None

Chapter 10

VECTOR-BORNE BACTERIA

<u>VECTOR TRANSMISSION:</u>
- **Arthropods are vectors**
- **Animals are reservoirs**
- **Humans are hosts**
- **Zoonotic transmission is possible in some cases**
- **Usually no Subsequent Horizontal or Vertical transmission**

FLEA-BORNE	**L**OUSE-BORNE	**M**ITE-BORNE	**T**ICK-BORNE

Yersinia pestis
(Reservoir = rats)
  Bubonic plague
  Septic plague
  Pneumonic plague
	Bartonella quintana
	(Reservoir = humans)
	  Trench fever
		Rickettsia akari
		(Reservoir = mice)
		  Rickettsial pox
			Ehrlichia chaffeensis
			(Reservoir =)
			  Human Ehrlichiosis

Rickettsia typhi
(Reservoir = rats)
Endemic flea-borne **typhus**
  (Murine typhus)
	Rickettsia prowazeckii
	(Reservoir = humans)
	Epidemic louse-borne **typhus**
	Brill-Zinsser disease
		Rickettsia tsutsugamushi
		(Reservoir = mice, rodents)
		Mite-borne **typhus**
		  (Scrub typhus)
			Rickettsia rickettsii
			#1 rickettsial borne disease
			(Reservoir =
			  dogs, mammals, ticks)
			Rocky mountain spotted fever

	Borrelia recurrentis
	(Reservoir = humans)
	(see Spirochetes)
	  Relapsing fever
			Borrelia burgdorferi
			#1 vector borne disease
			(Reservoir = deer, mice, ticks)
			(see Spirochetes)
			  Lyme disease

Yersinia pestis

GRAM STAIN:
NEG
BIPOLAR STAINING

VECTORS

AEROBIC

INTRACELLULAR

FEATURES:
- **Morphology:**
Rods:
  Coccobacilli
  Bipolar Staining
- **Grouping:**
- **Colonies:**
-Blood agar
-**Dangerous**

MOTILITY:
None

CAPSULE:
Protein Polysaccharide

GLYCOCALYX:
None

EXOTOXINS:
Enterotoxin is produced but without significance.

ENDOTOXIN:
- **Lipopolysaccharide (LPS)**

VIRULENCE FACTORS:
- **Endotoxin:** (O-antigens): provides antigenic variation.
- **Capsule:** (coded on plasmid)
  - **Envelope antigen F-1:** enhances survival within phagocytes.
- **Enzymes:**
  - **Coagulase:** causes blood to clot during mosquito blood meal.
  - **Fibrinolysin:**
- **Special Requirements:**
  - Calcium.
- **Ability to absorb organic iron**
  via siderophore-independent means.
- **Ability to resist serum complement** (coded on plasmid).
- **_Y. pestis_ has the ability to survive in animal blood and flea gut.**

LAB TESTS:
- **Oxidase**   Neg
- **Catalase**   **Pos**
- **Lactose**   Neg
- **Indole**   +/-
- **Methyl Red**   **Pos**
- **Voges-Proskauer** Neg
- **Simmon's citrate** +/-
- **Urease**   Neg
- **TSI (H$_2$S)**   Neg

SOURCE AND TRANSMISSION:
- **Animals** are reservoirs for _Y. pestis_; especially urban rats, and sylvatic (woodland) rats, squirrels, and prairie dogs.
- **Vector transmission** occurs via flea bite.
- **Zoonotic transmission** may occur via ingestion of infected animal, or rarely from contact with animals.
- **Horizontal transmission** is rare but may occur via inhalation of **infected human aerosols.**

CLINICAL:
- **Bubonic Plague:**
  - Symptoms: **fever**, chills, **sudden onset** of large, **painful buboes** (femoral, inguinal, axillary or cervical lymphadenitis). **B**acteremia and **sepsis** may ensue within days to cause high fever, tachycardia, hypotension and complete prostration. **Bubonic purpura** is a cutaneous manifestation of vasculitis which can lead to **gangrene** necrosis (hence **"Black Death"**). Infection is often fatal within days.
  - Symptoms arise a few days after the **flea bite**.
  - Symptoms resolve in weeks to months with treatment.
- **Septic Plague:**
  - Same symptoms and course as bubonic plague but **no buboes** arise.
- **Pneumonic Plague:** Bronchopneumonia
  - Symptoms: fever, cough with purulent sputum, and hemoptysis.
  - Arises via **hematogenous** spread of _Y. pestis_ from buboes, or from inhalation of infected aerosols. Rapid onset and usually **fatal.**

HOST DEFENSE AND IMMUNITY:
- **IgM and IgG antibodies** against various bacterial components.
- **Strong acute inflammatory response** with PMNs.
- **T-Cell mediated immunity** is important.
- **Vaccine** confers temporary immunity.
- **Complement is ineffective**.
- **Delayed hypersensitivity** causes granuloma formation.

TREATMENT:
- **Streptomycin**
- **IV fluids and pressors (dopamine)**
  For dehydration and hypotension.
- **Prevention:**
  Keep patient in isolation.
  Rodent control and insecticides.

VACCINE AND TOXOID:
- **Vaccine:**
Killed bacteria:
  For people who may be at risk: travelers, lab workers, etc.
  Boosters every 6 mos.
May no longer be available.

Rickettsia typhi

GRAM STAIN:
NEG
Stains Poorly

AEROBIC

INTRACELLULAR

VECTORS

FEATURES:
- **Morphology:**
Rods:
   Coccobacilli
- **Grouping:**
- **Colonies:**
-Requires **cell culture**
   or embryonated eggs
   or test animals.

MOTILITY:
None

CAPSULE:
None

GLYCOCALYX:
None

EXOTOXINS:
None

ENDOTOXIN:
- **Lipopolysaccharide (LPS)**

VIRULENCE FACTORS:
- **Endotoxin:** (O-antigens): provides antigenic variation.
- **Ability to survive within phagocytes** and to induce phagocytosis
   to gain entry into host's endothelial cells.
- **Ability to survive in rat blood and flea feces**.
- **Enzyme: Phospholipase A:**
   Causes lysis of phagosomal wall enabling the rickettsiae to
   escape into the host cell's cytoplasm.

LAB TESTS:
- **Giemsa** or **Gimenez stain**.
- **Weil-Felix Reaction:**
   (Types of Rickettsial-infected serum can
   agglutinate strains of *Proteus vulgaris*)

ox-19	**Pos**
ox-2	Neg
ox-K	Neg

- Guinea pig testicular swelling.

SOURCE AND TRANSMISSION:
- **Animals** are reservoirs for *R. typhi*; especially urban and suburban
   rats and opossums.
- **Vector transmission** occurs during flea bite.
   (Trans-ovarian transmission from **flea to flea** offspring occurs.)
- Mostly during **warm weather** in **crowded conditions**.

CLINICAL:
- **Endemic Flea-Borne Typhus (Murine Typhus):**
  - *R. typhi* Murine Typhus is a systemic infection which begins when
     the R. typhi bacteria enter the bloodstream via a **flea bite**.
     The rickettsemia progresses to cause **vasculitis** of the small
     vessels of many organs (especially **liver**) and skin lesions.
  - Symptoms: fever, chills, and **macular rash** mostly on the trunk.
  - Symptoms arise 1-2 weeks after flea bite.
  - Symptoms resolve in about 3 weeks, fatalities are rare.
  - **Note:** very small dose **less than 10 organisms can cause disease**.

HOST DEFENSE AND IMMUNITY:
- **IgM and IgG antibodies** against various bacterial components.
- **T-Cell mediated immunity** is important.
- **Previous infection** confers long lasting immunity.
- **Cross-immunity** against *R. typhi* is provided by previous infection
   with *R. Prowazekii* (the reverse is not true).

TREATMENT:
- **Doxycycline**
- **Chloramphenicol** during pregnancy.
- **Prevention:**
   Rodent control and insecticides.

VACCINE AND TOXOID:
None

Bartonella quintana

formerly *Rochalimaea quintana*

GRAM STAIN:
NEG

VECTORS

AEROBIC

EXTRACELLULAR

FEATURES:
- **Morphology:**
Rods:
  Small, curved
- **Grouping:**
- **Colonies:**
-Tan
-Circular
-Slow growth (1 month)
-Selective media

MOTILITY:
"Twitching"

CAPSULE:
None

GLYCOCALYX:
None

EXOTOXINS:
None

ENDOTOXIN:
- **Lipopolysaccharide (LPS)**

VIRULENCE FACTORS:
- **Endotoxin:**
- **Ability to survive in human blood and louse feces.**

LAB TESTS:
- **Oxidase**   Neg
- **Catalase**   Neg

SOURCE AND TRANSMISSION:
- **Humans** are the only reservoirs for *B. quintana*.
- **Vector transmission** occurs during **louse bite**.
- **Vector Transmission** can occur via **inhalation of lice-feces-aerosol** dust from clothing of infected patients.
- **Epidemics** may occur.
- Mostly during **cold weather** (lice infest clothing) in **crowded** conditions, or during wartime.

CLINICAL:
- **Trench Fever:**
  - *B. quintana* Trench Fever is a systemic infection which results in perivascular inflammation.
  - **Symptoms:** **fever** (may occur in cycles lasting about 5 days), chills, headache, severe **bone pain**, and a **transient rash**.
  - Symptoms arise about 2 weeks to 1 month after **louse bite**.
  - Symptoms may **relapse** many times over months or years, but the infection is most often self-limited after 2 months.
  - **Note:** very small dose **less than 10 organisms can cause disease**.

HOST DEFENSE AND IMMUNITY:
- **IgM and IgG antibodies** against various bacterial components.

TREATMENT:
- **Doxycycline**
- **Erythromycin** during pregnancy.
- **Prevention:** Insecticides.

VACCINE AND TOXOID:
None

Rickettsia prowazeckii

GRAM STAIN:
NEG
Stains Poorly

AEROBIC

INTRACELLULAR

VECTORS

FEATURES:
- **Morphology:**
Rods:
  Coccobacilli
- **Grouping:**
- **Colonies:**
-Requires **cell culture**
  or embryonated eggs
  or test animals.

MOTILITY:
None

CAPSULE:
None

GLYCOCALYX:
None

EXOTOXINS:
None

ENDOTOXIN:
- **Lipopolysaccharide (LPS)**

VIRULENCE FACTORS:
- **Endotoxin:** (O-antigens): provides antigenic variation.
- **Ability to survive within phagocytes** and to induce phagocytosis
  to gain entry into host's endothelial cells.
- **Ability to survive in human blood and louse feces**.
- **Enzyme: Phospholipase A:**
  Causes lysis of phagosomal wall enabling the rickettsiae to
  escape into the host cell's cytoplasm.

SOURCE AND TRANSMISSION:
- **Humans and flying squirrels** are reservoirs for *R. Prowazekii*.
- **Vector transmission** occurs during louse bite.
- **Vector transmission** can occur via **inhalation of lice-feces-aerosol**
  dust from clothing of infected patients.
- **Epidemics** may occur.
- Mostly during **cold weather** (lice infest clothing) in **crowded**
  conditions, or during wartime.

CLINICAL:
- **Epidemic Louse-Borne Typhus:**
  - *R. prowazekii* Epidemic Typhus is systemic infection which begins
    when the *R. prowazekii* enter the bloodstream via a **louse bite**.
    The rickettsemia progresses to cause **vasculitis** of the small
    vessels of many organs (especially **liver**), skin lesions, and
    clotting abnormalities.
  - **Symptoms**: high fever, chills, **macular rash** mostly on the trunk.
    The rash eventually becomes papular or petechial, coalesces
    and spreads **centrifugally** to involve the whole body **except**
    the face, palms, and soles.
  - Symptoms arise 1 week after louse bite.
  - Symptoms resolve in about 2 weeks, but complete recovery may
    take months, can be **fatal**.
  - **Note:** very small dose **less than 10 organisms can cause disease**.

- **Brill-Zinsser Disease:**
  - Recrudescent epidemic typhus.
  - Occurs months to years after recovery from initial infection.

HOST DEFENSE AND IMMUNITY:
- **IgM and IgG antibodies** against various bacterial components.
- **T-Cell mediated immunity** is important.
- **Vaccine** confers immunity.
- **Cross-immunity** against *R. typhi* is provided by previous infection
  with *R. Prowazekii* (the reverse is not true).

TREATMENT:
- **Doxycycline**
- **Chloramphenicol** during pregnancy.
- **Prevention:**
  Insecticides.

LAB TESTS:
- **Giemsa** or **Gimenez stain**.
- **Weil-Felix Reaction:**
  (Types of Rickettsial-infected serum can
  agglutinate strains of *Proteus vulgaris*)

ox-19	**Pos**
ox-2	Neg
ox-K	Neg

VACCINE AND TOXOID:
- **Vaccine:**
Killed bacteria:
  For people who may be at risk:
  travelers, lab workers, etc.
  and the patient's care-takers.

Rickettsia akari

GRAM STAIN:
NEG
Stains Poorly

VECTORS

AEROBIC

OBLIGATE INTRACELLULAR

FEATURES:
- **Morphology:**
Rods:
  Coccobacilli
- **Grouping:**
- **Colonies:**
-Requires **cell culture**
  or embryonated eggs
  or test animals.

MOTILITY:
None

CAPSULE:
None

GLYCOCALYX:
None

EXOTOXINS:
None

ENDOTOXIN:
- **Lipopolysaccharide (LPS)**

VIRULENCE FACTORS:
- **Endotoxin:** (O-antigens): provides antigenic variation.
- **Ability to survive within phagocytes** and to induce phagocytosis
  to gain entry into host's endothelial cells.
- **Ability to survive in mouse blood and in mites**.
- **Enzyme: Phospholipase A:**
  Causes lysis of phagosomal wall enabling the rickettsiae to
  escape into the host cell's cytoplasm.

LAB TESTS:
- **Giemsa** or **Gimenez stain.**
- **Weil-Felix Reaction:**
  (Types of Rickettsial-infected serum can
  agglutinate strains of *Proteus vulgaris*)
ox-19	Neg
ox-2	Neg
ox-K	Neg

SOURCE AND TRANSMISSION:
- **Mice** are reservoirs for *R. akari.*
- **Vector transmission** occurs during **mite bite**.
  (Trans-ovarian transmission from **mite to mite** offspring occurs.)
- During **warm weather**.

CLINICAL:
- **Rickettsial Pox:**
  - *R. akari* Rickettsial Pox is systemic infection which begins when
    the *R. akari* enter the bloodstream via a **mouse-mite bite**.
    The rickettsemia progresses to cause **vasculitis** of small vessels
    and skin lesions.
  - Symptoms: a **papule** develops at the bite-site then ulcerates to form
    an **eschar** (a dark scab). Rapid onset of **fever**, chills, headache,
    photophobia, and myalgia sometimes with mild, non-tender
    local lymphadenopathy; a general **papulo-vesicular** rash appears.
  - Symptoms arise 1 week after mite bite; papule - eschar occur first;
    after another 2 weeks, the other symptoms arise.
  - Symptoms resolve in about 3 weeks after pox-like lesions appear;
    disease is **self-limited**.
  - **Note:** very small dose **less than 10 organisms can cause disease**.

HOST DEFENSE AND IMMUNITY:
- **IgM and IgG antibodies** against various bacterial components.
- **T-Cell mediated immunity** is important.

TREATMENT:
- **Self-limited** sometimes without treatment.
- **Doxycycline** to speed recovery.
- **Chloramphenicol** during pregnancy.
- **Prevention:**
  Rodent control and insecticides.

VACCINE AND TOXOID:
None

Rickettsia tsutsugamushi

GRAM STAIN:
NEG
Stains Poorly

AEROBIC

OBLIGATE INTRACELLULAR

FEATURES:
- **Morphology:**
Rods:
   Coccobacilli
- **Grouping:**
- **Colonies:**
-Requires **cell culture**
   or embryonated eggs
   or test animals.

MOTILITY:
None

CAPSULE:
None

GLYCOCALYX:
None

EXOTOXINS:
None

ENDOTOXIN:
- **Note: No Endotoxin**

VIRULENCE FACTORS:
- **Many Serotypes:**
- **Ability to survive within phagocytes** and to induce phagocytosis
   to gain entry into host's endothelial cells.
- **Ability to survive in rodent blood and in mites**.
- **Enzyme: Phospholipase A:**
   Causes lysis of phagosomal wall enabling the rickettsiae to
   escape into the host cell's cytoplasm.

VECTORS

SOURCE AND TRANSMISSION:
- **Rodents** are reservoirs for *R. tsutsugamushi*.
- **Vector transmission** occurs during **mite larva bite (chigger)**.
   (Trans-ovarian transmission from **mite to mite** offspring occurs.)
- During **warm weather**.

CLINICAL:
- **Scrub Typhus** (Mite-Borne Typhus):
   - *R. tsutsugamushi* Scrub Typhus is systemic infection which begins
      when the *R. tsutsugamushi* enter the bloodstream via a rodent
      mite larva bite (chigger). The rickettsemia progresses to
      cause **vasculitis** of small vessels and skin lesions.
   - Rare in the United States, more common in Asia.
   - Symptoms: **papule** develops at the bite-site then ulcerates to form
      an **eschar** (a dark scab). Rapid onset of **high fever**, chills,
      headache, and myalgia with tender local lymphadenopathy;
      then a **maculo-papular rash** appears on the **trunk** and spreads
      centrifugally to the extremities.
   - Symptoms arise 1-2 weeks after mite-chigger bite; papule and
      eschar occur first; after another 5 days, the other symptoms arise.
   - Symptoms resolve in about 2 weeks after skin lesions appear;
      disease is often **self-limited**, but it can be **fatal**.
   - **Note:** very small dose **less than 10 organisms can cause disease**.

HOST DEFENSE AND IMMUNITY:
- **IgM and IgG antibodies** against various bacterial components.
- **T-Cell mediated immunity** is important.

TREATMENT:
- **Self-limited** sometimes without treatment.
- **Doxycycline** to speed recovery.
- **Chloramphenicol** during pregnancy.
- **Prevention:**
   Rodent control and insecticides.

LAB TESTS:
- **Giemsa** or **Gimenez** stain.
- **Weil-Felix Reaction:**
   (Types of Rickettsial-infected serum can
   agglutinate strains of *Proteus vulgaris*)
   ox-19   Neg
   ox-2   Neg
   ox-K   **Pos** (some Neg)

VACCINE AND TOXOID:
None

Ehrlichia chaffeensis

GRAM STAIN:
NEG
Stains Poorly

AEROBIC

OBLIGATE INTRACELLULAR

FEATURES:
- **Morphology:**
Rods:
    Coccobacilli
- **Grouping:**
- **Colonies:**
-Requires **cell culture**
-Not usually done

MOTILITY:
None

CAPSULE:
None

GLYCOCALYX:
None

EXOTOXINS:
None

ENDOTOXIN:
- **Note: No Endotoxin**

VIRULENCE FACTORS:
- **Ability to survive within Macros.**
- **Ability to survive in ticks.**

VECTORS

SOURCE AND TRANSMISSION:
- **Reservoir for *E. chaffeensis* is unknown**.
- **Vector transmission** occurs during **tick bite**.
- During **warm weather**.

CLINICAL:
- **Human Ehrlichiosis:**
  - *E. chaffeensis* Ehrlichiosis is a systemic infection which begins when the *E. chaffeensis* enter the bloodstream and lymphatics via a **tick bite**. The Ehrlichemia progresses to cause multi-organ dysfunction, but **no vasculitis**.
  - May be asymptomatic,
  - Symptoms: slow onset of **fever**, headache, chills, myalgia, nausea and anorexia; a **maculo-papular rash** may or may not appear. Disease may progress to **leukopenia**, **thrombocytopenia**, **pulmonary failure**, **renal failure**, **encephalitis**; and can be **fatal**.
  - Poor prognosis when infection occurs in the elderly.
  - Symptoms arise 1 week after **tick bite**.
  - Symptoms resolve in several weeks, or more rapidly with treatment.

- **Terminology:**
HME: Human Monocytotropic Ehrlichiosis by *E. chaffeensis*.
HGE: Human Granulocytotropic Ehrlichiosis by *E. phagocytophilia*

HOST DEFENSE AND IMMUNITY:
- **IgM and IgG antibodies** against various bacterial components.
- **Complement** is effective.
- ***E. chaffeensis* can survive in Macros** but not in PMNs.
- ***E. phagocytophilia* can survive in PMNs**

TREATMENT:
- **Doxycycline**
- **Prevention:**
    Prompt removal of ticks.

LAB TESTS:
- **Peripheral blood smear** shows **cytoplasmic inclusion** vacuole (**"morulae"** filled with bacteria) inside granulocytes.
- **Serology** shows increased **titer** for *E. chaffeensis* antibody, or for *E. phagocytophilia* antibody.

VACCINE AND TOXOID:
None

Rickettsia rickettsii

GRAM STAIN:
NEG
Stains Poorly

VECTORS

AEROBIC

OBLIGATE INTRACELLULAR

FEATURES:
- **Morphology:**
Rods:
   Coccobacilli
- **Grouping:**
- **Colonies:**
-Requires **cell culture**
   or embryonated eggs
   or test animals.

MOTILITY:
None

CAPSULE:
None

GLYCOCALYX:
None

EXOTOXINS:
None

ENDOTOXIN:
- **Lipopolysaccharide (LPS)**

VIRULENCE FACTORS:
- **Endotoxin:** (O-antigens): provides antigenic variation.
- **Ability to survive within phagocytes** and to induce phagocytosis
   to gain entry into host's endothelial cells.
- **Ability to survive in animal blood and in ticks**.
- **Enzyme: Phospholipase A:**
   Causes lysis of phagosomal wall enabling the rickettsiae to
   escape into the host cell's cytoplasm.

SOURCE AND TRANSMISSION:
- **Animals and ticks** are reservoirs for *R. rickettsii*.
- **Vector transmission** occurs during **tick bite**.
   (Tick must remain attached for 6-8 hours or longer.)
   (Trans-ovarian transmission from **tick to tick** offspring occurs.)
- During **warm weather**.

CLINICAL:
- **Rocky Mountain Spotted Fever:**
   - *R. rickettsii* Rocky Mountain Spotted Fever is a systemic infection
      which begins when the *R. rickettsii* enter the bloodstream via
      a **tick bite**. The rickettsemia progresses to cause **vasculitis** of
      small vessels of many organs (especially **lungs**), skin lesions,
      and fulminant disease.
   - **Most common Rickettsial disease in the United States**.
   - Symptoms: often there is no mark noticed at bite site. **Rapid onset**
      of **high fever**, headache, nausea, **vomiting**, and myalgia; then
      a **maculo-papular rash** appears on the wrists, **palms** and **soles**.
      The rash may become **petechial** then necrotic and **gangrenous**.
      Disease may progress to **pulmonary failure**, **renal failure**,
      encephalitis and coma; and it can be **rapidly fatal**.
   - Worst prognosis in the elderly, in males, and in **G6PD deficiency**.
   - Symptoms arise 1 week after tick bite; fever and nausea occur first;
      after another 5 days, the rash begins.
   - Symptoms resolve in 3 weeks with early aggressive treatment.
   - **Note:** very small dose **less than 10 organisms can cause disease**.

HOST DEFENSE AND IMMUNITY:
- **IgM and IgG antibodies** against various bacterial components.
- **T-Cell mediated immunity** is important.
- **Previous infection** confers long lasting immunity.

TREATMENT:
- **Doxycycline**
   Must be administered very early in the course of disease.
- **Admission to ICU** may be necessary.
- **Chloramphenicol** during pregnancy.
- **Prevention:**
      Rodent control, insecticides, and prompt removal of ticks.

LAB TESTS:
- **Giemsa** or **Gimenez stain**.
- **Weil-Felix Reaction:**
   (Types of Rickettsial-infected serum can
   agglutinate strains of *Proteus vulgaris*)

ox-19	**Pos**
ox-2	**Pos**
ox-K	Neg

VACCINE AND TOXOID:
None

Chapter 11

GRAM POSITIVE RODS
Acid-Fast and Modified Acid-Fast Bacteria

TUBERCULOUS MYCOBACTERIUM	NON-TUBERCULOUS MYCOBACTERIUM	MODIFIED ACID-FAST	LEPROSY

Mycobacterium tuberculosis
 Primary tuberculosis
 Secondary tuberculosis
 Miliary tuberculosis
 Extra-pulmonary tuberculosis
     Pott's disease (skeletal)
     Chronic meningitis
     Scrofuloderma (skin)
 Tuberculosis and AIDS
	MAI: *Mycobacterium avium-intracellulare complex*
	     (a.k.a. *MAC*)
	 MAI pulmonary disease in AIDS
	
	 Non-Tuberculous *Mycobacterium*
	     Group I:
	         M. kansasii
	         M. marinum
	     Group II:
	         M. scrofulaceum
	     Group III:
	         MAI
	     Group IV:
	         M. smegmatis
	         M. abscessus
	         M. chelonei
	         M. fortuitum
		Nocardia asteroides
		 Nocardosis
		     Pulmonary abscess
		     Sepsis
		     Brain abscess
		 Mycetoma
			Mycobacterium leprae
			 Tuberculoid leprosy
			 Lepromatous leprosy
			 Borderline leprosy

Mycobacterium bovis
 (Zoonotic)
 Pulmonary tuberculosis
 Extra-pulmonary tuberculosis
     GI tract
     Scrofuloderma (skin)			

Mycobacterium tuberculosis

GRAM STAIN: POS (Stains Poorly)	ZIEHL-NEELSEN OR KINYOUN STAIN: ACID-FAST ("Alcohol Acid Fast")

OBLIGATE AEROBE

INTRACELLULAR

FEATURES:
Morphology:
  Rods
Grouping:
  Grow in **cords**
Colonies:
  -Slow growth
  -Special media

MOTILITY:
None

CAPSULE:
Lipid and Polypeptide
Complex coat

GLYCOCALYX:
None

EXOTOXINS:
None

VIRULENCE FACTORS:
- **Cord Factor (trehalose dimycolate):**
  Gathers *M. tuberculosis* in chains.
- **Abundant Peptide Antigens of outer coat:**
  - **Stimulate actively self-destructive host immunity.**
  - **Note:** There are no enzymes or toxins to cause destruction.
- **Isoniazid Resistance:**
  (**Note:** Isoniazid requires catalase for its activation)
  - **Random mutation** occurs to cause **loss of catalase activity**.
- **Production of substances to allow survival within Macros**.
- **Ability to survive acidic, alkaline, or drying conditions**.
- **Lipid-rich cell wall (mycolic acid, wax D, etc.):**
  Provides resistance to disinfectants.

LAB TESTS:
- **Acid-fast stain** of sputum smear.
- **Culture** of sputum.
- **Chest X-Ray**.
- **PPD skin test (Mantaux):**
  Inject TB antigen sub-dermally and check at **48-72 hrs**:
  - Induration **>10 mm = POS**.
  - Redness or induration **< 5mm = NEG**.
  - Induration **5mm-10 mm** indicates immunocompromised state
- **Catalase   POS**
- **Generates Niacin**.
- No pigment production.
- **Nitrate reduction**.

SOURCE AND TRANSMISSION:
- **Humans** are the only reservoirs.
- **Horizontal transmission** occurs via respiratory droplets from actively infected person.
- **Rare horizontal transmission** may occur via skin contact (scrofuloderma), especially to pathologists during autopsies.

CLINICAL:
- **PPD Positive:**
  - Indicates exposure to *M. tuberculosis* and intact T-cell response.
  - May be permanently inactive and asymptomatic.
- **Primary Tuberculosis:**
  - *M. tuberculosis* lodges **initially in lower lobe** of lung.
  - **Tubercle formation: granuloma** of *M. tuberculosis* inside Macros; surrounded by **Langhans cells**, Epithelioid cells, and Lymphos. Central area may undergo **caseating necrosis** or **calcification**. *M. tuberculosis* may survive for many years like this.
  - **Ghon complex** = primary tubercle plus associated swollen lymph node. Shows well on chest x-ray.
- **Secondary Tuberculosis:**
  - Infection **reactivates in upper lobe** due to higher oxygenation.
  - This form of disease usually results due to **impaired immunity**.
  - Sputum smear becomes acid-fast POS, cavitating lesions may occur.
  - Infection may spread by local extension to nearby tissues.
  - Disease becomes contagious.
- **Miliary Tuberculosis:**
  - Widespread **hematological dissemination** of *M. tuberculosis* results in "shot-gun pellet" type lesion in lungs, CNS, GI tract, kidney, or almost any other organ, including the bones.
- **Extra-pulmonary TB:**
  - **Pott's Disease** (skeletal).
  - **Chronic Meningitis**; or **CNS Tuberculoma**.
  - **Scrofuloderma** (skin); etc.
- **Tuberculosis in AIDS:**
  - Fulminant course and more extra-pulmonary symptoms.
  - **PPD may become NEG** due to weak cellular immunity.
- **Note:**
TB causes more world-wide fatalities than any other infectious disease.

HOST DEFENSE AND IMMUNITY:
- **T-cell mediated delayed hypersensitivity**.
- **Antibodies are ineffective**.
- **Cytokines are important to activate both Lymphos and Macros**; this enhances the intracellular killing of *M. tuberculosis*.
- **Macrophages fuse to form Langhans Giant Cells**.
- **Granulomas** form with epithelioid cells surrounding central necrosis.

TREATMENT:
- **Isoniazid (INH)** for PPD POS; Also for HIV POS prophylaxis; and for contacts of active TB.
- **Multi-Drug Therapy:**
  1. **Isoniazid** plus Vitamin B6
  2. **Rifampin** (or Ketoconazole if on birth control)
  3. **Pyrazinamide**
  4. **Ethambutol** or Streptomycin (not in pregnancy) (not in children)
- **Warning:** use of immunosupressive drugs (e.g. steroids) can re-activate TB (Secondary TB).
- **Isolation** may be necessary due to airborne transmission.

VACCINE AND TOXOID:
- **BCG Vaccine:** Live attenuated bacteria. Does not stop infection. Not available in USA.

Mycobacterium bovis

GRAM STAIN:	ZIEHL-NEELSEN OR KINYOUN STAIN:
POS	**ACID-FAST**
(Stains Poorly)	("Alcohol Acid Fast")

OBLIGATE AEROBE

INTRACELLULAR

FEATURES:
Morphology:
 Rods
Grouping:
 Grow in **cords**
Colonies:
 -Slow growth
 -Special media

ZOONOTIC

MOTILITY:	CAPSULE:
None	**Lipid and Polypeptide**
	Complex coat
	GLYCOCALYX:
	None

EXOTOXINS:
None

VIRULENCE FACTORS:
- **Abundant Peptide Antigens of outer coat:**
  - **Stimulate actively self-destructive host immunity.**
  - **Note:** There are no enzymes or toxins to cause destruction.
- **Isoniazid Resistance:**
  - (**Note:** Isoniazid requires catalase for its activation)
  - **Random mutation** occurs to cause **loss of catalase activity**.
- **Production of substances to allow survival within Macros**.
- **Ability to survive acidic, alkaline, or drying conditions**.
- **Lipid-rich cell wall** (mycolic acid, wax D, etc.):
  Provides resistance to disinfectants.

SOURCE AND TRANSMISSION:
- **Humans** are the only reservoirs.
- **Horizontal transmission** occurs via respiratory droplets from actively infected person.
- **Rare horizontal transmission** may occur via skin contact (scrofuloderma), especially to pathologists during autopsies.

CLINICAL:
- **_M. bovis_ Tuberculosis:**
  - **GI tract infection,**
  - **Pulmonary infection,**
  - **Scrofuloderma.**
  - Very **rare** in the USA.

HOST DEFENSE AND IMMUNITY:
- **T-cell mediated delayed hypersensitivity**.
- **Antibodies are ineffective**.
- **Cytokines are important to activate both Lymphos and Macros**; this enhances the intracellular killing of *M. bovis*.
- **Macrophages fuse to form Langhans Giant Cells**.
- **Granulomas** form with epithelioid cells surrounding central necrosis.

TREATMENT:
- **Isoniazid (INH)** for PPD POS;
  Also for HIV POS prophylaxis; and for contacts of active TB.
- **Multi-Drug Therapy:**
  1. **Isoniazid** plus Vitamin B6
  2. **Rifampin** (or Ketoconazole if on birth control)
  3. **Pyrazinamide**
  4. **Ethambutol** or Streptomycin (not in pregnancy) (not in children)
- **Warning:** use of immunosupressive drugs (e.g. steroids) can re-activate TB (Secondary TB).
- **Isolation** may be necessary.

LAB TESTS:
- **Acid-fast stain** of sputum smear.
- **Culture** of sputum.
- **Chest X-Ray**.
- **PPD skin test (Mantaux): POS**.
- **Catalase:** NEG
- Does not generate Niacin.
- **No pigment** production.
- No nitrate reduction.

VACCINE AND TOXOID:
- **BCG Vaccine:** Live attenuated bacteria.
  Does not stop infection.
Note: used only for **farm animals** in the USA.

Mycobacterium avium-intracellulare complex
aka *MAI*   aka *MAC*

GRAM STAIN:
POS
(Stains Poorly)

ZIEHL-NEELSEN OR KINYOUN STAIN:
ACID-FAST
("Alcohol Acid Fast")

OBLIGATE AEROBE

INTRACELLULAR

FEATURES:
Morphology:
  Rods
Grouping:
Colonies:
  -Slow growth
  -Special media

MOTILITY:
None

CAPSULE:
Lipid and Polypeptide
  Complex coat

GLYCOCALYX:
None

EXOTOXINS:
None

VIRULENCE FACTORS:
- **Low virulent organisms** *MAI* usually cause only **opportunistic infections**.
- **Isoniazid Resistance:**
  (**Note:** Isoniazid requires catalase for its activation)
  - Resistant strains of *MAI* **do not produce catalase**.
- **Production of substances to allow survival within Macros**.
- **Ability to survive acidic, alkaline, or drying conditions**.

SOURCE AND TRANSMISSION:
- **Ubiquitous in nature** *MAI* organisms cause disease by **opportunistic** infections in **birds** and **immunocompromised** humans, especially **AIDS** patients with **low CD4 T-cell count**.

CLINICAL:
- *MAI* **Pulmonary infection:**
  - This a **very common infection among AIDS** patients.
  - Causes disease mostly in AIDS patients with **CD4 count < 100**.
  - *MAI* causes **pulmonary disease** similar to TB. Can lead to **cavitation** or **infiltration**.
  - *MAI* quickly **disseminates** to cause lesions in every organ. The **GI tract is very often involved**. The lesions are granulomas with Macros filled with organisms.
  - *MAI* infection is usually **fatal** within months.
  - Infection is very difficult to distinguish from TB; cultures must be made from sputum or blood; then **DNA probes** must be used.

HOST DEFENSE AND IMMUNITY:
- **T-cell mediated delayed hypersensitivity**.
- **Antibodies are ineffective**.
- **Cytokines are important to activate both Lymphos and Macros**; this enhances the intracellular killing of *MAI*.
- **Macrophages fuse to form Langhans Giant Cells**.
- **Granulomas** form with epithelioid cells surrounding central necrosis.

TREATMENT:
- **Multi-Drug Therapy:**
  1. **Rifampin**
  2. **Ethambutol**
  3. **Streptomycin**
- **Clarithromycin**
  Can be used instead of Streptomycin for disseminated disease.
- **Rifampin prophylaxis** in AIDS at CD4 counts <100.

LAB TESTS:
- **Acid-fast stain** of sputum smear or biopsy specimen.
- **Culture** of sputum or biopsy specimen.
- **Chest X-Ray**.
- **Broncoscopy** to obtain biopsy specimen.
- **PPD skin test (Mantaux):** sometimes **POS**.
- **Catalase:** NEG
- Does not generate Niacin.
- No pigment production.
- No nitrate reduction.

VACCINE AND TOXOID:
None

Nontuberculous Mycobacterium spp aka NTM

GRAM STAIN:
POS
(Stains Poorly)

ZIEHL-NEELSEN OR KINYOUN STAIN:
ACID-FAST
("Alcohol Acid Fast")

OBLIGATE AEROBE

INTRACELLULAR

FEATURES:
Morphology:
  Rods
Grouping:
Colonies:
-Slow growth
-Special media
-Group IV is exception:
  They grow rapidly.

MOTILITY:
None

CAPSULE:
Lipid and Polypeptide
  Complex coat

GLYCOCALYX:
None

EXOTOXINS:
None

VIRULENCE FACTORS:
- **Low virulent organisms** *NTM* usually cause only **opportunistic infections.**
- **Isoniazid Resistance:**
  (**Note:** Isoniazid requires catalase for its activation)
  - Resistant strains of *NTM* **do not produce catalase.**
- **Multiple drug resistance.**
- **Production of substances to allow survival within Macros.**
- **Ability to survive acidic, alkaline, or drying conditions.**

SOURCE AND TRANSMISSION:
- **Ubiquitous in nature (soil and water):** these atypical *Mycobacteria* cause **opportunistic** infections mostly in the **immunocompromised.**

CLINICAL:
- **Group I:**
  Photochromogens: produce yellow pigment upon exposure to light.
  - *M. kansasii*: causes pulmonary infection similar to TB.
  - *M. marinum*: causes **"swimming pool granuloma"** at abrasion site.
- **Group II:**
  Scotochromogens: produce yellow pigment in the dark.
  - *M. scrofulaceum*: causes **Scrofula** (cervical lymphadenitis).
- **Group III:**
  Non-chromogens: produce no pigments.
  see *MAI = M. avium-intracellulare complex*: see previous page.
- **Group IV:**
  Non-chromogens: rapid growers.
  - *M. smegmatis*: collects under penis foreskin as **smegma.**
  - *M. abscessus, M. chelonei, M. fortuitum*: cause **wound infections.**

HOST DEFENSE AND IMMUNITY:
- **T-cell mediated delayed hypersensitivity.**
- **Antibodies are ineffective.**
- **Cytokines are important to activate both Lymphos and Macros;** this enhances intracellular killing.

TREATMENT:
- **Group I:**
  M. kansasii: same treatment as TB.
  M. marinum: Rifampin + Ethambutol.
- **Group II:**
  M. scrofulaceum: same treatment as TB.
- **Group III:**
  see *MAI* on previous page.
- **Group IV:**
  M. smegmatis: Amikacin
  M. abscessus, M. chelonei, and *M. fortuitum*: Amikacin + Cefoxitin.

VACCINE AND TOXOID:
None

LAB TESTS:
- **Acid-fast stain** of sputum smear.
- **Culture** of sputum.
- **Chest X-Ray.**
- **PPD skin test (Mantaux):** sometimes **POS.**
- **Catalase:** +/-
- Does not generate Niacin.
- **Pigment production** as noted.
- Nitrate reduction: +/-

Nocardia asteroides

GRAM STAIN:
POS

ZIEHL-NEELSEN OR KINYOUN STAIN:
ACID-FAST
("Alcohol Acid Fast")

AEROBIC

EXTRACELLULAR

FEATURES:
Morphology:
  Rods
  Coccobacilli
Grouping:
  Filamentous
  Branched chains
Colonies:
  -Pigmented or not

MOTILITY:
None

CAPSULE:
None

GLYCOCALYX:
None

EXOTOXINS:
None

VIRULENCE FACTORS:
●**Enzymes:**
  ▪**Catalase and Superoxide Dismutase** enable *N. asteroides* to
    resist the PMN intracellular oxidative burst.
●**Filament formation** enables *N. asteroides* to resist phagocytosis.

LAB TESTS:
●**Modified Ziehl-Neelsen stain**
    of sputum smear or pus smear.
●**Gram stain** of biopsy.
●**Culture**.
●**Catalase   POS**
●Pigment production: +/-

SOURCE AND TRANSMISSION:
●**Ubiquitous in soil** *N. asteroides* organisms cause **opportunistic**
  infections in **immunocompromised** humans, especially **AIDS**
  patients with **low CD4 T-cell count**, and especially any patient
  on **corticosteroid medication**.
●**Respiratory or skin trauma** are the most likely routes of infection.

CLINICAL:
●**Nocardosis:**
  ▪**Pulmonary Abscesses:**
    May cause cavitating lesions; may resemble TB.
  ▪**Septic Nocardosis:**
    Spreads from pulmonary lesions; may spread to any organ.
  ▪**Brain Abscesses:**
    Result from disseminated infection.
  ▪Not contagious.
  ▪Disease can be **fatal**; or may **relapse** after effective treatment.

●**Mycetoma:** "aerobic actinomyces" or "actinomycetoma"
  ▪Caused by *N. asteroides* in combination with others *Nocardia spp.*
  ▪A **chronic granulomatous** infection of sub-cutaneous tissues.
  ▪**Sinus-tract formation** occurs with draining pus open on skin.
  ▪**Foot** is the usual site of infection, due to trauma.

HOST DEFENSE AND IMMUNITY:
●**Acute pyogenic inflammation** with PMN phagocytosis is the
  primary host reaction.
●**Antibodies are necessary** to defend against the filamentous form of
  N. asteroides.
●**Cytokines are important** to activate both phagocytes and T-cells.
●**Activated CD8 T-cells** are capable of killing *N. asteroides* directly.

TREATMENT:
●**Sulfonamide**
●**TMP-SMZ prophylaxis**
    in organ transplant patients taking immunosuppressive medication.
●**Amikacin plus Impenem** in sulfa allergy.
●**Debridement** of mycetoma.

VACCINE AND TOXOID:
None

Mycobacterium leprae

GRAM STAIN:
POS
(Stains Poorly)

FITE STAIN:
ACID-FAST

OBLIGATE AEROBE

INTRACELLULAR

FEATURES:
Morphology:
    Rods
Grouping:
Grow in **Globi bundles:**
    Encapsulated globs
    of Rods in tissue
Colonies:
-Never on media
-Only **foot pad of mice**

MOTILITY:
None

CAPSULE:
Lipid and Polypeptide
    Complex coat

GLYCOCALYX:
None

EXOTOXINS:
None

VIRULENCE FACTORS:
- **PGL-1 (phenolic glycolipid 1) Capsule:**
  - Scavenges free radicals.
  - Enables *M. leprae* to survive phagocytosis.
- **Lipoarabinomannan glycoprotein plus PGL-1:**
  - Cause immunologic anergy in host.
- **Preference for lower temperature:**
  - Limits infection to **skin** and **naso-pharynx.**
- **Intracellular Survival within:**
  - **Skin histiocytes.**
  - **Schwann cells.**

LAB TESTS:
- **Lepromin Skin test:**
  POS in Tuberculoid form:
      (induration at 3-4 weeks)
  NEG in Lepromatous form.
- **Serology test for PGL-1**
- **FITE Acid-fast stain** of biopsy.
- Loss of acid-fastness by Pyridine extraction.
- **Catalase:** NEG
- **Dopa-oxidase: POS**
- Does not generate Niacin.
- No pigment production.
- No Nitrate reduction.

SOURCE AND TRANSMISSION:
- **Humans and nine-banded armadillos** are the only reservoirs for *M. leprae.*
- **Horizontal transmission** occurs via respiratory droplets due to long term close personal contact.
- **Other routes of transmission suspected:** Direct contact via skin trauma, zoonotic from armadillos, and vector-borne routes.

CLINICAL:
- **Tuberculoid Leprosy:** (associated with HLA-DR3 genotype.)
  - **Symptoms:**
    Well-defined asymmetrical **cutaneous macular rash** with erythematous borders and **pigment loss in center**; associated with areas of sensory loss (fine touch, pain, temperature).
  - **Disfigurement** from trauma secondary to permanent sensory loss.
  - Symptoms halt their progression with treatment but may relapse.
  - Incubation after respiratory transmission is 3-6 years.
  - **Biopsy** of lesion **Fite stain** shows <u>few</u> *M. leprae* organisms.
  - **Lepromin** skin test **POS.**

- **Lepromatous Leprosy:** (associated with HLA-MTI genotype.)
  - **Symptoms:**
    Symmetrical **cutaneous nodular lesions** associated with areas of **permanent sensory loss** (fine touch, pain, temperature) and upper respiratory congestion. Widespread dissemination is due to *M. leprae* **specific immune anergy.**
  - **Disfigurement** from trauma secondary to permanent sensory loss, especially along ulnar nerve, hands, feet, nose, ears, eyes, testes.
  - Symptoms, except sensory loss and severe disfigurement, halt their progression with treatment, but may relapse.
  - Incubation after respiratory transmission is 3-10 years.
  - **Biopsy** of lesion **Fite stain** shows <u>many</u> *M. leprae* organisms.
  - **Lepromin** skin test **NEG.**

- **Borderline Leprosy:**
  - Most patients have mixture of Tuberculoid and Lepromatous forms.

HOST DEFENSE AND IMMUNITY:
- **Tuberculoid form:**
  - **Weak** antibody response.
  - Cytokines are important.
  - **T-cell mediated delayed hypersensitivity.**
  - Macros form **Langhans Giant Cells.**
  - **Granulomas** form with epithelioid cells.
- **Lepromatous form:**
  - **Strong** antibody response
  - Weak production of cytokines.
  - *M. leprae* **specific T-cell immune anergy.**
  - *M. leprae* **specific Macrophage anergy.**

TREATMENT:
- **Emotional support.**
- **Multi-Drug Therapy:**
  1. **Dapsone**
  2. **Rifampin**
  3. Clofazimine is added for Lepromatous form
- **Treatment lasts for many years.**
- **Ostyomyelitis and skin infections**
  Require surgical debridement and additional antibiotic treatment.
- **Physical therapy** may be necessary due to nerve damage.
- **Hot Wax baths**
  Of extremities helps slow the progression of infection without the scalding effect of hot water on skin that has lost sensation.

VACCINE AND TOXOID:
- **BCG Vaccine:** Live attenuated bacteria.
  Does not stop infection.
  Not available in USA.
  Questionable efficacy.

Chapter 12

SPIROCHETES

TREPONEMA SPIROCHETES	ZOONOTIC SPIROCHETES	VECTOR-BORNE SPIROCHETES	
Treponema pallidum Primary syphilis Secondary syphilis Latent syphilis Secondary syphilis relapse Tertiary syphilis Congenital syphilis	*Leptospira interrogans* (Zoonotic) 　　Leptospirosis 　　Weil syndrome	*Borrelia burgdorferi* (Vector-borne) 　　Lyme disease *Borrelia recurrentis* (Vector-borne) 　　Relapsing fever	
Treponema pallidum-endemicum Bejel 　(oral lesions in children)			
Treponema carateum Pinta 　(hypopigmenting skin 　　lesions in children)			
Treponema pallidum-pertenue Yaws 　(papillomatous skin 　　lesions in children)			

Treponema pallidum

MICROAEROPHILIC

EXTRACELLULAR

FEATURES:
- **Morphology:**
Spirochetes
  Spiral Rods
  Thin
  Tightly coiled
- **Grouping:**
- **Colonies:**
-Never

MOTILITY:
Rotates
via fibrils
at both ends

CAPSULE:
Membrane structure
Complex

GLYCOCALYX:
None

EXOTOXINS:
None

ENDOTOXIN:
- **Lipopolysaccharide (LPS)**

VIRULENCE FACTORS:
- **Endotoxin:**
- **Outer membrane enhances adherence.**
- **Enzymes:**
  - **Hyaluronidase** mediates perivascular invasion.

LAB TESTS:
- **Microscopy:**
  Spirochetes seen in skin specimen:
    Darkfield
    Immunofluorescent
    Gram stain ineffective
- **Non-Treponemal blood tests:**
  Become POS upon infection,
  but **titers decrease during recovery.**
  POS indicates <u>current active</u> disease.
    RPR (ART)
    VDRL
- **Treponemal blood tests:**
  Become POS upon infection,
  and **remain POS for patient's lifetime.**
  POS indicates <u>past</u> infection.
    FTA-abs
    MHA-TP (TPHA)

SOURCE AND TRANSMISSION:
- **Horizontal transmission** occurs via sexual contact.
- **Vertical transmission** via transplacental route in utero.
- **Horizontal transmission** may also occur via blood transfusions or direct contact with infected tissue or contaminated fomites.

CLINICAL:
Note: less than 10 treponemal spirochetes can cause disease.
- **Primary Syphilis:**
  - <u>Symptoms</u>: indolent (**painless**) **chancre** forms at the site of entry of *T. pallidum* (external genitalia, oral, anal, and cervix sites). Chancre starts as red, indurated (hard), **papule** then **ulcerates.** <u>Incubation</u> is about 3 weeks before symptoms begin. Symptoms last about 4-6 weeks; chancre heals **without scar.**
  - Syphilis is **contagious** during the **primary stage.**
  - *T. pallidum* can be isolated from the chancre.
- **Secondary Syphilis:**
  - <u>Symptoms</u>: **maculo-papular**, centripetal **rash** develops first on **trunk**, then spreads centrifugally to **palms, soles**, genitalia, and **mucus membranes** due to post-chancre **spirochetemia.** Constitutional symptoms: fever, **sore throat**, and general **lymphadenopathy** (especially epitrochlear nodes). *T. pallidum* invades **any organ** (hence **"the great pretender"**). <u>Symptoms</u> begin about 3 weeks to 3 months after untreated chancre is resolved, and may last 2 weeks to many months.
  - Secondary Syphilis is **contagious.**
  - *T. pallidum* can be isolated from the muco-cutaneous rash.
- **Latent syphilis:** No symptoms, but POS serological tests for *T. pallidum.*
- **Secondary Syphilis Relapse:** Disease actives from latent stage. Usually occurs within 2 years of latency. **Condyloma Latum** occur.
- **Tertiary Syphilis:** ("Late Syphilis," "**Lues**," or "Luetic disease"):
  - Late manifestation may occur upto 40 years after latency. **Not contagious:** *T. pallidum* found in CSF only.
  - May affect any organ: **Neurosyphilis:** Tabes dorsalis, Argyll Robertson pupil, seizures. **Cardiovascular:** ascending-aorta Aneurysm, obliterated vasovasorum **Gumma formation:** bones, mucocutaneous sites, anywhere; benign.
- **Congenital Syphilis:**
  - **Transplacental transmission** from mother to fetus during primary, secondary, latent syphilis. Can cause: fetal death, blindness, CNS problems, deafness, "saddle nose," "saber shins," skin rash.
  - **Warning:** Child is extremely **infectious at birth.**

HOST DEFENSE AND IMMUNITY:
- **Plasma cells** accumulate in **chancre** formation.
- **IgM and IgG antibodies** develop, especially during secondary syphilis, to provide some humoral immunity.
- **T-cell mediated immunity** is important in **gumma** formation.
- **Prolonged infection confers only partial immunity.**

TREATMENT:
- **Benzathine Penicillin** for early syphilis and for prophylaxis.
- **Penicillin G** for late syphilis, congenital syphilis, and neurosyphilis.
- **Penicillin desensitization** Necessary to treat syphilis in penicillin-allergic patient during pregnancy.
- **Sexual partner must be treated.**

VACCINE AND TOXOID:
None

Treponema pallidum-endemicum

SOURCE AND TRANSMISSION:
- **Horizontal transmission** occurs via direct person-to-person contact and via **sharing of eating or drinking utensils**.
- **Infection occurs only in children of central Africa, west Asia.**

MICROAEROPHILIC

EXTRACELLULAR

FEATURES:
- **Morphology:**
Spirochetes
  Spiral Rods
  Thin
  Tightly coiled
- **Grouping:**
- **Colonies:**
-Never

MOTILITY:
Rotates
via fibrils
at both ends

CAPSULE:
Membrane structure
  Complex

GLYCOCALYX:
  None

EXOTOXINS:
None

ENDOTOXIN:
- **Lipopolysaccharide (LPS)**

VIRULENCE FACTORS:
- **Endotoxin:**
- **Outer membrane enhances adherence**.
- **Enzymes:**
  - **Hyaluronidase** mediates perivascular invasion.

CLINICAL:
- **Bejel: (Endemic Syphilis):**
  - **Primary:**
    Oral lesions; quickly resolve.
  - **Secondary:**
    Oral papules, mucosal lesions, condyloma lata.
  - **Latent:** asymptomatic.
  - **Late:**
    Gummas of bone, skin, and nasopharynx.

HOST DEFENSE AND IMMUNITY:
- **IgM and IgG antibodies** provide some humoral immunity.
- **T-cell mediated immunity** is important in **gumma** formation.
- **Prolonged infection confers only partial immunity**.

LAB TESTS:
- **Microscopy:**
    Spirochetes seen in skin specimen:
      Darkfield
      Immunofluorescent
      Gram stain ineffective
- **Non-Treponemal blood tests:**
    Become POS upon infection,
    but **titers decrease during recovery.**
    POS indicates current active disease.
      RPR (ART)
      VDRL
- **Treponemal blood tests:**
    Become POS upon infection,
    and **remain POS for patient's lifetime**.
    POS indicates past infection.
      FTA-abs
      MHA-TP (TPHA)

TREATMENT:
- **Penicillin G** for patients and contacts.

VACCINE AND TOXOID:
None

Treponema carateum

SOURCE AND TRANSMISSION:
- **Horizontal transmission** occurs via direct person-to-person contact
- **Infection occurs only in children of rural Central America, Mexico and South America.**

MICROAEROPHILIC

EXTRACELLULAR

FEATURES:
- **Morphology:**
Spirochetes
  - Spiral Rods
  - Thin
  - Tightly coiled
- **Grouping:**
- **Colonies:**
- -Never

MOTILITY:
Rotates
via fibrils
at both ends

CAPSULE:
Membrane structure
Complex

GLYCOCALYX:
None

EXOTOXINS:
None

ENDOTOXIN:
- **Lipopolysaccharide (LPS)**

VIRULENCE FACTORS:
- **Endotoxin:**
- **Outer membrane enhances adherence.**
- **Enzymes:**
  - **Hyaluronidase** mediates perivascular invasion.

CLINICAL:
- **Pinta:** (Cutaneous treponematosis)
  - **Primary:**
    Cutaneous pruritic papules develop, enlarge, and coalesce.
    Incubation is about 2 weeks; symptoms last months or years;
    may resolve with residual **permanent hypopigmentation**.
  - **Secondary:**
    Pintids (small cutaneous scaly papules) develop at the same
    sites as primary lesions. Pintids may become **dyschromic**
    blue, brown, or gray.
    Symptoms begin about 3 months to 10 years after untreated
    primary lesions are resolved.
  - **Latent:** asymptomatic.
  - **Late:**
    Permanent **achromic** (de-pigmented) macular lesions develop
    at elbows, ankles, and wrists.

Note: Pinta is disfiguring, but does not shorten life span.

HOST DEFENSE AND IMMUNITY:
- **IgM and IgG antibodies** provide some humoral immunity.
- **T-cell mediated immunity** is important.
- **Prolonged infection confers only partial immunity**.

LAB TESTS:
- **Microscopy:**
  Spirochetes seen in skin specimen:
    Darkfield
    Immunofluorescent
    Gram stain ineffective
- **Non-Treponemal blood tests:**
  Become POS upon **Secondary lesions**,
  but **titers decrease during recovery**.
  POS indicates <u>current active</u> disease.
    RPR (ART)
    VDRL
- **Treponemal blood tests:**
  Become POS upon **Secondary lesions**,
  and **remain POS for patient's lifetime**.
  POS indicates <u>past</u> infection.
    FTA-abs
    MHA-TP (TPHA)

TREATMENT:
- **Penicillin G** for patients and contacts.
- **Tetracycline** in penicillin allergy.

VACCINE AND TOXOID:
None

Treponema pallidum-pertenue

SOURCE AND TRANSMISSION:
- **Horizontal transmission** occurs via direct person-to-person contact
- **Infection occurs only in children of rural tropical areas around the world.**

MICROAEROPHILIC

EXTRACELLULAR

FEATURES:
- **Morphology:**
Spirochetes
   Spiral Rods
   Thin
   Tightly coiled
- **Grouping:**
- **Colonies:**
-Never

MOTILITY:
Rotates
via fibrils
at both ends

CAPSULE:
Membrane structure
Complex

GLYCOCALYX:
   None

EXOTOXINS:
None

ENDOTOXIN:
- **Lipopolysaccharide (LPS)**

VIRULENCE FACTORS:
- **Endotoxin:**
- **Outer membrane enhances adherence.**
- **Enzymes:**
   - **Hyaluronidase** mediates perivascular invasion.

CLINICAL:
- **Yaws: (Papillomatous treponematosis)**
  - **Primary:**
     Cutaneous papules develop on **extremities** then enlarge to become **papillomatous** nodules.
     Incubation is about 4 weeks; symptoms resolve in 6 months.
  - **Secondary:**
     Widespread development of **papillomatous nodules**.
     Symptoms begin weeks or months after untreated primary lesions are resolved. 2° lesions may resolve in months.
  - **Latent:** asymptomatic.
  - **Secondary Relapse:**
     Multiple relapses of 2° lesions may occur over many years.
  - **Late:**
     Cutaneous nodules and ulcers; hyperkeratosis of palms and soles; and **gummas** of bone, skin, and nasopharynx.

HOST DEFENSE AND IMMUNITY:
- **IgM and IgG antibodies** provide some humoral immunity.
- **T-cell mediated immunity** is important in **gumma** formation.
- **Prolonged infection confers only partial immunity**.

LAB TESTS:
- **Microscopy:**
     Spirochetes seen in skin specimen:
          Darkfield
          Immunofluorescent
          Gram stain ineffective
- **Non-Treponemal blood tests:**
     Become POS upon infection,
     but **titers decrease during recovery.**
     POS indicates <u>current active</u> disease.
          RPR (ART)
          VDRL
- **Treponemal blood tests:**
     Become POS upon infection,
     and **remain POS for patient's lifetime.**
     POS indicates <u>past</u> infection.
          FTA-abs
          MHA-TP (TPHA)

TREATMENT:
- **Penicillin G** for patients and contacts.
- **Tetracycline** in penicillin allergy.

VACCINE AND TOXOID:
None

Leptospira interrogans

ZOONOTIC

OBLIGATE AEROBE

EXTRACELLULAR

FEATURES:
- **Morphology:**
Spirochetes
Spiral Rods
Thin
Tightly coiled
Question mark shaped
"Interrogans"
- **Grouping:**
- **Colonies:**

MOTILITY:
Flagella
One at each end

CAPSULE:
Membrane structure
Complex

GLYCOCALYX:
None

EXOTOXINS:
None

ENDOTOXIN:
- **Lipopolysaccharide (LPS)**

VIRULENCE FACTORS:
- **Endotoxin:**
- **Ability to penetrate mucus membranes**.
- **Ability to multiply very rapidly**.
- **Great antigenic variation** results in over 200 serotypes.
- **Enzymes:**
  - **Hyaluronidase** mediates perivascular invasion.

SOURCE AND TRANSMISSION:
- **Animal kidneys** are reservoirs for *L. interrogans*.
- **Zoonotic transmission** occurs via contact with **animal urine**.
- **Wild or domestic animals, especially dogs**, carry *L. interrogans*.
- **Survival in streams, ponds, and moist soil** for weeks or months contaminated by wild or domestic animals.
- **Abattoir workers:** farmers, veterinarians, backpackers, hunters are at risk.

CLINICAL:
- **Leptospirosis: (Anicteric):**
  - Symptoms: Biphasic:
  First phase (septic phase)
    Occurs due to widespread dissemination with constitutional symptoms such as fever, chills, headache and myalgia.
    Incubation is about 1 week then first phase lasts about 1 week.
    An asymptomatic period of 2-3 days intervenes.
  Second phase (immune phase)
    Occurs due to circulating antibody and meningitis with severe headache, nausea, vomiting, and myalgia.
    Symptoms of second phase last for a few days.

- **Weil Syndrome: (Icteric):**
  - Symptoms: severe form of leptospirosis, with a similar progression. **Hepatic and renal dysfunction** lead to **jaundice** and **renal failure**. **Myocarditis** and cardiogenic shock may occur. Can be **fatal**.

HOST DEFENSE AND IMMUNITY:
- **IgM and IgG antibodies** provide some humoral immunity.
- **Immune complex deposition** may be involved in the disease process.

LAB TESTS:
- **Serologic tests**.
- **Cultures:**
  Blood and CSF:
    take specimen between 3 and 10 days after infection.
  Urine:
    take specimen between 1 week and 1 month after infection.

TREATMENT:
- **Penicillin G** for patients and contacts.
- **Doxycycline** in penicillin allergy, and for prophylaxis.

VACCINE AND TOXOID:
None

Borrelia burgdorferi

VECTORS

AEROBIC

EXTRACELLULAR

FEATURES:
- **Morphology:**
Spirochetes
  Spiral Rods
  Long
  Loosely coiled
- **Grouping:**
- **Colonies:**
-Slow growth
-Special media

MOTILITY:
Multiple Flagella

CAPSULE:
Membrane structure
Complex

GLYCOCALYX:
None

EXOTOXINS:
None

ENDOTOXIN:
- **Lipopolysaccharide (LPS)**

VIRULENCE FACTORS:
- **Endotoxin:**
- **Ability to survive in human blood and in ticks**.
- **Ability to resist phagocytosis**.
- **Ability to adhere to and penetrate epithelial cells**.
- **Ability to sequester itself** in joints, skin and CNS,
    thus enabling **relapses** in spite of treatment.

LAB TESTS:
- **Serologic tests**.
  Blood, CSF
- **Cultures:**
  From biopsy of stage one rash only.

SOURCE AND TRANSMISSION:
- **White-foot mouse, Whitetail deer and Ixodes ticks** are reservoirs
    for *B. burgdorferi*.
- **Vector transmission** occurs during **tick bite**
    (tick must remain attached for **24 hours** or longer).
- Horizontal transmission from **tick to tick** occurs.
- **Vertical transmission** occurs transplacents in utero, rare.
- **Occurs world wide** Lyme disease
    is the **most common vector-borne disease in the USA**.

CLINICAL:
- **Lyme Disease:**
  - **Stage One: Erythema Chronicum Migrans:**
    Red macule occurs at the tick bite site, this expands to become
    an **annular rash** (sometimes multiple) with **central clearing**
    (the center of the rash heals as the rash grows in diameter).
    The rash progresses to large diameter with raised **red border**.
    The rash is **painless** and **not infectious**.
    B. burgdorferi may be cultured from biopsy of the rash.
    Incubation is about 2 weeks; symptoms resolve in 1-2 months.
  - **Stage Two: Neurologic and Cardiac:**
    Neurologic: meningitis, **encephalitis**, Bell's palsy (CN VII),
    peripheral neuropathy, etc.
    Cardiac: transient A-V block. **Eyes:** conjunctivitis
    Symptoms begin weeks or months after beginning stage one.
    Stage 2 lesions may resolve in months, years or never.
  - **Latent:** asymptomatic.
  - **Stage Three (Late):**
  Migratory arthritis; chronic neurologic; and musculoskeletal:
    Intermittent and **migratory arthritis**, joint pain and swelling of
    the large joints, especially the knees.
    CNS: **encephalitis**; altered sensorium, memory and speech.
    Symptoms begin 2 months to 2 years after beginning stage one.
    Late stage symptoms may resolve in months, years or never.

- **Congenital Lyme Disease:**
  - Very rare **transplacental** transmission may occur **in utero**.
  - May be **fatal** for neonate.

HOST DEFENSE AND IMMUNITY:
- **IgM and IgG antibodies** against various spirochete components.
- **Classic complement pathway** aids in opsonization.
- **T-cell mediated delayed hypersensitivity** and immune-complex
    deposition may have role in joint inflammation.

TREATMENT:
- **Doxycycline**
- **Amoxicillin** for children and during pregnancy.
- **Erythromycin** for children with penicillin allergy.
- **IV Ceftriaxone** for neurologic or cardiac symptoms.

VACCINE AND TOXOID:
- **Vaccine**
Synthesized Lipo-protein.

Borrelia recurrentis

VECTORS

AEROBIC

EXTRACELLULAR

FEATURES:
- **Morphology:**
Spirochetes
  - Spiral Rods
  - Long
  - Loosely coiled
- **Grouping:**
- **Colonies:**
- -Slow growth
- -Special media

MOTILITY:
Multiple Flagella

CAPSULE:
Membrane structure
Complex

GLYCOCALYX:
None

EXOTOXINS:
None

ENDOTOXIN:
- **Lipopolysaccharide (LPS)**

VIRULENCE FACTORS:
- **Endotoxin:**
- **Variable Major Protein:**
  - Surface antigen protein may be **varied** many times throughout the course of infection. This enables *B. recurrentis* to escape opsonization by antibody and complement, thus **relapses** occur.
- **Ability to survive in human blood and in lice lymph**.
- **Ability to resist phagocytosis**.
- **Ability to adhere to and penetrate epithelial cells**.
- **Ability to sequester itself** in internal organs during afebrile periods, thus enabling **relapses**.

SOURCE AND TRANSMISSION:
- **Humans** are reservoir for *B. recurrentis*.
- **Vector transmission** occurs during **human lice** being crushed on mucus membranes or skin; the spirochetes then penetrate the epithelium and travel in the blood.
  Note: Transmission is not via lice bites or feces.
- **Relapsing fever occurs world wide**.

CLINICAL:
- **Relapsing Fever:**
  - **First Febrile Attack:**
    Lice get **crushed** on skin, the *B. recurrentis* spirochetes get released then **penetrate** through epithelium to invade the blood stream.
  - Symptoms: **high fever**, chills, headache, myalgia and splenomegaly.
  - Incubation is about 1 week then first attack lasts about 1 week.
  - **Latent phase:**
    Antibodies effectively clear spirochetes from the bloodstream, but some survive by **sequestration** in various organs, especially the **spleen and liver**. Patient becomes **afebrile** during latency. Latency lasts about 1 week.
  - **Relapse phase:**
    Symptoms return for a few days as the surface antigens get changed to enable *B. recurrentis* to evade antibodies, thus a second spirochetemia ensues to cause fever.
  - **Latent phase again:**
    A second asymptomatic interval intervenes.
  - **Relapse phase again:**
    Symptoms return again. **2 or 3 relapses are common**.

Note: Infection may be **fatal**, usually due to hypotension and shock during the first febrile attack.

HOST DEFENSE AND IMMUNITY:
- **IgM and IgG antibodies** against various spirochete surface antigens. Ability of *B. recurrentis* to vary its antigens make antibodies ultimately **ineffective**.
- **Cytokines** play an important role.

LAB TESTS:
- **Peripheral blood smear:**
  - Dark-field microscopy
  - Giemsa stain
  - Wright stain.

TREATMENT:
- **Doxycycline**
- **Erythromycin** for children and during pregnancy.

VACCINE AND TOXOID:
None

Chapter 13

CHLAMYDIA

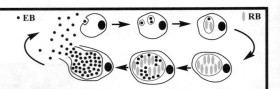

• EB   RB

RESPIRATORY CHLAMYDIA	ZOONOTIC CHLAMYDIA	SEXUALLY TRANSMITTED CHLAMYDIA	
Chlamydia pneumoniae Atypical pneumonia Bronchitis	*Chlamydia psittaci* (Zoonotic) Atypical pneumonia	*Chlamydia trachomatis* Sexually transmitted diseases Urethritis Proctitis Cervicitis PID Lymphogranuloma Venereum Trachoma (eye infection) Neonatal infections Reiter syndrome	

Chlamydia pneumoniae

GRAM STAIN:
NULL
Stains Poorly
NO PEPTIDOGLYCAN

OBLIGATE ANAEROBE

EB = EXTRACELLULAR

RB = OBLIGATE INTRACELLULAR

FEATURES:
- **Biphasic:**
Infectious Extracellular form:
  Elemental Bodies (EB)
    "Pear shaped"
Obligate Intracellular form:
  Reticulate Bodies (RB).

- **Colonies:**
-Require **cell culture**.

MOTILITY:
None

CAPSULE:
None

GLYCOCALYX:
None

EXOTOXINS:
None

ENDOTOXIN:
- **Lipopolysaccharide (LPS)** similar to gram negative bacteria.

VIRULENCE FACTORS:
- **Unique life cycle:**
  Elementary Bodies (EB=300 nm) enter host cells via several mechanisms; EBs organize as **Reticulate Bodies** (RB=1000nm) which replicate to produce new Elemental Bodies; the host cell ruptures to release the EBs so the cycle can continue.
- *Chlamydia pneumoniae* **survive in Macros or epithelial cells**; but are killed in PMNs.
- **Ability to cause recurrent or persistent infections** often leads to greater tissue damage and scarring than the initial infection.

LAB TESTS:
- **PCR** may be useful.
- Few tests, if any, are helpful.
- **Chest X-Ray**.

SOURCE AND TRANSMISSION:
- **Humans** are the only reservoirs for *C. pneumoniae*.
- **Horizontal transmission** occurs via **respiratory droplets**.
- **Epidemics** can occur.

CLINICAL:
- **Pneumonia: Atypical Pneumonia.**
  - Respiratory infection by *C. pneumoniae* is **very common**. Infection is usually mild or asymptomatic, but can be fatal.
  - Symptomatic infection occurs most often in the elderly.
  - **Chest X-ray** usually shows unilateral, lower lobe involvement.
  - Symptoms: **interstitial pneumonia** with **non-productive cough** and inspiratory crackles, fever, chills, headache, and chest pain.
  - Symptoms begin gradually over days to weeks.
  - Symptoms may last for weeks or months, and **relapses** may occur.

- **Bronchitis**.

HOST DEFENSE AND IMMUNITY:
- **PMNs** are the most effective defense.
- **T-cells, Macros, Eosinophils and plasma cells** are all activated.
- **Cytokines** are effective.
- **Previous infection confers no protective immunity** against subsequent infection.

TREATMENT:
- **Doxycycline**.
- **Azithromycin**
    For children and pregnant women.

VACCINE AND TOXOID:
None

Chlamydia psittaci

GRAM STAIN:
NULL
Stains Poorly
NO PEPTIDOGLYCAN

ZOONOTIC

OBLIGATE ANAEROBE

EB = EXTRACELLULAR

RB = OBLIGATE INTRACELLULAR

FEATURES:
- **Biphasic:**
Infectious Extracellular form:
   Elemental Bodies (EB)
Obligate Intracellular form:
   Reticulate Bodies (RB).

- **Colonies:**
-Require **cell culture.**

MOTILITY:
None

CAPSULE:
None

GLYCOCALYX:
None

EXOTOXINS:
None

ENDOTOXIN:
- **Lipopolysaccharide (LPS)** similar to gram negative bacteria.

VIRULENCE FACTORS:
- **Unique life cycle:**
   Elementary Bodies (EB=300 nm) enter host cells via several
   mechanisms; EBs organize as **Reticulate Bodies** (RB=1000nm)
   which replicate to produce new Elemental Bodies; the host cell
   ruptures to release the EBs so the cycle can continue.
- *Chlamydia psittaci* **survive in Macros or epithelial cells**;
   but are killed in PMNs.
- **Ability to cause recurrent or persistent infections** often leads
   to greater tissue damage and scarring than the initial infection.

LAB TESTS:
- **Serology** tests for high titer of complement-fixing
   antibodies may be useful for diagnosis, but it is
   not species-specific.
- **Cell-culture** may be done, but it is **dangerous.**
- **Chest X-Ray.**

SOURCE AND TRANSMISSION:
- **Birds and poultry** are reservoirs for *C. psittaci.*
- **Zoonotic transmission** occurs via contact with **birds** and poultry
- **Transmission from bird to bird, or to bird offspring**, is how the
   reservoir population of *C. psittaci* is maintained.
- **Abatoir workers:** veterinarians, farmers, pet shop owners,
   zookeepers, or anyone in contact with an infected bird is at risk.

CLINICAL:
- **Pneumonia: Atypical Pneumonia.**
   - Infection is usually mild or asymptomatic, but can be **fatal.**
   - Symptomatic infection occurs most often in the **elderly.**
   - **Chest X-ray** usually shows unilateral, lower lobe involvement.
   - Symptoms: **interstitial pneumonia** with **non-productive cough**
      and inspiratory crackles, fever, chills, headache, and chest pain.
   - Incubation is about 1-2 weeks
   - Symptoms may last for weeks or months, and **relapses** may occur.

- **C. psittaci spread to the Reticulo-Endothelial System (RES):**
   - Hepatosplenomegaly with **jaundice.**

- **C. psittaci disseminate then via hematogenous route to:**
   - **CNS:** encephalitis, seizures, and coma, can be **fatal.**
   - **Heart:** pericarditis, myocarditis, and endocarditis; can be **fatal.**
   - **GI Tract:** nausea, vomiting, and diarrhea.
   - **Thyroid:** thyrotoxicosis.
   - *C. psittaci* complications can affect **any organ.**

HOST DEFENSE AND IMMUNITY:
- **PMNs** are the most effective defense.
- **T-cells, Macros, Eosinophils and plasma cells** are all activated.
- **Cytokines** are effective.
- **Previous infection confers no protective immunity** against
   subsequent infection.

TREATMENT:
- **Doxycycline.**
- **Azithromycin**
      For children and pregnant women.
- **Prevention:**
      Prophylactic Doxycycline for **birds.**

VACCINE AND TOXOID:
None

Chlamydia trachomatis

GRAM STAIN:
NULL
Stains Poorly
NO PEPTIDOGLYCAN

OBLIGATE ANAEROBE

EB = EXTRACELLULAR

RB = OBLIGATE INTRACELLULAR

FEATURES:
- **Biphasic:**
Infectious Extracellular form:
  Elemental Bodies (EB)
Obligate Intracellular form:
  Reticulate Bodies (RB).

- **Colonies:**
-Require **cell culture.**

MOTILITY:
None

CAPSULE:
None

GLYCOCALYX:
None

EXOTOXINS:
None

ENDOTOXIN:
- **Lipopolysaccharide (LPS)** similar to gram negative bacteria.

VIRULENCE FACTORS:
- **Unique life cycle:**
  Elementary Bodies (EB=300 nm) enter host cells via several mechanisms; EBs organize as **Reticulate Bodies** (RB=1000nm) which replicate to produce new Elemental Bodies; the host cell ruptures to release the EBs so the cycle can continue.
- *Chlamydia trachomatis* **survive in Macros or epithelial cells**; but are killed in PMNs.
- **Ability to cause recurrent or persistent infections** often leads to greater tissue damage and scarring than the initial infection.

LAB TESTS:
- **Specimens:** are obtained from female endocervical cytobrushing; male urethral swabbing; or scraping of infected conjunctiva.
- **Direct immunofluorescent, Iodine, ELISA or Giemsa** stained smears show triangular-shape intra-cytoplasmic inclusion bodies (the RBs).
- **Direct immunofluorescent or ELISA** staining of specimen may reveal EBs.
- **Prior to testing, specimens may be cultured** by cell-culture techniques, for greater specificity.
- **DNA probe and PCR amplification or EIA** using Urine specimen.
- **Serological tests are not helpful.**

SOURCE AND TRANSMISSION:
- **Humans** are the only reservoirs for *C. trachomatis.*
- **Horizontal transmission** occurs via **sexual contact.**
- **Autoinoculation** of infection to other parts of the body is possible.
- **Vertical transmission** from mother to neonate occurs **during birth,** by passage through infected vagina.

CLINICAL:
- **Note:** *Chlamydia trachomatis* is the #1 cause of STD in the USA.
- **Male STD:**
  - **Urethritis, Epididymitis:**
    Symptoms: **urethral discharge**, dysuria, and **hemospermia.**
    Most often **asymptomatic in men.**
  - **Proctitis:** in homosexual men from anal intercourse.

- **Female STD:**
  - **Cervicitis, endometritis, salpingitis,** and **PID:**
    Symptoms: **vaginal discharge**, dysuria, pain, bleeding.
    Often **asymptomatic in women.** May cause **sterility.**
  - **Proctitis:** from anal intercourse.

- **Lymphogranyuloma Venereum STD:**
  - Incubation about 2 weeks, **females** often remain **asymptomatic.**
  - Stage one: Genital/anal papule at site of infection; heals rapidly.
  - Stage two: **Inguinal lymphadenopathy - "buboes"** - along with constitutional symptoms such as **fever**, headache, myalgia. May present as proctitis due to anal intercourse.
  - Symptoms may spontaneously resolve or become chronic.

- **Trachoma: Ophthalmological infection:**
  - **Chronic inflammation of eye** due to hand-eye **autoinoculation.**
  - Often leads to **blindness**, does not occur as a neonatal infection.

- **Neonatal infections:** (Due to passage through infected vagina)
  - **Inclusion Conjunctivitis:** 1to 2 weeks after birth; no blindness.
  - **Infant Atypical Pneumonia:** 5 to 25 weeks after birth.

- **Post-Chlamydia Reiter Syndrome - Arthritis:**
  - Arthritic disease associated with HLA-B27 genotype.

HOST DEFENSE AND IMMUNITY:
- **PMNs** are the most effective defense.
- **T-cells, Macros, Eosinophils and plasma cells** are all activated.
- **Cytokines** are effective.
- **Previous infection confers no protective immunity** against subsequent infection.

TREATMENT:
- **Doxycycline.**
- **Azithromycin** For children and pregnant women.
- **Cefoxitin plus Doxycycline** for concurrent *N. gonorrhea* infection.
- **Lymphogranuloma venereum** Requires aspiration of lymph nodes.
- **Sexual partner must be treated.**
- **Prevention:** Condoms and sex education.

VACCINE AND TOXOID:
None

Chapter 14
MYCOPLASMA AND UREAPLASMA

RESPIRATORY DISEASE MYCOPLASMA	SEXUALLY TRANSMITTED MYCOPLASMA	SEXUALLY TRANSMITTED UREAPLASMA	

Mycoplasma pneumoniae
 Atypical pneumonia
 Bronchitis
	Mycoplasma hominis
	 Sexually transmitted diseases
	     UTI
	     PID
	 Perinatal Diseases
	     Post-partum fever
	     Post-abortion fever
		Ureaplasma urealyticum
		 Sexually transmitted diseases
		     Urethritis
		 Perinatal Diseases
		     Low birthweight newborns
		     Chorioamnionitis	

Mycoplasma pneumoniae

GRAM STAIN:
NULL
Stains Poorly
NO CELL WALL

AEROBIC

EXTRACELLULAR

FEATURES:
- **Smallest free-living organisms**.
  Pliable membrane contains
  sterols, and no cell wall.

- **Colonies:**
  -Agar media:
    Extracellular growth
    Microscopic characteristic
    "mulberry"colonies.
  -Cell culture:
    Intracellular growth.

MOTILITY:
None

CAPSULE:
None

GLYCOCALYX:
None

EXOTOXINS:
None

ENDOTOXIN:
None

VIRULENCE FACTORS:
- **Antimicrobial Resistance:**
  - Lack of cell wall foils drugs that target cell wall components.
- **Adhesin Protein P1:**
  - Enables attachment to epithelial cells, especially ciliated cells.
- **Hydrogen Peroxide Production:**
  - May contribute to mucosal damage.
- **_M. pneumonia_ has the ability to survive intracellularly**,
  but does most damage to host cells at extracellular locations.
- **Special Nutrient Requirements:**
  - **Cholesterol**, nucleic acid precursors, amino acids, etc.
- **Sterol Cytoplasmic Membrane:**
  - Unique feature of *Mycoplasmataceae* family.

LAB TESTS:
- **Culture** of sputum; takes weeks.
- **Gram Stain** of sputum to rule out
    other causative organisms.
- **Cold Agglutinins   POS**
    (special RBC IgM blood test)
- **Glucose fermentation   POS**
- **Tetrazolium Dye reduction: Blue to Yellow**.

SOURCE AND TRANSMISSION:
- **Humans** are the only reservoirs for *M. pneumoniae*.
- **Horizontal transmission** occurs via **respiratory droplets**
    mostly among **college students** and **military troops** worldwide.
- **Epidemics** can occur.

CLINICAL:
- **Pneumonia: Atypical Pneumonia.**
  - *M. pneumoniae* **the most common cause of Atypical pneumonia.**
    Infection is usually mild or asymptomatic, but can be fatal.
  - Infection occurs most often in **teenagers** and **young adults**.
    especially **college students** and **military troops**.
  - **Chest X-ray** usually shows unilateral, lower lobe involvement.
  - Symptoms: **interstitial pneumonia** with **non-productive cough**
    and inspiratory crackles, fever, chills, headache, and chest pain.
  - Incubation is 2-3 weeks.
  - Symptoms may last for weeks or months, and **relapses** may occur.
  - Complications:
    Raynauds phenomena may occur in *M. pneumonia* infection
    due to **cold-agglutinin** antibodies, this can lead to necrosis of
    fingers and toes if it occurs in **Sickle cell anemia** patients.

- **Bronchitis.**

HOST DEFENSE AND IMMUNITY:
- **Antibodies and T-cells** are important.
- **Autoantibodies are produced:**
    Several autoagglutinins, especially
    IgM Cold Isohemagglutinins
- **Cytokines are activated, except IL-2**.
- **Previous infection** confers **no protective immunity** against
    subsequent infection.

TREATMENT:
- **Doxycycline**.
- **Azithromycin**
    For children and pregnant women.

VACCINE AND TOXOID:
None

Mycoplasma hominis

GRAM STAIN:
NULL
Stains Poorly
NO CELL WALL

AEROBIC

EXTRACELLULAR

FEATURES:
- **Smallest free-living organisms**.
  Pliable membrane contains
  sterols, and no cell wall.

- **Colonies**:
- Agar media:
  Extracellular growth
  Microscopic characteristic
  "fried egg"colonies.
- Cell culture:
  Intracellular growth.

MOTILITY:
None

CAPSULE:
None

GLYCOCALYX:
None

EXOTOXINS:
None

ENDOTOXIN:
None

VIRULENCE FACTORS:
- **Antimicrobial Resistance**:
  - Lack of cell wall foils drugs that target cell wall components.
- **Adhesin Protein P1**:
  - Enables attachment to epithelial cells, especially ciliated cells.
- **Hydrogen Peroxide Production**:
  - May contribute to mucosal damage.
- **_M. hominis_ has the ability to survive intracellularly**,
  but does most damage to host cells at extracellular locations.
- **Special Nutrient Requirements**:
  - **Cholesterol**, nucleic acid precursors, amino acids, etc.
- **Sterol Cytoplasmic Membrane**:
  - Unique feature of *Mycoplasmataceae* family.

LAB TESTS:
- **Culture**:
  From genitourinary tract.
  Grows in 1-2 weeks.
- Glucose fermentation   NEG
- **Metabolizes Arginine**.

SOURCE AND TRANSMISSION:
- **Humans** are the only reservoirs for *M. hominis*.
- **Horizontal transmission** occurs via **sexual contact**.
- **Temporary colonization of neonates** may occur by passage through
  infected vagina **during birth**; usually **inconsequential**.

CLINICAL:
- **UTI: Acute Pyelonephritis**:
  - Symptoms: flank pain, **fever**, dysuria.
  - May progress to **PID**.

- **Perinatal Infection**:
  - **Post-Partum Fever and Post-Abortion Fever**:
    Fever will last a few days following birth or following abortion.

HOST DEFENSE AND IMMUNITY:
- **Antibodies and T-cells** are important.
- **Previous infection** confers **no protective immunity** against
  subsequent infection.

TREATMENT:
- **Doxycycline**.
- **Azithromycin**
  For children and pregnant women.
  also for doxycycline-resistant strains.

VACCINE AND TOXOID:
None

Ureaplasma urealyticum

GRAM STAIN:
NULL
Stains Poorly
NO CELL WALL

AEROBIC

EXTRACELLULAR

FEATURES:
- **Smallest free-living organisms**.
  Pliable membrane contains **sterols**, and no cell wall.

- **Colonies:**
-Agar media:
  Extracellular growth
  Small colonies
  Microscopic characteristic
  "fried egg"colonies.
-Cell culture:
  Intracellular growth.

MOTILITY:
None

CAPSULE:
None

GLYCOCALYX:
None

EXOTOXINS:
None

ENDOTOXIN:
None

VIRULENCE FACTORS:
- **Antimicrobial Resistance:**
  - Lack of cell wall foils drugs that target cell wall components.
- **U. urealyticum has the ability to survive intracellularly**,
  but does most damage to host cells at extracellular locations.
- **Special Nutrient Requirements:**
  - **Cholesterol**, nucleic acid precursors, amino acids, etc.
- **Sterol Cytoplasmic Membrane:**
  - Unique feature of *Mycoplasmataceae* family.
- **U. urealyticum can split urea** as an energy source.

LAB TESTS:
- **Culture:**
  From genitourinary tract.
  Grows within 2 days.
  Very TINY colonies.
  Requires Urea.
- Glucose fermentation   NEG

SOURCE AND TRANSMISSION:
- **Humans** are the only reservoirs for *U. urealyticum*.
- **Horizontal transmission** occurs via **sexual contact**
- **Temporary colonization of neonates** may occur by passage through infected vagina **during birth**; usually **inconsequential**.

CLINICAL:
- **Urethritis:** does not progress to PID.

- **Perinatal Infection:**
  - **Low Birth-Weight Newborns**.
  - Chorioamnionitis: rare.

HOST DEFENSE AND IMMUNITY:
- **Antibodies and T-cells** are important.
- **Previous infection** confers **no protective immunity** against subsequent infection.

TREATMENT:
- **Doxycycline**.
- **Azithromycin**
  For children and pregnant women.
  also for doxycycline-resistant strains.

VACCINE AND TOXOID:
None

Chapter 15

BACTERIA CROSS REFERENCE

OBLIGATE AEROBES
Pseudomonas aeruginosa
Mycobacterium spp
Leptospira interrogans

OBLIGATE ANAEROBES
Clostridium botulinum
Clostridium difficile
Clostridium perfringens
Clostridium tetani
Actinomyces israelii
Peptostreptococcus spp
Propionibacterium acnes
Bacteroides fragilis
Fusobacterium spp
Prevotella spp
Chlamydia spp

MICROAEROPHILIC
Helicobacter pylori
Campylobacter jejuni
Treponema spp

BIPOLAR STAINING
"Safety pin pattern" ⊂▭▭⊃
Haemophilus influenzae
Francisella tularensis
Pasteurella multocida
Yersinia pestis

OBLIGATE INTRACELLULAR
Rickettsia spp
Ehrlichia spp
Chlamydia spp

INTRACELLULAR
Listeria monocytogenes
Neisseria spp
Legionella pneumophilia
Salmonella spp
Shigella spp
Brucella spp
Coxiella burnetii
Francisella tularensis
Yersinia pestis
Mycobacterium spp
Nocardia asteroides

PIGMENT PRODUCING
Corynebacterium diphtheriae
    (gray-black)
Pseudomonas aeruginosa
    (blue-green)
Serratia marcescens
    (red)
Prevotella melaninogenica
    (brown)
Legionella pneumophilia
    (brown)
Nontuberculous Mycobacteria
    (yellow)

UNUSUAL SHAPE BACTERIA
Corynebacterium diphtheriae
    (club; Chinese letter clumps)
Listeria monocytogenes
    (Chinese letter clumps)
Clostridium tetani
    (club or tennis racquet)
Neisseria spp (coffee bean pairs)
Helicobacter pylori
    ("S" or comma)
Vibrio spp ("S" or comma)
Bacillus anthracis (boxcar)
Campylobacter jejuni
    ("S"or comma)
Actinomyces spp (filamentous)
Mycobacterium tuberculosis
    (cords)
Nocardia spp (filamentous)
Chlamydia spp
    (elemental/reticulate bodies)

MOTILITY
Bacillus cereus
Listeria monocytogenes (tumble)
Clostridium difficile
Clostridium tetani
Proteus spp
Morganella spp
Providencia spp
Enterobacter cloacae
Serratia marcescens
Uropathogenic E. coli
Legionella pneumophilia
Pseudomonas aeruginosa
Helicobacter pylori (cork screw)
Vibrio spp
Enteric E. coli
Salmonella spp
Campylobacter jejuni (darting)
Yersinia (in culture only)
Bartonella spp (twitching)
Treponema spp (rotate)
Leptospira interrogans
Borrelia spp

NO CELL WALL
[Require cholesterol culture]
Mycoplasma
Ureaplasma

GRAM NULL
[Do not stain with Gram stain]
All Spirochetes
Chlamydia spp
Mycoplasma
Ureaplasma

GRAM VARIABLE
[POS or NEG with Gram stain}
Gardnerella vaginalis

CAPSULES
Group A Streptococcus
    (Hyaluronic acid)
Group B Streptococcus
Streptococcus pneumoniae
Neisseria spp
Moraxella catarrhalis
Bordetella pertussis
Haemophilus influenzae
Klebsiella pneumoniae
E. coli (sometimes)
Salmonella spp
Bacillus anthracis
    (polypeptide D-glutamate)
Francisella tularensis (lipid)
Pasteurella multocida
Yersinia pestis
    (protein-polysaccharide)
Bacteroides fragilis
Prevotella melaninogenica
Mycobacterium spp
    (lipid/polypeptide)

GLYCOCALYX
Staphylococcus epidermidis
Streptococcus Viridans Group
Pseudomonas aeruginosa

SPORES
Bacillus spp
    (spores need oxygen)
Clostridium spp (anaerobic)
Coxiella burnetii

NO INVITRO GROWTH
Mycobacterium leprae
    (foot pad of living mouse only)
Treponema spp

CELL CULTURE GROWTH
Coxiella burnetii
Rickettsia spp
Ehrlichia spp
Chlamydia spp

UNUSUAL CULTURES
Proteus spp
    (swarming, putrid)
Corynebacterium diphtheriae
    (black)
Pseudomonas aeruginosa
    (blue-green, fruity)
Mycoplasma and **Ureaplasma**
    (fried egg)
Mycoplasma pneumoniae
    (mulberry)

EXOTOXIN PRODUCING
Staphylococcus aureus
Group A Streptococcus
Bacillus spp
Corynebacterium diphtheriae
Listeria monocytogenes
Clostridium spp
Uropathogenic E. coli
Bordetella pertussis
Pseudomonas aeruginosa
Vibrio spp
Entero Toxigenic E. coli
Entero Hemorrhagic E. coli
Shigella spp

IgA PROTEASE
Streptococcus pneumoniae
Neisseria spp
Haemophilus influenzae

FEW ORGANISMS NEEDED
TO CAUSE INFECTION
Shigella spp
Coxiella burnetii
Rickettsia spp
Bartonella spp
Treponema pallidum
Chlamydia spp

MANY ORGANISMS NEEDED
TO CAUSE INFECTION
Salmonella spp
Vibrio spp

Categories of Common Bacterial Toxins

ADP-Ribosylating Toxins
V. cholera Cholera Toxin
ETEC Cholera-like LT Toxin

C. diphtheriae Diphtheria Toxin
   (Blocks host EF2)
P. aeruginosa Exotoxin A
   Diphtheria-like toxin
   (Blocks host EF2)

C. botulinum C2 Enterotoxin
(This in not botulism neurotoxin)
C. perfringens Iota Toxin

B. pertussis Pertussis Toxin

Adenylate Cyclase Toxins
B. pertussis
   Adenylate Cyclase Toxin
   (This is not pertussis toxin)
B. anthracis
   Edema Factor

Toxins ⇧ Adenylate Cyclase:
⇧ cAMP:
B. pertussis
   Adenylate Cyclase Toxin
   (This is not pertussis toxin)
B. anthracis
   Edema Factor

V. cholera Cholera Toxin
ETEC Cholera-like LT Toxin

Toxins ⇧ cGMP:
ETEC Cholera-like ST Toxin

G-Protein Mediated Toxins:
V. cholera Cholera Toxin
   (Turn on the "on signal")
ETEC Cholera-like LT Toxin
   (Turn on the "on signal")

B. pertussis Pertussis Toxin
   (Turn off the "off signal")

Metallo Protease Toxins
C. botulinum Botulinum Toxin
C. tetani Tetanus toxin
B. anthracis Lethal Factor

Neuro Toxins
C. botulinum Botulinum Toxin
   (Flaccid paralysis)
C. tetani Tetanus toxin
   (Spastic paralysis)

RNA Glycosidas Toxins
Shigella spp Shiga Toxin
(blocks 28s rRNA of 60s subunit)
EHEC Shiga-like Toxin (SLT)
(blocks 28s rRNA of 60s subunit)

Protein Synthesis Inhibition
Shigella spp Shiga Toxin
(blocks 28s rRNA of 60s subunit)
EHEC Shiga-like Toxin (SLT)
(blocks 28s rRNA of 60s subunit)

C. diphtheriae Diphtheria Toxin
   (Blocks host EF2)
P. aeruginosa Exotoxin A
   Diphtheria-like toxin
   (Blocks host EF2)

Enterotoxins
S. aureus Toxin A, Toxin F
B. cereus Enterotoxin
C. botulinum C2 Enterotoxin
(This in not botulism neurotoxin)
C. difficile Enterotoxin
C. perfringens Enterotoxin

V. cholera Cholera Toxin
ETEC Cholera-like LT Toxin
ETEC Cholera-like ST Toxin

V. parahaemolyticus Enterotoxin

Shigella spp Shiga Toxin
(blocks 28s rRNA of 60s subunit)
EHEC Shiga-like Toxin (SLT)
(blocks 28s rRNA of 60s subunit)

NOTE: 1. These light microscope color plates represent typical specimens (not ideal specimens) as encountered in clinical practice.
2. All of the color plates on this page are magnified to equal high power to allow meaningful comparison of relative sizes.

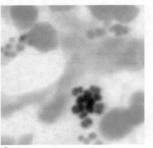

Streptococcus aureus
Abcess (Gram stain)

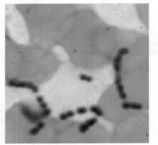

Streptococcus Group A
Blood (Gram stain)

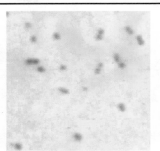

Streptococcus Group B
CSF (Gram stain)

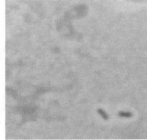

Streptococcus pneumoniae
Sputum (Gram stain)

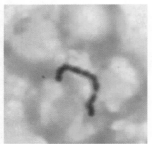

Streptococcus viridans
Blood (Gram stain)

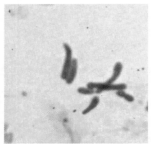

Corynebacterium diphtheriae
Culture (Gram stain)

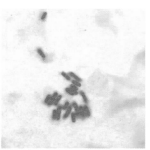

Listeria monocytogenes
Sputum (Gram stain)

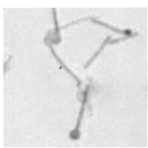

Clostridium teteni
Culture (Gram stain)

Actinomyces israelii
Brain abscess (Gram stain)

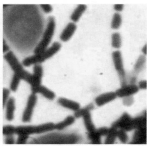

Bacillus anthracis
Tissue biopsy (Gram stain)

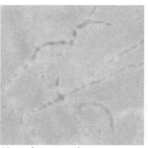

Nocardia asteroides
Brain abscess (MAF stain)

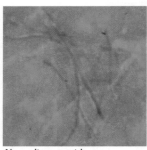

Nocardia asteroides
Brain abscess (Gram stain)

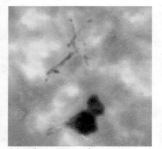

Mycobacterium tuberculosis
Lung biopsy (AF sain)

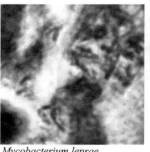

Mycobacterium leprae
Skin biopsy (Fite stain)

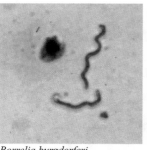

Borrelia burgdorferi
Skin biopsy (Silver stain)

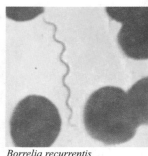

Borrelia recurrentis
Blood smear (Giemsa stain)

NOTE: 1. These light microscope color plates represent typical specimens (not ideal specimens) as encountered in clinical practice.
2. All of the color plates on this page are magnified to equal high power to allow meaningful comparison of relative sizes.

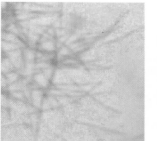

Fusobacterium spp
Abscess (Gram stain)

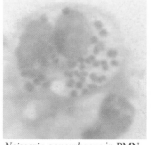

Neisseria gonorrhoeae in PMN
Urethral discharge (Gram stain)

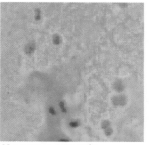

Neisseria meningitides
CSF (Gram stain)

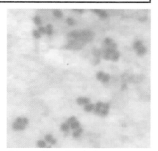

Moraxella catarrhalis
Sputum (Gram stain)

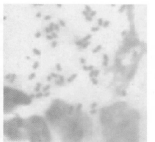

Haemophilus influenzae
Sputum (Gram stain)

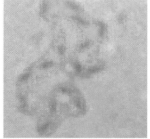

Klebsiella pneumoniae
Sputum (Gram stain)

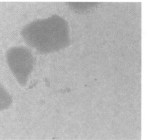

Pseudomonas aeruginosa
Sputum (Gram stain)

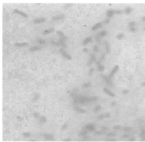

Pseudomonas aeruginosa
Sputum Cystic Fibrosis (Gram stain)

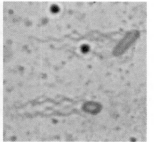

Proteus vulgaris
Urine (Flagella stain)

Hilicobacter pylori
Stomach biopsy (Gram stain)

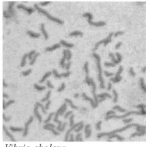

Vibrio cholera
Culture (Gram stain)

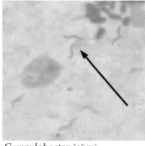

Campylobacter jejuni
Feces (Gram stain)

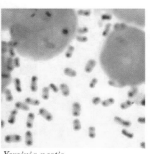

Yersinia pestis
Blood (Gram stain)

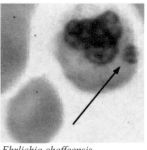

Ehrlichia chaffeensis
Blood smaer (Giemsa stain)

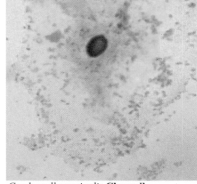

Gardneralla vaginalis **Clue cell**
Vaginal smear (Gram stain) Medium power

Chapter 16

DNA VIRUSES

Single-strand linear DNA
Icosahedral
No envelope

Parvovirus

B19 virus
  Erythema Infectiosum
  Hydrops Fetalis
  Sickle cell aplastic crisis
Dependovirus
  Asymptomatic

Double-strand linear DNA
Icosahedral
No envelope

Adenovirus

  1, 2, 3, 5 Intussusception
  3, 7 Pharyngoconjunctivitis
  3, 4, 7 Atypical pneumonia
  8, 19, 37 Keratoconjunctivitis
  11, 21 Hemorrhagic cystitis
  40, 41 Diarrhea

Partial double-strand
                Circular DNA
Icosahedral
Envelope

Hepadnavirus

Hepatitis B virus
  Acute Hepatitis
  Chronic Hepatitis
  Carrier State Hepatitis
  Hepatocellular carcinoma
Hepatitis D virus
Single-strand circular RNA
Double envelope
Defective virus
  Acute Hepatitis
  Chronic Hepatitis
  Carrier State Hepatitis
  Hepatocellular carcinoma

Double-strand linear DNA
Icosahedral
Envelope

Herpes virus

Alpha virus
  HSV-1
    Herpes labialis
  HSV-2
    Herpes genitalis
  VZV
    Chicken pox
    Herpes zoster
    Reye syndrome
Beta virus
  CMV
    Mononucleosis
    Retinitis
    Congenital encephalitis
Gamma virus
  EBV
    Mononucleosis
    Malignancy
  HHV-6
    Roseola

Double-strand Circular DNA
Icosahedral
No envelope

Papovavirus

Human Papillomavirus
    HPV-1, HPV-2
        Common warts
    HPV-6, HPV-11
        Genital warts
    HPV-16, HPV-18
        Cervical carcinoma
Polyomavirus
    JC virus
        PML
    BK virus
        Asymptomatic

Double-strand Linear DNA
Complex nucleocapsid
Double envelope

Pox virus

Orthopoxvirus
        Vaccinia virus
            Cow pox
        Variola virus
            Small pox
Molluscum contagiosum virus
            Genital infection

Family:

PARVO VIRUS

GENERA AND SPECIES:

Parvovirus:
B19

Dependovirus:
Adeno-associated virus
Herpes-associated virus

LOCATION OF REPLICATION:
Nucleus

EFFECT ON HOST CELLS:
Lysis

GENOME:
SS Linear DNA
+ or (-) Sense

SEGMENTATION:
No other segments

NUCLEOCAPSID:
Icosahedral

ENVELOPE:
No Envelope

SPECIAL FACTS:

● **Parvoviruses**
The only single-stranded DNA virus
Single strands may be **positive sense**
or **negative sense,** depends on strain.

● **Parvoviruses**
Very durable, can survive many years
in the environment, can endure high
temperatures for many hours.

Genus:
Parvovirus

SPECIES: B19 Virus
● Diseases:
▪ **Erythema Infectiosum:** "Slapped cheeks"
Red macular facial rash, limited to cheeks.

▪ **Erythroid Precursor Lysis:**
Destroys RBC precursors of host bone marrow;
causes hemolytic anemia.
　Fatal Aplastic Crisis occurs when RBC
　　precursors are destroyed in a patient with
　　sickle cell disease.
　Fatal Hemolytic Anemia occurs when
　　RBC precursors are destroyed in patient
　　with prior aplastic anemia.
　Chronic anemia occurs when RBC
　　precursors are destroyed in immunocom-
　　promised patient.

▪ **Hydrops Fetalis:**
Causes abortion of fetus if mother gets infected
during pregnancy.

　▪ **Arthritis.**

● Transmission:
▪ **Horizontal** via respiratory route.
▪ **Horizontal** via blood transfusions.
▪ **Vertical** mother to fetus via transplacental route
▪ **Spring season.**

● Geographic Range:
▪ World-wide.

● Diagnosis: Serology:
▪ **B19 DNA**
　　　indicates current infection.
▪ **B19-specific IgM antibody**
　　　indicates recent infection.
▪ **B19-specific IgG antibody**
　　　indicates past infection.

● Treatment:
▪ Infection often **benign** and **self-limited**.
▪ **Blood transfusion**
　　　in severe aplastic crisis.
▪ **IV immunoglobulin**
　　　for immunocompromised cases.
▪ **Avoid infection during pregnancy**.

● Immunity:
▪ Post-infectious immunity is long lasting.

● Vaccine: none.

Genus:
Dependovirus

SPECIES:
Adeno-dependent Dependovirus
● **Note:**
All **Dependoviruses** require **co-infection**
with a **double-stranded DNA virus** in order to
establish infection.
● Infection is not known to cause disease.

SPECIES:
Herpes-dependent Dependovirus
● **Note:**
All **Dependoviruses** require **co-infection**
with a **double-stranded DNA virus** in order to
establish infection.
● Infection is not known to cause disease.

Family:

ADENO VIRUS

GENERA AND SPECIES:

Adenovirus:
47 serotypes.

LOCATION OF REPLICATION:
Nucleus

EFFECT ON HOST CELLS:
Lysis

GENOME:
DS Linear DNA

SEGMENTATION:
No other segments

NUCLEOCAPSID:
Icosahedral
with **Fiber Spikes**

ENVELOPE:
No Envelope

SPECIAL FACTS:

●**Hemagglutinin fibers** protrude from each of 12 vertices of nucleocapsid; Provides serotype-specific antigens.

●**Capsid** basic structure is a unique combination of **triangles** which form hexagons and occasionally pentagons. Hexagons and pentagons form **sphere**.

●Adenovirus genes encode proteins which interfere with the expression of host MHC, therefore APCs cannot present the virus and the virus evades host immunity.

●Adenovirus causes tumors in some animals; may cause latent infections in humans.

Genus:
Adenovirus

SPECIES:
Adenovirus serotypes
(more than 47types)

●Diseases:
▪**1, 2, 3, 5:**
   Intussusception: in children.
▪**3, 7:**
   Pharyngoconjunctival Fever:
      Conjunctivitis and pharyngitis in children.
▪**3, 4, 7:**
   Respiratory Infections; Atypical Pneumonia:
      In young adults, especially military.
▪**8, 19, 37:**
   Epidemic Keratoconjunctivitis: in adults.
▪**11, 21:**
   Hemorrhagic Cystitis: mostly in children.
▪**40, 41:**
   Diarrhea:
      Common cause of diarrhea in infants.

●Transmission:
▪**Fecal-oral** route.
▪**Respiratory** route.

●Geographic Range:
▪World-wide.

●Diagnosis:
▪Based on clinical presentation.
▪Virus isolation, serology, tissue culture, etc. rarely performed.

●Treatment:
▪Symptomatic relief; often self-limited.

●Immunity:
▪Post-infectious, long-lasting, type-specific immunity (IgG).

●Vaccine:
▪**Live virus vaccine** is made with non-attenuated **strains 4 and 7**. Vaccine comes as an enteric-coated capsule (to withstand stomach acid). After ingestion, the **strains 4 and 7** generated an immune response which builds type-specific antibody. No infection arises; **strains 4 and 7** can only infect the respiratory tract, not the GI tract, due to temperature tropism. Vaccine is used for **military personnel**.

Family:

PAPOVA VIRUS

GENERA AND SPECIES:

Human Papillomavirus:
More than 50 serotypes.

Human Polyomavirus:
JC virus
BK virus

LOCATION OF REPLICATION:
Nucleus

EFFECT ON HOST CELLS:
Variable, depends on strain

GENOME:
DS Circular DNA

SEGMENTATION:
No other segments

NUCLEOCAPSID:
Icosahedral

ENVELOPE:
No Envelope

SPECIAL FACTS:

● **PROLIFERATION** is Hallmark of **Human Papillomavirus** infection.

● **Note:**
HPV-1, HPV-2, HPV-6, HPV-11:
DNA inserts into the host cells as **Episomes.**

● **Note:**
HPV-16, HPV-18:
DNA inserts into the host cells as **integrated into the host DNA.**

Genus:
Human Papillomavirus

SPECIES: HPV-1, HPV-2

● Disease: **Common Warts:**
  Occur on hands, feet. Regress spontaneously.
● Transmission: direct contact.
● Geographic Range: **World-wide.**
● Diagnosis: clinical presentation.
● Treatment:
  ▪ **Salicylic acid-Lactic acid** topical ointment.
  ▪ **Cryotherapy.**

SPECIES: HPV-6, HPV-11

● Disease:
▪ **Anal, Oral, or Genital Warts:**
  "**Condyloma Acuminata**" Flesh-colored, pedunculated papules which may "accumulate." Occur on penis, vagina, cervix, urethra, anus. Rarely regress, often **recur** even after treatment. May grow very large during pregnancy or immunosuppression.
▪ **Malignant transformation:**
  may occur at sites of infection.
● Transmission:
  ▪ **Horizontal** via sexual contact: very common.
  ▪ **Vertical** at birth via passage through vagina.
● Geographic Range:
  ▪ World-wide.
● Diagnosis:
  ▪ Clinical presentation.
  ▪ **5% Acetic acid:**
    Causes whitening (but not specific for HPV).
● Treatment:
  ▪ **Emotional support:** infection can be relentless.
  ▪ **Podophyllin; Cryotherapy; or Surgery:**
    For cosmesis.
● Vaccine: none.

SPECIES: HPV-16, HPV-18

● Disease: **Cervical Carcinoma:** can be **fatal.**
● Transmission: horizontal via **sexual contact.**
● Geographic Range: **World-wide.**
● Diagnosis: **Pap smear** shows **Koilocytes.**
● Treatment: surgery.
● Vaccine: none.

Genus:
Polyomavirus

SPECIES: JC Virus

● Disease: **PML:**
▪ **Progressive Multifocal Leukoencephalopathy:**
  Infection of Brain **oligodendrocytes** leads to progressive **demyelination.** Occurs mostly in **AIDS** and otherwise **immunocompromised** patients (eg organ transplant immunosuppression)
● Symptoms: hemiparesis, visual field problems, and focal deficits progress to dementia, coma. PML is **rapidly fatal** (mos.).
● Transmission: most all humans are seropositive. Virus remains **latent** in the host **kidney.**
● Geographic Range:
  ▪ World-wide.
● Diagnosis:
  ▪ **CT scan:** multiple white matter hypodensities.
  ▪ **MRI:** multiple white matter increase T2 signal.
  ▪ **Brain biopsy** shows oligodendrocyte basophilic intranuclear inclusion body.
  ▪ **PCR of urine or CSF** to detect JC Virus DNA.
● Treatment: no effective treatment.
  May improve if immunosuppression is reversed, or in cases of AIDS, if CD4 count is elevated by effective use of antiretroviral medications.
● Vaccine: none.

SPECIES: BK Virus

● Disease: mostly **asymptomatic.**
● Transmission: most all humans are seropositive. Virus remains **latent** in the host **kidney.**
● Geographic Range: World-wide.
● Diagnosis:
  PCR of **urine** to detect BK Virus DNA.
● Treatment: none.
● Vaccine: none.

Family:

HEPADNAVIRUS

GENERA AND SPECIES:
Hepatitis B Virus:
Hepatitis B
Defective Virus:
Hepatitis D Virus

LOCATION OF REPLICATION:
Nucleus

EFFECT ON HOST CELLS:
Buds from plasma membrane, no Lysis

GENOME:
Partial DS
Circular DNA

SEGMENTATION:
No other segments

NUCLEOCAPSID:
Icosahedral

ENVELOPE:
Envelope

SPECIAL FACTS:
▪ HBV has unique DNA: circular and mostly double stranded,but has single stranded "missing portion" of DNA.

▪**Three forms in human blood:**
Whole virions.
Spherical pieces.
Filamentous pieces.

▪**Three different major antigens:**
HBsAg protein of envelope surface;
HBcAg and HBeAg proteins of the capsid core.

Pathogenesis: HBV Life Cycle:
1. HBV travel in blood to adhere to host hepatocytes.

2. After entry and uncoating, viral DNA polymerase replicates the "missing portion" of viral genome

3. Some portions of viral DNA get integrated into the host genome, other portions serve as templates for mRNA transcription.

4. Some newly transcribed mRNA gets "reverse transcribed" in viral genomic DNA by process similar to Retroviral reverse transcriptase.

5. The virion forms in the cytoplasm then buds from the hepatocyte plasma membrane.

Genus:
Hepatitis B Virus [HBV]

SPECIES: Hepatitis B many types
Note: HBV is known as the **"Dane Particle"**
●Diseases:
▪**Asymptomatic:** new infected or chronic carriers may remain asymptomatic; anicteric (no jaundice).
▪**Acute hepatitis:** 2 month incubation period, symptoms of hepatic inflammation begin such as fever, nausea, right upper quadrant pain, icterus (jaundice), dark urine. Symptoms resolve after 2-3 months. Relapses rarely occur, but may progress to chronic carrier state or chronic active hepatitis.
▪**Chronic carrier:** sub-clinical persistence of HBV in hepatocytes is detected by HBsAg in blood. Neonatal infection may lead to chronic carrier state.
▪**Chronic active hepatitis:** symptomatic, persistent icteric infection that usually results from initially mild infection. Can lead to liver cirrhosis. Can be fatal.
▪**Fulminant hepatitis:** rapid progression liver necrosis. Acute, severe, symptomatic, and rapidly fatal.
▪**Hepatocellular Carcinoma:** in chronic carriers, or in chronic active hepatitis patients. This is fatal.
●Transmission:
▪**Horizontal** via sexual contact, close personal contact.
▪**Horizontal** via IV drug abuse, sharing needles.
▪**Horizontal** patient to health care worker by needle stick
▪**Iatrogenic** Blood transfusions, organ transplants, etc.
▪**Vertical** mother to child via breast milk or during birth.
●Geographic Range: World-wide.
●Diagnosis: **Serology:**
▪**HBeAg:** indicates active infection, and transmissibility.
▪**HBsAg:** indicates active infection; most common test. Continued presence indicates carrier state.
▪**HBcAg-specific antibody:** arises at "window period" after HBsAg disappears but before HBsAg-specific antibody appears.
▪**Liver Function Test** (LFT): Elevated **ALT** enzyme.
●Treatment:
▪**Acute Hepatitis:** symptom relief. **Note:** disappearance of HBeAg and appearance of **HBeAg-specific antibody** indicates end of transmissibility. Disappearance of HBsAg and presence of **HBsAg-specific antibody** indicates end of infection.
▪**Chronic Carriers:** education to prevent transmission.
▪**Chronic Hepatitis: Interferon-α** temporarily effective.
▪**Chronic Hepatitis** may require liver transplant surgery; but HBV may infect the new liver, due to latency of the virus elsewhere in the host's body.
▪**Fulminant Hepatitis** may require liver transplant. The new liver is unlikely to become infected because the HBV is usually restricted to the old liver.
●Immunity: post-infectious immunity is long lasting.
●Vaccine:
▪**Active immunization:** Inactivated HBV particles: spheres and filaments which contain HBsAg.
▪**Passive immunization: HBsAg-specific IgG antibody.**
●Prevention: avoid risky sexual behavior; use condoms. Health care workers must use universal precautions.

Genus:
Hepatitis D Virus [HCV]

Note:
HDV is an RNA virus, it is included here because it requires components of HBV in order to survive within a human host.

SPECIES: Hepatitis D
Note: HDV is known as **"Delta Agent"**
●Virion:
GENOME:
SS(-) Circular RNA
The RNA codes for one protein: HDV antigen (Delta antigen). HDV is similar to a virioid but cannot be considered a virioid.
ENVELOPE:
Double Envelope:
Inner layer is HDVAg envelope
Outer layer is HBsAg envelope donated to HDV by HBV

●Pathogenesis:
HDV = "defective" virus, in order to be infectious, it requires either coinfection concurrently with a new primary HBV infection or superinfection upon a pre-existing chronic or carrier-state HBV infection. In either case, HBV donates an outer envelope coat to HDV to make HDV a whole, infectious virus.

●Disease:
▪**Chronic carrier state** leads to cirrhosis.
▪**Chronic Hepatitis** leads to cirrhosis.
▪**Fulminant Hepatitis** high mortality.

●Transmission:
▪IV drug abusers who share needles.

●Geographic Range:
▪World-wide.

●Diagnosis: **Serology:**
▪**HDV-specific IgM antibody.**
▪**HDV RNA.**
▪**Coinfection: HDV-specific IgM** and **HBcAg-specific IgM** are present together in the same serum sample.
▪**Superinfection: HDV-specific IgM** and HBsAg present in same serum sample.
▪**Liver Function Test** (LFT): Elevated **ALT** enzyme.

●Treatment: high dose **Interferon-α** May be helpful.

●Vaccine:
No vaccine, no passive immunity, however Hepatitis B vaccine will prevent Hepatitis D infections, by eliminating the Hepatitis B virus.

Family:

HERPES VIRUS

GENERA AND SPECIES:
Alpha Virus:
Herpes Simplex Virus 1 (HSV-1)
Herpes Simplex Virus 2 (HSV-2)
Varacella Zoster Virus (VZV)
Beta Virus:
Cytomegalovirus (CMV)
Gamma Virus:
Epstein-Barr Virus (EBV)
Human Herpes Virus-6 (HHV-6)

LOCATION OF REPLICATION:
Nucleus

EFFECT ON HOST CELLS:
Buds from host cell **Nucleus** then escapes from host cell through pore or else causes cell **Lysis**.
Note: Herpes is the only virus to bud from the nucleus

GENOME:
DS Linear DNA

SEGMENTATION:
No other segments

NUCLEOCAPSID:
Icosahedral

ENVELOPE:
Envelope

SPECIAL FACTS:

●All Herpes viruses can cause persistent and **latent** infections: initial infection is the **primary** infection; recrudescent or relapsing infection is known as the **secondary** infection.

●All Herpes viruses tend to form **intra-nuclear inclusions**.

●Size comparison of Herpes virus genomes: **From smallest to largest:**
VZV HSV HHV6 EBV CMV

●Herpes viruses are **intracellular** they spread from infected cell to neighboring cell; they do not survive long extracellularly.

Genus:
Alpha Virus

SPECIES:
Herpes Simplex Virus 1 [HSV-1]
Herpes Simplex Virus 2 [HSV-2]
●Diseases: **HSV-1:**
▪**Gingivostomatitis, Herpes Labialis** (cold sores) Painful, relapsing vesicular lesions of lips/mouth.
▪**Keratoconjunctivitis**
▪**Herpetic Whitlow:** vesicular finger skin lesions.
▪**Adult Necrotizing Encephalitis:** rapidly fatal. Temporal lobe, seizures, personality changes

●Diseases: **HSV-2:**
▪**Herpes Genitalis:** painful, relapsing vesicular lesions of genitalia, groin, anus.
▪**Herpetic Whitlow:** vesicular finger skin lesions.
▪**Neonatal skin lesions and Encephalitis:** fatal.
▪**Aseptic meningitis.**

●Transmission: (primary incubation: 2-10 days).
Note: infectious virus may be **shed** even when vesicles are absent.
▪**HSV-1: Horizontal** via **direct contact.**
▪**HSV-2: Horizontal** via **sexual contact.**
▪**HSV-2: Vertical** mother to child during birth.
▪**Health care workers:** risk for HSV-1, HSV-2.

●Diagnosis:
▪**Tzanck smear:** shows multinucleated giant cells Scrape skin at vesicle base, mount on slide, fix in methyl alcohol, use Giemsa or Wright stain.
▪**HSV PCR of CSF** for encephalitis diagnosis.
▪**CT Scan** in encephalitis shows unilateral medial temporal lobe inflammation.
▪**CSF** may show **blood** in meningitis cases.

●Treatment:
▪**Acyclovir:**
Activated by **viral thymidine kinase**; serves to block viral **DNA polymerase**; helps symptoms. No cure.
▪**Emotional support** necessary due to relentless nature of infection. Education is necessary to prevent spread, and to protect neonate.

●Immunity: may become **persistent** or **latent**.
▪**HSV-1** latent in **Trigeminal** sensory ganglia.
▪**HSV-2** latent in **Lumbo-Sacral** sensory ganglia.

●Prevention: No vaccine.
▪**C-section** at birth may protect neonates.
▪**Condoms** may **not** be effective.

SPECIES:
Varicella Zoster Virus [VZV]
●Disease: **Chicken Pox:** (late winter season)
▪**Rash:** itchy, centripetal, vesicular, on trunk first: **"dew drop on rose petal."** Rash stages: papule, vesicle, crust. Note: lesions at different stages may be present at same time. Benign, self-limited, but can be more serious in adults than in children.
▪**Cellulitis superinfection.**
By *S. pyogenese*, or *S. aureus*.
▪**Pneumonitis in immunocompromised** often fatal
▪**Hemorrhagic pox** in childhood leukemia.
▪**Reye Syndrome** in children who use **aspirin**.

●Disease: **Herpes zoster: "Shingles"**
▪**Reactivation of latent VZV** from sensory ganglia due to stress, immunocomromised state, old age.
▪**Painful vesicular skin lesions within dermatomes.**
▪**Post-Herpetic Neuralgia** intermittent nerve pain that can last for years after the zoster rash heals.

●Transmission: (primary incubation: 1-2 weeks):
▪**Horizontal** via **respiratory** route: mostly among children, highly contagious. Patients are infectious at 48 hrs prior to rash, until all vesicles crusted.
▪**Horizontal** via contact with **Herpes zoster** patient can cause chicken pox.

●Diagnosis:
▪**Tzanck smear:** shows multinucleated giant cells.

●Treatment:
▪**Isolation** of patient and seronegative contacts.
▪**Skin kept clean** to prevent superinfection, may require oral/topical antibiotics for superinfection.
▪**Topical** lotion, oral antihistamines for pruritus.
▪**Acyclovir** may help in immunocompromised.
▪**Must not use aspirin.**
▪**Tricyclic antidepressants** or **gabapentin** used for post-herpetic neuralgia pain.

●Immunity:
▪Post-infectious immunity long lasting, however initial infection becomes **latent**, relapses as zoster.
▪**VZV** tends to be latent in **Trigeminal** sensory ganglia, sometimes cervical-thoracic dorsal-root sensory ganglia. (Rarely ventral horn.)

●Vaccine:
▪**Active immunization:** Oka-strain **live VZV**.
Not in immunocompromised or pregnant patients.
▪**Passive immunization:** (VZIG, VIP)
VZV-specific IgG antibody. Use within 96 hrs of exposure; for immunocompromised or pregnant.

Family:

HERPES VIRUS (continued)

Genus:
Beta Virus

SPECIES:
Cytomegalovirus [CMV]one serotype

- **Diseases:**
  - Most CMV infections are asymptomatic.
  - **Infectious Mononucleosis: "Heterophile-NEG"**
    Symptoms: lymphocytosis, atypical lymphocytes, fever, hepatosplenomegaly; 20-30 yr age group.
  - **Retinitis/ Blindness** in immunocompromised
    Common in AIDS patients with CD4 count<50.
    Funduscopic exam: "pizza pie retina."
  - **Interstitial pneumonitis** in immunocompromised
  - **Hepatitis** in immunocompromised.
  - **Cytomegalic Inclusion Disease** Congenital CMV
    Encephalitis, brain calcifications; seizures, mental retardation, and nerve deafness.

- **Transmission:** (primary incubation: 1-2 months).
  - **Note:** most humans are infected with CMV.
  - **Horizontal** via **sexual** or intimate contact:
    Present in semen, cervical fluids, saliva, urine, etc.
  - **Iatrogenic:** organ transplant, blood products.
  - **Vertical** mother to fetus transplacentally in utero causes congenital infection.
  - **Vertical** transmission mild infection may occur during delivery due to **vaginal secretions**, or may occur post-partum due to **breast feeding**.
  - **Reactivation** of latent CMV ("secondary CMV") as consequence of immunocompromised state.

- **Diagnosis:**
  - **Serology:** CMV-specific IgM or IgG
  - **Tissue samples:**
    "**Owl-Eye**" nuclear/cytoplasmic inclusion.
  - **CT scan:** focal calcifications in brain.

- **Treatment:**
  - No effective treatment of CMV infection.
  - **Ganciclovir** or **Foscarnet** for CMV retinitis and for transplant patients, but relapse occurs when treatment is halted.

- **Immunity:**
  - Infections may become persistent or latent.
  - CMV is latent in many organs and leukocytes.

- **Vaccine:** none.

Genus:
Gamma Virus

SPECIES:
Epstein-Barr Virus [EBV]

- **Diseases:**
  - Asymptomatic in children.
  - **Infectious Mononucleosis: "Heterophile-POS"**
    Symptoms: lymphocytosis, atypical lymphocytes, fever, hepatitis, **splenomegaly**, pharyngitis exudate coated tongue, anorexia, swollen tonsils, **fatigue**.
    Occurs mostly in 15-20 yr "**college**" age group.
    Infection is usually benign and self-limited.
  - **Cancer associations:**
    Burkett's Lymphoma in Africa.
    Nasopharyngeal Carcinoma in China.
  - **Note:** EBV replicates primarily within B-cells; therefore T-cells proliferate as the host response.

- **Transmission:** (primary incubation: 1-2 months).
  - **Horizontal** oral/intimate contact; kissing (saliva)

- **Diagnosis:**
  - **Serology:**
    EBVcapsid-antigen-specific IgM antibody.
  - **Serology:**
    Heterophile-agglutinin (Monospot test): POS.
  - **Peripheral Smear:** atypical T-lymphocytes:
    The T-lymphocytes attack B-lymphocytes.
  - **Liver Function Test** (LFT): elevated **ALT**

- **Treatment:**
  - Acetaminophen for constitutional symptoms
  - Avoid sports: may rupture spleen.
  - **Note:** Avoid ampicillin: it causes non-itchy maculopapular rash.

- **Immunity:**
  - Infections may become persistent or latent.
  - EBV tends to be latent in B-lymphocytes.

- **Vaccine:** none.

SPECIES:
Human Herpesvirus-6 [HHV-6]

- **Disease: Roseola (Exanthem subitum):**
  Mostly **children** 6mos-12mos.
- **Symptoms:** sudden onset high **fever** lasts 3 days.
  Pink, **rose-color rash** on **trunk** when fever ends.
- **Horizontal transmission** via **respiratory** route.
- **Treatment:** symptomatic relief;
  infection is brief and self-limited.

Family:

POX VIRUS

GENERA AND SPECIES:
Orthopoxvirus:
Vaccinia virus
Variola virus
Unclassified:
Molluscum contagiosum virus

LOCATION OF REPLICATION:
Cytoplasm
Note: Pox Virus is the only DNA
   virus to replicate in cytoplasm

EFFECT ON HOST CELLS:
No cell Lysis
No budding from host cell

GENOME:
DS Linear DNA

SEGMENTATION:
No other segments

NUCLEOCAPSID:
Complicated

ENVELOPE:
Double Envelope

SPECIAL FACTS:

●Pox viruses, the only DNA viruses
that do not replicate in the host cell
nucleus, they must carry their own
DNA-dependent-RNA-polymerase
enzymes.

●Pox viruses cause no host cell lysis;
do not bud from plasma membrane.
Unique double-layered envelope is
acquired at the host golgi apparatus.

●Pox viruses are the **largest**
and **most complex** viruses.

Genus:
Orthopoxvirus

SPECIES: Vaccinia virus
●Disease: **Cowpox:** Vesicular lesion on fingers
due to milking of infected cows by hand.

●Live attenuated Vaccinia virus Vaccine is used
to protect against smallpox. **Rare side-effects:**
  ▪Vesicular rash; encephalitis; viremia in
   immunocompromised,
  ▪**Vaccinia Necrosum** necrosis and gangrene at
   inoculation site progresses throughout body;
   this can be fatal.

●Treatment: mostly self-limited.
Vaccinia immunoglobulin is sometimes effective.

SPECIES: Variola virus Two Strains
●Disease: **Smallpox:**
Vesicular rash: face/trunk spreads to extremities.
Stages: macules, papules, vesicles, then crust.
Differentiated from rash of chicken pox:
Smallpox: all lesions are at same stage.
Chicken pox: various stages present concurrently.

●Strains:
  Variola Major: 50% mortality.
  Variola minor: 1% mortality.

●Pathogenesis:
1. Variola establishes infection in respiratory tract.
2. Spreads to blood as primary viremia.
3. Infects internal organs.
4. Infects skin as vesicular rash.

●Transmission:
▪**Horizontal** via **respiratory** route.

●Geographic Range: none.
▪**Note:** Smallpox eliminated worldwide.

●Diagnosis: Clinical presentation, Virus isolation.

●Treatment: symptomatic relief.
  Sometimes Variola immunoglobulin.

●Immunity:
Post-infectious, long-lasting immunity (IgG).

●Vaccine: Live, attenuated Vaccinia virus:
  Now only for military use.

Note: Successful elimination of smallpox due to:
(Last case was 1977.)
1. Humans are the only reservoir.
2. Safe vaccine causes rapid antibody production.
3. Only two serotypes (maybe just one).
4. Clinically easy to recognize.
5. No carrier or sub-clinical states.

Genus:
Unclassified Poxvirus

SPECIES:
Molluscum Contagiosum Virus
●Disease:
▪**Genital Tumors:** benign, self-limited, firm, pink
pedunculated, papules on genitals, in adults.
▪**Disseminated:** progress to systemic infection in
immunocompromised. Large skin tumors arise.
▪**Skin tumors:** small, benign, self-limited, warts
cutaneous papules in children and adults.

●Transmission:
▪**Horizontal** via **direct** contact.
▪**Horizontal** via **sexual** contact.

●Geographic Range:
▪World-wide.

●Diagnosis:
▪Electron microscopy of biopsy.

●Treatment:
▪**Local lesions**: surgery, laser, cryotherapy.
▪**Disseminated:** no effective treatment.

●Vaccine: none.

Chapter 17

RNA VIRUSES

Positive-sense
Single-strand linear RNA
Icosahedral
No envelope

Picornavirus
Rhinovirus
    Coryza (common cold)
Enterovirus
    Coxsackie A virus
      Aseptic meningitis
      Hand-foot-mouth disease
    Coxsackie B virus
      Aseptic meningitis
      Pleurodynia
      Myopericarditis
    Echo virus
      Aseptic meningitis
    Enterovirus 70
      Conjunctivitis
    Enterovirus 71
      Encephalitis
    Hepatitis A virus
      Acute Hepatitis
    Polio virus
      Aseptic meningitis
      Polio

Calicivirus
    Norwalk virus
      Gastroenteritis
    Hepatitis E virus
      Acute Hepatitis

Positive-sense
Single-strand linear RNA
Icosahedral
Envelope

Togavirus
Alphavirus
  Eastern equine encephalitis
  Western equine encephalitis
  Venezuelan equine encephalitis
Rubivirus
  Rubella virus
    German measles
    Congenital Rubella

Flavivirus
Mosquito-borne epidemic types
  Yellow fever virus
  Dengue fever virus
  St. Louis encephalitis virus
  Japanese encephalitis virus
Hepatitis C virus
    Acute Hepatitis
    Chronic Hepatitis
    Carrier State Hepatitis
    Hepatocellular carcinoma

Negative-sense
Single-strand linear RNA
Helical
Envelope

Rhabdovirus
  Lyssavirus
    Rabies virus
      Rabies encephalitis

Paramyxovirus
  Paramyxo virus
    Mumps virus
      Mumps
    Parainfluenza virus
      Croup
  Morbillivirus
    Measles virus
      Measles
      SSPE
  Pneumovirus
    RSV
      Bronchiolitis

Filovirus
  Ebola virus
      Hemorrhagic fever
  Marbug virus
      Hemorrhagic fever

Negative-sense
Single-strand linear RNA
Segmented
Helical
Envelope

Orthomyxovirus
  Influenza A virus
    Flu
    Atypical pneumonia
    Reye syndrome
  Influenza B virus
    Flu
    Reye syndrome
  Influenza C virus
    URI

Negative-sense
Single-stranded circular RNA
Segmented
Helical
Envelope

Arenavirus
  Lymphocytic Choriomeningitis
    Aseptic meningitis
  Lassa Fever virus

Bunyavirus
  California encephalitis virus
  LaCrosse virus

Positive-sense-non-infectious
DIPLOID segmented
Single-strand linear RNA
Complex nucleocapsid
Envelope

Retrovirus
Oncovirus
  HTLV-1
    T-cell Leukemia/Lymphoma
    Tropical spastic paraparesis
  HTLV-2
    Hairy cell Leukemia

Lentivirus
  HIV-1
    ARC
    AIDS
    Malignancies
    Opportunistic infections
  HIV-2
    AIDS-like infection

Spumavirus
  Human foamy virus
    Asymptomatic

Double-strand linear RNA
Segmented
Icosahedral
No envelope

Reovirus
  Rotavirus
    Rotavirus Groups A, B, C
      Diarrhea
  Coltivirus
    Colorado Tick Fever virus
      Colorado tick fever

Positive-sense
Single-strand linear RNA
Helical
Envelope

Coronavirus
    Coryza (common cold)

Family:

PICORNAVIRUS

GENERA AND SPECIES:
Rhinovirus:
    100 types
Enterovirus:
    Coxsackie A virus
    Coxsackie B virus
    Echo virus
    Enteroviruses
    Hepatitis A virus
    Polio virus

LOCATION OF REPLICATION:
Cytoplasm

EFFECT ON HOST CELLS:
Lysis

GENOME:
SS+ Linear RNA
    Infectious RNA

SEGMENTATION:
No other segments

NUCLEOCAPSID:
Icosahedral

ENVELOPE:
No Envelope

SPECIAL FACTS:

PATHOGENESIS:
▪Horizontal transmission: fecal-oral. (except Rhinovirus)
▪In general, GI tract gets colonized, Peyers patches get infiltrated, then viremia carries virus to sites of focal involvement.
▪Usually summer/autumn.

Genus:
Rhinovirus

SPECIES: **Rhinovirus 1-100** 100 Types
- Disease: **Common Cold: Coryza**
  Rhinoviruses grow best at 33°C so infection is limited to the upper airway.
- Transmission: **Respiratory** route; during winter.
- Diagnosis: By clinical presentation.
- Treatment: symptom relief; self-limited.
- Immunity:
  Post-infectious, type-specific immunity (IgG).
- Vaccine: none.

Genus:
Enterovirus

SPECIES: **Coxsackie A** many types
- Disease: mucus membrane/skin manifestations
  ▪**Aseptic Meningitis.**
  ▪**Hand-foot-mouth Disease:** vesicular rash on hands, feet, with ulcerations in mouth.
  ▪**Herpangina:** vesicular eruption in throat.
- Transmission: **Fecal-oral**, mostly **Children**.
- Diagnosis: Clinical presentation, cell culture.
- Treatment: Symptom relief; often self-limited.
- Immunity:
Post-infectious, type-specific immunity (IgG).
- Vaccine: none.

SPECIES: **Coxsackie B** many types
- Disease: organ dysfunction.
▪**Aseptic Meningitis:** common.
▪**Pleurodynia:"Devil's grip"** pleuritic chest pain.
▪**Myopericarditis:** can be rapidly fatal.
▪**Pancreatic damage** may lead to **diabetes.**
- Transmission: **Fecal-oral**, mostly **Children.**
- Diagnosis: Clinical presentation, cell culture.
- Treatment: Symptom relief; often self-limited.
- Immunity:
Post-infectious, type-specific immunity (IgG).
- Vaccine: none.

SPECIES: **Echo** many types
- Disease:
▪**Aseptic Meningitis:** #1 causative organism.
▪**Neonatal Encephalitis** and Sepsis: can be fatal.
▪**Neonatal Fulminant Hepatitis:** mostly fatal.
▪**Diarrhea.**
- Transmission: **Fecal-oral**, mostly **children.**
- Diagnosis: Clinical presentation, cell culture.
- Treatment: Symptom relief; often self-limited.
- Immunity:
Post-infectious, type-specific immunity (IgG).
- Vaccine: none.

SPECIES: **Enterovirus 70**
- Disease: **Acute Hemorrhagic Conjunctivitis:** Common, highly contagious, transient. Sometimes also caused by Coxsackie A24

SPECIES: **Enterovirus 71**
- Disease: Paralysis and Encephalitis: can be fatal.

SPECIES:
Hepatitis A [Enterovirus 72] One Type
- Disease: **Acute Hepatitis:** hepatic inflammation asymptomatic in children. Causes fever, elevated Liver Function Test, jaundice, dark urine in adults. **No chronic sequelae,** and **no carrier state.**
- Transmission: fecal-oral; contaminated water; mostly children; world-wide, USA.
- Diagnosis: ↑ALT, **Hepatitis A-specific IgM.**
- Treatment: Symptom relief; self-limited.
- Immunity:
  Post-infectious, long-lasting immunity (IgG).
- Vaccine:
  Active immunity inactivated virus vaccine.
  Passive immunity with IgG immunoglobulin.

SPECIES: **Polio virus** Three Types
- Disease: (polio infection is very **rare**)
▪**Aseptic Meningitis:** common, non-paralytic.
▪**Polio Myelitis:** necrosis of anterior horn cells: Paralysis. Fatal if bulbar respiratory areas effected
- Transmission: **Fecal-oral**, mostly children.
- Diagnosis:
  Clinical presentation, isolate virus, serology.
- Treatment: Symptom relief; respiratory support. Normal function may return in several months.
- Immunity:
  Post-infectious, type-specific immunity (IgG).
- Vaccine: both vaccines generate **Ig M and IgG:**
▪**Salk IPV:** dead virus. **No IgA** created. GI tract vulnerable to infection; infection **cannot** progress.
▪**Sabin OPV:** live virus. **IgA created** to protect GI tract. Causes disease in immunocompromised: if given to compromised patient or to children in household who shed the virus after vaccination.

Family:

CALICIVIRUS

GENERA AND SPECIES:

Gastroenteritis group:
  Norwalk Virus
Hepatitis Group:
  Hepatitis E Virus

LOCATION OF REPLICATION:
Cytoplasm

EFFECT ON HOST CELLS:
Lysis

GENOME:
SS+ Linear RNA
  Infectious RNA

SEGMENTATION:
No other segments

NUCLEOCAPSID:
Icosahedral

ENVELOPE:
No Envelope

Genus:
Gastroenteritis Group

SPECIES: **Norwalk Virus**

● Disease: **Gastroenteritis:**
Nausea, abdominal cramps, vomiting, diarrhea.
Lasts 3 days. Infection by Norwalk is **common**
Can cause **epidemics**.

● Transmission: **Fecal-oral**.
Note: Some people not susceptible:
   They do not absorb the virus.

● Geographic Range:
  ▪World-wide.

● Diagnosis:
  ▪**Serology: Norwalk-specific IgM antibody**.
  ▪Immune electron microscopy of stool sample.
  ▪PCR is effective
  ▪Culture has not been achieved.

● Treatment: Oral fluid replacement.

● Immunity:
  ▪Post-infectious immunity is **not** long lasting.
  ▪**Re-infection** is possible after several months.

● Vaccine: none.

Genus:
Hepatitis Group

SPECIES: **Hepatitis E** One Type

● Diseases:
▪**Acute Hepatitis:** hepatic inflammation mostly
asymptomatic in children, causes fever, elevated
Liver Function Test, jaundice, dark urine in adults.
No chronic sequelae, and **no carrier state**.
▪**Fulminant Hepatitis of Pregnant Women:**
Fatal for mother if infected in first trimester.

● Transmission: **Fecal-oral**; mostly adults.

● Geographic Range:
▪Tropical and semitropical developing countries.

● Diagnosis:
▪↑ALT; process of elimination of other causes.
▪Immune electron microscopy of stool sample.
▪Hepatitis E-specific IgM test not widely available

● Treatment: Symptom relief; self-limited.

● Immunity:
▪Post-infectious immunity is **not** long lasting.

● Vaccine:
▪**Passive immunity** with IgG immunoglobulin.

Family:

REOVIRUS

GENERA AND SPECIES:

Rotavirus: (11 segments RNA)
  Rotavirus A, B, C
Coltivirus: (12 segments RNA)
  Colorado tick fever

LOCATION OF REPLICATION:
Cytoplasm

EFFECT ON HOST CELLS:
Lysis

GENOME:
DS Linear RNA

SEGMENTATION:
10-12 RNA segments

NUCLEOCAPSID:
Icosahedral
Double Layer

ENVELOPE:
No Envelope

SPECIAL FACTS:

●**Double-layer capsid:** "Wheel" structure on Electron microscopy.

●**No eclipse period:** Virus remains intact within host cells; virus does not go through uncoating process.

●**Antigenic variation:** Presence of many RNA segments allows for the resortment of genetic material, and the presentation of different antigens.

Genus:
Rotavirus

SPECIES:
Rotavirus Groups A, B, C
●<u>Disease</u>: **Gastroenteritis:**
Rotavirus is #1 cause of Diarrhea in children.
Diarrhea is significant cause of childhood fatality.

●<u>Transmission</u>:
  ▪Fecal-oral.
  ▪Winter season.

●<u>Geographic Range</u>:
  ▪World-wide.

●<u>Diagnosis</u>:
  ▪Rotavirus Detection in stool sample by ELISA.
  ▪Immune electron microscopy of stool sample.

●<u>Treatment</u>:
  ▪Oral fluid and electrolyte replacement.

●<u>Immunity</u>:
  ▪Post-infectious immunity is **not** long lasting.
  ▪**Re-infection** possible after several months, most likely due to antigenic variation from resortment.

●<u>Vaccine</u>: none.

Genus:
Coltivirus

SPECIES:
Colorado Tick Fever   Many Types
  (Formerly classified in the Genus *Orbivirus*)
●<u>Diseases</u>: **Colorado Tick Fever:**
▪<u>Biphasic symptoms</u>:
High fever, rash, nausea, vomiting.
Remission for a few days.
Fever returns but symptoms resolve in few weeks.
▪<u>Note</u>:
A unique aspect of Colorado Tick Fever viremia is that the virus survives within red blood cells.

●<u>Transmission</u>:
      Vector = **tick**
      <u>Reservoir</u> = **squirrels, chipmunks**
      <u>Hosts</u> = **Humans**
        ▪Late **spring**, early summer.

●<u>Geographic Range</u>:
  ▪Western North America.

●<u>Diagnosis</u>:
▪Direct immunofluorescent stain of virus in RBC.
▪Serology.

●<u>Treatment</u>:
▪Supportive care.
▪Acetaminophen for fever.

●<u>Immunity</u>:
Post-infectious, type-specific immunity (IgG).

●<u>Vaccine</u>: none.

Family:

TOGAVIRUS

GENERA AND SPECIES:

Alphavirus:
Eastern equine encephalitis
Western equine encephalitis
Venezuelan equine encephalitis
Rubivirus:
Rubella virus

LOCATION OF REPLICATION:
Cytoplasm

EFFECT ON HOST CELLS:
Buds from plasma membrane, no Lysis

GENOME:
SS+ Linear RNA
Infectious RNA

SEGMENTATION:
No other segments

NUCLEOCAPSID:
Icosahedral
C-Protein only

ENVELOPE:
Envelope
H-Protein Spike

Genus:
Alphavirus

SPECIES:
Eastern Equine Encephalitis
- **Disease: Encephalitis:**
  CNS infection with high fever.
  50% fatal. Can cause **epidemics.**

- **Transmission:**
  Vector = **mosquito**
  Reservoir = **birds**
  Hosts = **Humans, horses**

- **Geographic Range: South-east USA,** very rare.
- **Diagnosis:** Virus isolation, serology.
- **Treatment:** Intensive supportive care.
- **Immunity:**
  Post-infectious, type-specific immunity (IgG).
- **Vaccine:** For animals only.

SPECIES:
Western Equine Encephalitis
- **Disease: Encephalitis:**
  CNS infection with high fever.
  Can be fatal. Can cause **epidemics.**

- **Transmission:**
  Vector = **mosquito**
  Reservoir = **birds**
  Hosts = **Humans, horses**

- **Geographic Range: Western USA,** rare.
- **Diagnosis:** Virus isolation, serology.
- **Treatment:** Intensive supportive care.
- **Immunity:**
  Post-infectious, type-specific immunity (IgG).
- **Vaccine:** For animals only.

SPECIES:
Venezuela Equine Encephalitis
- **Disease: Encephalitis:**
  CNS infection with high fever.
  Can be fatal. Can cause **epidemics.**

- **Transmission:**
  Vector = **mosquito**
  Reservoir = **birds**
  Hosts = **Humans, horses**

- **Geographic Range:**
  South and Central America, common.
- **Diagnosis:** Virus isolation, serology.
- **Treatment:** Intensive supportive care.
- **Immunity:**
  Post-infectious, type-specific immunity (IgG).
- **Vaccine:** For animals only.

Genus:
Rubivirus

SPECIES: **Rubella Virus** One Type
- **Diseases:**
- **German Measles:**
Fever and maculopapular **rash on face** and then extremities. Lasts 3 days. Can cause **epidemics.**
- **Congenital Rubella:**
Rubella virus is teratogen, especially if mother is infected in first trimester. Viremia cross placenta to cause disease in the fetus:
  - **Heart:** patent ductus arteriosus (PDA)
  - **Eyes:** cataracts, glaucoma.
  - **CNS:** mental retardation, **deafness.**
- **Note:** Children infected **in-utero** may continue to **shed** the virus for many months. This is **risk** to **pregnant women** and **immunocompromised.**

- **Transmission:**
German Measles: **Horizontal Respiratory** route.
Congenital: **Vertical transplacental** in-utero.

- **Diagnosis:**
- Clinical presentation.
- Cell-culture.
- Serology shows Rubella-specific IgM antibody.

- **Treatment:** Symptom relief.

- **Immunity:**
Post-infectious, type-specific immunity (IgG).

- **Vaccine:**
- **Live virus:** as part of **MMR** vaccine.
- **Note:**
Vaccine causes disease in **immunocompromised:** if given to compromised patient or to children in household who **shed** the virus after vaccination. However, MMR is given in **HIV** infected patients.

Family: FLAVIVIRUS

GENERA AND SPECIES:

Mosquito-Borne Epidemic Types
Yellow Fever Virus
Dengue Fever Virus
St. Louis Encephalitis Virus
Japanese Encephalitis Virus

Hepatitis C Virus:
Hepatitis C Virus

LOCATION OF REPLICATION:
Cytoplasm

EFFECT ON HOST CELLS:
Buds from plasma membrane, no Lysis

GENOME:
SS+ Linear RNA
Infectious RNA

SEGMENTATION:
No other segments

NUCLEOCAPSID:
Icosahedral

ENVELOPE:
Envelope
E and H-Protein Spikes

SPECIAL FACTS:

● Clinically, HCV infection is nearly indistinguishable from HBV. However, HCV is more likely to cause persistent, chronic infections.

● Diagnostic tests do not include tests for HCV-specific antibodies because the immune system, for unknown reasons, cannot launch an effective defense.

● Details about the life cycle of HCV are unknown.

Genus: Mosquito-Borne Epidemic Types

SPECIES: Yellow Fever Virus One Type

● Disease: **Yellow Fever:**
Fever, headache. Remission for few days. Fever again with jaundice, hemorrhage, hematemesis. Mild to severe, bit can be fatal.
● Transmission: Vector = **mosquito**
Reservoir = **monkeys** ("jungle fever")
Hosts = **Humans** ("urban fever")
● Geographic Range: **South America and Africa**.
● Diagnosis: Virus isolation, serology.
● Treatment: Intensive supportive care; Acetaminophen (fever); Antacid (stomach bleed).
● Immunity:
Post-infectious type-specific immunity (IgG).
● Vaccine: **Live virus:** given every 10 years.

SPECIES: Dengue Fever Virus 4 Types

● Diseases: ▪**Dengue Fever "Breakbone Fever":**
Biphasic symptoms: high fever, rash, nausea, bone pain. Remission for few days. Fever returns with maculapapular rash. Resolves in 2 weeks.
▪**Hemorrhagic Fever:** high fever, hypotension, hemorrhages (GI bleed), shock, severe, fatal. Usually due to second or third time infection.
● Transmission: Vector = **mosquito (Daytime)**
Reservoir = **Humans**
● Geographic Range: **Urban**, world-wide tropics.
● Diagnosis: Virus isolation, serology.
● Treatment: Intensive care; fluid replacement.
● Immunity:
Post-infectious, type-specific immunity (IgG).
● Vaccine: none.

SPECIES: St. Louis Encephalitis Virus

● Disease: **Encephalitis:**
CNS infection; **asymptomatic** to severe illness. Can be **fatal**, especially in the **elderly**.
● Transmission:　Vector = **mosquito**
Reservoir = **birds**
Hosts = **Humans**
● Geographic Range: North America.
● Diagnosis: Virus isolation, serology.
● Treatment: Intensive care; anticonvulsants.
● Immunity:
Post-infectious, type-specific immunity (IgG).
● Vaccine: none

SPECIES: Japanese Encephalitis Virus

● Disease: **Encephalitis:**
CNS infection; **asymptomatic** to severe illness. Can be **fatal**, especially in **children**.
● Transmission: Vector = **mosquito (Nighttime)**
Reservoir = **birds**, **pigs**
Hosts = **Humans**
　▪Usually occurs at **Night** in Monsoon season.
● Geographic Range: **Rural Asia** and **India**.
● Diagnosis: Virus isolation, serology, CSF.
● Treatment: Intensive care; anticonvulsants.
● Immunity:
Post-infectious, type-specific immunity (IgG).
● Vaccine: **Dead virus:** used in south east Asia.

Genus: Hepatitis C Virus

SPECIES: Hepatitis C Virus
Known as the **"Post-Transfusion Hepatitis"**
● Diseases:
▪**Asymptomatic/anicteric (no jaundice):**
Newly infected people or chronic carriers.
▪**Acute hepatitis:** after 6 week incubation period: Hepatic inflammation, fever, nausea, right upper quadrant pain, icterus (jaundice), dark urine. Resolves after 2-3 months. Relapse is common. May progress to chronic carrier state or chronic active hepatitis.
▪**Neonatal HCV infection is rare**.
▪**Chronic carrier:** sub-clinical persistence of HCV in host hepatocytes detected by serology.
▪**Chronic active hepatitis:** prolonged, icteric, persistent HCV infection usually follows course of relapses and remissions. Causes liver **cirrhosis**. Can be **fatal**.
▪**Fulminant hepatitis:** Rapid progression to liver necrosis is **rare** with HCV infection.
▪**Hepatocellular Carcinoma:** arises in chronic carriers, or chronic active hepatitis patients. **Fatal**.

● Transmission:
▪**Horizontal** via IV drug abuse, sharing needles.
▪**Iatrogenic:** Blood transfusions, organ transplants
▪**Horizontal** via sexual contact, unlikely.
▪**Vertical** is possible, but unlikely.

● Geographic Range: World-wide.

● Diagnosis: Fabricated HCV antigen can indirect-ly detect serum antibody, real **HCV** antigen is not available to measure real HCV-specific antibody.
▪ELISA tests Recombinant HCVspecific antibody.
NS4 sequence: **c100-3** antigen.
NS3 sequence: **c33-C** or **c200** antigens.
Core Protein: **c22-3** antigen.
▪Confirmatory Recombinant HCVspecific antibody **RIBA** (Recombinant immunoblot assay).
▪**HCV RNA PCR** to check viral load.
▪**Liver Function Test** (LFT); elevated **ALT**.

● Treatment:
▪**Acute Hepatitis:** Symptom relief, usually mild.
▪**Chronic Carriers:** Education to prevent spred.
▪**Chronic Hepatitis:** Interferon-α is helpful.
▪**Chronic Hepatitis** may require liver transplant but HCV may infect the new liver, due to latency of the virus elsewhere in the host's body.
▪**Fulminant Hepatitis** requires liver transplant. The new liver is unlikely to get infected because the HCV is usually restricted to the old liver.

● Immunity:
Post-infectious immunity is ineffective.

● Vaccine: none.

Family:

RHABDOVIRUS

GENERA AND SPECIES:

Lyssavirus:
Rabies virus

LOCATION OF REPLICATION:
Cytoplasm

EFFECT ON HOST CELLS:
Buds from plasma membrane, no Lysis

GENOME:
SS(-) Linear RNA
Infectious RNA

SEGMENTATION:
No other segments

NUCLEOCAPSID:
Helical

ENVELOPE:
Envelope
    Bullet-Shape

SPECIAL FACTS:
● **Negri Bodies:**
Eosinophilic cytoplasmic inclusion bodies in neurons of hippocampus and of cerebellum purkinje cells infected by Rabies Virus.
● **Note:** Rabies Virus surface protein antigens have ability to move from virion surface to virion interior to escape host antibody opsonization.
● **Note:** Rabies Virus infection is the most deadly infection known: untreated **mortality is 100%.**

PATHOGENESIS:
● **Zoonotic transmission** occurs via animal bite. First, sensory neurons are infected. The virus moves to the CNS by axonal transport. The virus multiplies in the CNS then travels down cranial nerves and other peripheral nerves to various organs and to salivary glands.
● **Horizontal transmission** occurs, especially among health care workers by contact with bodily fluids from infected patient (saliva, tears, urine).

Genus:
Lyssavirus

SPECIES:
Rabies Virus many types
● Disease: **Rabies:**
▪ **Hydrophobia:** painful swallowing, foaming at mouth: due to cranial nerve involvement. Severe dehydration from nausea with vomiting.
▪ **Aerophobia:** painful muscle spasms in response to air being fanned over the patient's face or body.
▪ **Encephalitis:** demyelination and neuron death: confusion, lethargy leading to seizures, coma, death.

● Transmission:
▪ **Zoonotic via animal bite** from unprovoked encounter with an unusually aggressive animal.
    ▪ Animals are infectious one week before they die.
    ▪ Bats may remain asymptomatic while infectious.
    ▪ Birds, opossum, rabbits, reptiles, rodents, squirrels, do **not** carry Rabies.
▪ **Horizontal via bodily fluids:** saliva, tears, urine, CSF.
    ▪ Health care workers are at risk.

● Geographic Range:
▪ World-wide, except Japan and England.

● Diagnosis:
▪ History of **unprovoked animal bite** sufficient evidence.
▪ History of **bat bite or contact** is sufficient evidence.
▪ There are no diagnostic tests prior to onset of symptoms.
▪ Once symptoms begin, diagnostic tests are useless because **death is certain.**
▪ Negri Bodies seen in brain at autopsy: human or animal.
▪ Rabies Virus-specific antigen immunofluorescence of corneal scrapings or of skin biopsy can be done.

● Treatment:
▪ Step #1: **Wash** the bite site thoroughly.
▪ Step #2: **Passive** immunization by systemic injection of **HRIG** (Human Rabies immune globulin): One dose (IM in gluteal).
▪ Step #3: Inject HRIG around the bite site.
▪ Step #4: **Active** immunization with **HDCV** or RVA dead virus vaccine given IM in deltoid on days 0, 3, 7, 14, 28 following bite.
▪ **Note:** injections must begin within 48 hours, but no later than 4-5 days, otherwise the infection is **100% fatal.**

● Immunity: Antibodies are slow to develop and are ineffective once symptoms begin.

● Vaccine:
▪ **Passive immunization** HRIG
            (Human Rabies Immune Globulin).
▪ **Active immunization** HDCVor RVA dead virus vaccine.

● Prevention:
▪ **Pre-exposure HDCV** vaccination for anyone who may be at risk for contact with infected animals. Three doses gives protection for 2 years.
▪ **Vaccination of domestic and farm animals.**

Family:

PARAMYXOVIRUS

GENERA AND SPECIES:

Paramyxovirus:
Mumps: F, H, N proteins
Parainfluenza: F, H, N proteins
Morbillivirus:
Measles (Rubeola): F, H proteins
Pneumovirus:
Respiratory Syncytial virus:
F-protein only

LOCATION OF REPLICATION:
Cytoplasm

EFFECT ON HOST CELLS:
Buds from plasma membrane, no Lysis

GENOME:
SS(-) Linear RNA

SEGMENTATION:
No other segments

NUCLEOCAPSID:
Helical

ENVELOPE:
Envelope
F, H, N - Proteins

SPECIAL FACTS:

● **F-protein: Fusion protein:**
Enables fusion with host cells.
● **H-protein: Hemagglutinin:**
Enhances attachment to host cells.
● **N-protein: Neuraminidase:**
Breaks down neuraminic acid of mucus

PATHOGENESIS:
● **Horizontal transmission**
Respiratory route: upper respiratory
tract and bronchial mucus membranes
become infected. Measles and Mumps
progress to viremia.

Genus:
Paramyxovirus

SPECIES:
Mumps F,H,N: One Type

● **Disease: Mumps:**
▪ **Parotitis:** painful swelling of parotid glands
with fever; symptoms last about 2 weeks.
▪ **Orchitis:** painful unilateral swelling of testes.
(Sterility results from bilateral infection.)
▪ **Aseptic Meningitis:** #1 cause of meningitis
among non-immunized patients.
▪ **Self-limited** symptoms; more severe in adults.

● Transmission: respiratory route, mostly children.

● Geographic Range: World-wide.

● Diagnosis: Clinical presentation, serology.

● Treatment: Symptom relief.

● Immunity:
Post-infectious, long-lasting immunity (IgG).

● Vaccine: **Live virus:** part of **MMR** vaccine.
▪ **Note:**
Vaccine causes disease in **immunocompromised**:
if given to compromised patient or to children in
household who **shed** the virus after vaccination.
However, MMR is given in **HIV** infected patients.

SPECIES:
Parainfluenza F,H,N: Many Types
● Disease:
▪ **Croup (Laryngotracheobronchitis):**
Characteristic cough.
▪ **Upper Respiratory Tract Infections (URIs):**
Otitis media, pharyngitis, common cold.
▪ **Atypical Pneumonia.**

● Transmission:
▪ Respiratory route, mostly young children.
▪ Autumn season.

● Geographic Range: World-wide.

● Diagnosis:
▪ Clinical presentation, cell culture, and serology.

● Treatment: Symptom relief.

● Immunity:
Post-infectious, type-specific immunity (IgG).

● Vaccine: none.

Genus:
Morbillivirus

SPECIES:
Measles (Rubeola) F,H: One Type
● Diseases:
▪ **Measles:** cough, high fever and Koplik spots
(red spots with gray center, on buccal mucosa).
Rash on face first, spreads to trunk, extremities.
Measles virus is **highly contagious**.
▪ **Atypical Pneumonia:**
Seen in **immunocompromised**, can be fatal.
▪ **Encephalitis** and other complications occur.
▪ **Subacute Sclerosing Panencephalitis** [SSPE].

● Transmission: respiratory route, mostly children.

● Diagnosis:
▪ Clinical presentation, **Koplik spots**, serology.

● Treatment: Symptom relief.
Note: immunocompromised patients need passive
immunization with immunoglobulin.

● Immunity:
Post-infectious, long-lasting immunity (IgG).

● Vaccine: **Live virus:** part of **MMR** vaccine.
▪ **Note:**
Vaccine causes disease in **immunocompromised**:
if given to compromised patient or to children in
household who **shed** the virus after vaccination.
However, MMR is given in **HIV** infected patients.

Genus:
Pneumovirus

SPECIES:
Respiratory Syncytial Virus F
● Diseases: ▪ **Bronchiolitis-Pneumonia:**
#1 cause of infant lower respiratory tract infection
Symptoms: wheezing, narrow bronchioles.
Chest X Ray shows air trapped in lungs.
▪ **Upper Respiratory Tract Infections** (URIs).

● Transmission: Respiratory:
▪ Infants < 6 months get Bronchiolitis.
▪ Older children and adults get URI.
▪ Winter season.

● Geographic Range: World-wide.

● Diagnosis: clinical presentation, cell culture.

● Treatment: Intense care; **Ribavirin** (rarely used)

● Immunity: **Reinfection** occurs, immunity is
incomplete, and there is viral antigenic variation.

● Vaccine: none.

Family:

ORTHOMYXOVIRUS

GENERA AND SPECIES:

Influenza A virus:
Antigenic subtypes based on H and N envelope protein spike combinations.

Influenza B virus:

Influenza C virus:

LOCATION OF REPLICATION:
Transcription/Replication in **Nucleus**. Assembles/buds from plasma membr.

EFFECT ON HOST CELLS:
Buds from plasma membrane, no Lysis

GENOME:
SS(-) Linear RNA

SEGMENTATION:
8 RNA Segments

NUCLEOCAPSID:
Helical

ENVELOPE:
Envelope
H, N proteins

SPECIAL FACTS:
●**H-protein: Hemagglutinin:** Enhances attachment to host cells.
●**N-protein: Neuraminidase:** Degrades neuraminic acid of mucus.
●**Note:**
H-protein has 3 types: H1, H2, H3. N-protein has 3 types: N1, N2, N3.
▪**Viral types** represented by protein combinations: Ex: Influenza A/H3N2
▪**Epidemic types** by city and year: Ex: Influenza A/Singapore/86/H1N1.

●**Antigenic Variation:**
▪**Antigenic Drift:** changes in surface antigen proteins due to minor random mutations. No epidemics.
▪**Antigenic Shift:** changes in surface antigen proteins due to resortment of RNA segments. Only Influenza A may lead to epidemics or pandemics.

PATHOGENESIS:
●**Horizontal transmission** is via **Respiratory** route: Upper respiratory tract, bronchial mucus membranes, and ciliated epithelial cells become infected and disrupted.

Genus:
Influenza A

SPECIES:
Influenza A virus Many Types
●Diseases:
▪**Influenza ("flu"):** constitutional symptoms: Fever, chills, headache, myalgia, cough for 3 days.
▪**Atypical Pneumonia:** can be rapidly fatal.
▪**Secondary Bacterial Pneumonia:** destruction of respiratory cilia by initial flu infection enhances infection by *S. aureus* and other bacteria such as *S. pneumoniae* or *H. influenzae*. Can be fatal.
▪**Reye Syndrome:** CNS complications may arise in children during Influenza infection, especially if given **aspirin**. Can cause seizures and coma. Mostly fatal.

●Special Outbreaks:
▪**Endemic:** Influenza A infection has world-wide baseline prevalence at all times.
▪**Epidemic:** Influenza A has sudden outbreaks above baseline, but restricted to one region.
▪**Pandemic:** Influenza A has sudden outbreaks above baseline to spread across the whole world. Due to **Antigenic Shift**.

●Antigenic Shift:
▪Influenza A generates new combinations of its surface glycoproteins (H and N), continuously.

●Transmission: Respiratory route, **winter** season.

●Geographic Range: World-wide.

●Diagnosis:
Clinical presentation, virus isolation, serology.

●Treatment:
▪Symptomatic relief for mild cases.
▪**Zanamivir** oral inhaler or **Oseltamivir**.
▪**Amantadine** or **Rimantadine** in some cases.
▪Antibiotics for cases of 2° bacterial pneumonia.
▪Aspirin must NEVER be given.

●Immunity:
Post-infectious, type-specific immunity (IgG).

●Vaccine: **Dead virus:**
New annual vaccine every **autumn**.

Genus:
Influenza B

SPECIES:
Influenza B virus Many Types
●Diseases:
▪**Influenza ("flu"):** constitutional symptoms: Fever, chills, headache, myalgia, cough for 3 days.
▪**Atypical Pneumonia:** can be rapidly fatal.
▪**Secondary Bacterial Pneumonia:** can be fatal.
▪**Reye Syndrome:** CNS complications may arise in children during Influenza infection, especially if given **aspirin**. Can cause seizures and coma. Mostly fatal.

●Special Outbreaks:
▪**Endemic:** Influenza B infection has world-wide baseline prevalence at all times.
▪**Epidemic:** Influenza B has sudden outbreaks above baseline, but restricted to one region.
▪**Note:** Influenza B does not cause pandemics.

●Transmission: Respiratory route, **winter** season.

●Geographic Range: World-wide.

●Diagnosis:
Clinical presentation, virus isolation, serology.

●Treatment:
▪Symptomatic relief for mild cases.
▪Antibiotics for cases of 2° bacterial pneumonia.
▪Aspirin must NEVER be given.

●Immunity:
Post-infectious, type-specific immunity (IgG).

●Vaccine: **Dead virus:**
New annual vaccine every **autumn**.

Genus:
Influenza C

SPECIES:
Influenza C virus
●Diseases: minor respiratory illness.
●No epidemics due to no antigenic variation.
●No treatment, self-limited.
●No vaccine.

Family:

ARENAVIRUS

GENERA AND SPECIES:

Lymphocytic Choriomeningitis:
Lymphocytic Choriomeningitis

Lassa Fever virus:
Lassa Fever virus

LOCATION OF REPLICATION:
Cytoplasm

EFFECT ON HOST CELLS:
Buds from plasma membrane, no Lysis

GENOME:
SS(-) Circular RNA

SEGMENTATION:
2 RNA Segments
End to end to form a Circle

NUCLEOCAPSID:
Helical

ENVELOPE:
Envelope

SPECIAL FACTS:

●**Arena = "Sandy"**
Refers to ribosomes on inner surface of envelope.

●**Note:** very unique RNA structure sometimes called **"Ambisense"** due to the way proteins are translated.

Genus:
Lymphocytic Choriomeningitis Virus

SPECIES:
Lymphocytic Choriomeningitis Virus
●Disease: **Aseptic Meningitis:**
CNS infection, high fever, headache, myalgia.
▪**Chorioretinitis** (eye infection), **Hydrocephalus** of fetus if LCV infection occurs during pregnancy.
▪Other infections: orchitis, myocarditis, arthritis.

●Transmission:
▪**Zoonotic transmission** via human contact with rodent **feces** or **urine** infected with virus:
Reservoir = **mice**
Host = **human**
●Geographic Range:
▪**N. America, S. America, Europe.**

●Diagnosis: Virus isolation from blood and CSF.

●Treatment: Supportive care, self limited.

●Immunity:
Post-infectious, type-specific immunity (IgG).

●Vaccine: none.

Genus:
Lassa Fever Virus

SPECIES:
Lassa Fever Virus
●Diseases: **Lassa Fever:**
Symptoms: fever, sore throat, myalgia, GI bleed. Can progress to increased capillary permeability, multiorgan dysfunction and shock. Can be fatal, especially in children, often mild and self-limited.
▪**Abortion:** if Lassa Fever Virus infection occurs during pregnancy, often fatal to the mother.

●Transmission:
▪**Zoonotic transmission** via human contact with rodent **aerosols, feces, urine** infected with virus.
Reservoir = **mice**
Host = **human**
▪Lab workers at risk while handling specimens.
▪**Horizontal transmission** personal contact.

●Geographic Range: **West Africa.**

●Diagnosis:
▪Virus isolation from blood and CSF.
▪Serology.
▪**Liver Function Test** (LFT): Elevated **AST** correlates to poor prognosis.

●Treatment: Supportive care; **IV Ribavirin.**

●Immunity:
Post-infectious, type-specific immunity (IgG).

●Vaccine: none.

Family:

RETROVIRUS

GENERA AND SPECIES:

Oncovirus Type C:
Human T-Cell Lymphotrophic Virus 1
Human T-Cell Lymphotrophic Virus 2

Lentivirus:
Human Immunodeficiency Virus 1
Human Immunodeficiency Virus 2

Spumavirus:
Human Foamy Virus

LOCATION OF REPLICATION:
Retrovirus RNA is not infectious;
Does not encode RNA polymerase.
**RNA polymerase is required to
directly produce new viral RNA.**

EFFECT ON HOST CELLS:
Bud from CD4 cell Plasma membrane.
HTLV: T-cell **Proliferation**, no Lysis.
HIV: T-cell **Lysis**, **Depletes** CD4 cells.

GENOME:
**SS+ Circular RNA
DIPLOID**

SEGMENTATION:
2 RNA Strands

NUCLEOCAPSID:
Complex

ENVELOPE:
Envelope

HTLV GENES AND PROTEINS:

●**GAG** Antigen Proteins:
Capsid and **Core** proteins.
  Packaging of virion core contents.
●**POL** Enzyme Proteins:
Protease:
  Cleaves GAG/POL coded proteins
  from precursors.
Reverse Transcriptase:
  RNA-dependent DNA-polymerase
  also has RNAase activity to destroy
  the RNA template.
Integrase:
  Splices the proviral DNA into the
  host-cell genome.
●**ENV** Antigen Glycoproteins:
Envelope surface glycoproteins:
  For HTLV attachment to host cells.
Transmembrane glycoproteins:
  For HTLV attachment to host cells.
●**TAX** Promoter Protein:
Transactivation of viral and host
  DNA transcription.
●**REX** Regulation/Transport Protein:
Regulates RNA splicing.
Transports mRNA out of nucleus.
●**LTR** Long Terminal Repeats:
Promoter and **Enhancer** regions.

Genus:
Oncovirus

SPECIES: HTLV-1
Human T-Cell Lymphotrophic Virus Type 1
●Disease:
▪**Adult T-Cell Leukemia/Lymphoma:**
Malignant proliferation of mature T-cells:
General lymphadenopathy, hepatosplenomegaly,
widespread cutaneous papulo-nodular lesions.
Complications due to impaired immunity:
Opportunistic infections: Pneumocystis carinii
pneumonia, fungal infections, Herpes virus.
▪**Tropical Spastic Paraparesis:**
Bilateral progressive weakness of lower limbs:
with stiffness, some sensory loss. Hyper reflexes.

●Pathogenesis: Hallmarks of HTLV-1:
 1. Mostly **mature CD4 T-cells** are infected.
 2. Causes **Proliferation** of these T-cells.

●Transmission:
▪**Horizontal** male to female via **sexual** contact.
  (Virus is present in semen.)
▪**Horizontal** male to male, homosexual contact.
▪**Horizontal** via IV drug abuse, sharing needles.
▪**Iatrogenic:** Blood transfusions, organ transplants
  and artificial insemination.
▪**Vertical** mother to child via breast milk.
  (No transplacental infection occurs.)

●Latency: up to **30-40 years**.

●Geographic Range:
**Japan, S.E. USA, Caribbean, S. America, and
major cities worldwide.**

●Diagnosis:
▪**Serology** test for HTLV-I specific antibody.
▪**Peripheral blood smear:** atypical lymphocytes.
▪**Presence of HTLV-I provirus in leukemic cells.**
▪**Elevated WBC** as high as 100,000 cells/mm^3.

●Treatment: lymphoma chemotherapy.

●Vaccine: none.

SPECIES: HTLV-2
Human T-Cell Lymphotrophic Virus Type 2
●Disease: **Hairy Cell Leukemia:**
HTLV-2 infection is associated with this disease.

●Pathogenesis: similar to HTLV-I infection.

●Transmission:
▪**Horizontal** male to female via **sexual** contact.
  (Virus is present in semen.)
▪**Horizontal** male to male, homosexual contact.
▪**Horizontal** via IV drug abuse, sharing needles.
▪**Iatrogenic:** Blood transfusions, organ transplants
  and artificial insemination.
▪**Vertical** mother to child via breast milk.
  (No transplacental infection occurs.)

●Latency: long time; unknown.

●Geographic Range: Worldwide.

●Diagnosis:
▪**Serology** test for HTLV-II specific antibody.

●Treatment: no effective treatment.

●Vaccine: none.

Family:
RETROVIRUS (continued)

Genus:
Lentivirus

Convention of CD4 notation:

● **CD4** or **CD4+** or **CD4 POS**
Designate host cells possessing CD4 surface marker (often helper T-cells).

● **CD4(-)** or **CD4 NEG**
Designate host cells which do not possess CD4 surface marker.

● **CD4 Count:**
Number of CD4 cells per mm^3 blood. The CD4 count in **HIV** infection follows a characteristic pattern: Decreases rapidly on initial infection; increases rapidly back to normal; but gradually and irreversibly declines over many years.

SPECIAL FACTS:

● **HIV** has ability to **rapidly mutate** due to the highly error-prone reverse transcriptase enzyme. This generates a widely variable genetic diversity, especially among envelope antigens.

● This renders potential vaccines and antigen-targeted antiviral medications immediately ineffective. This enables HIV to escape host immune defense.

● **HIV** is a highly inefficient virus due to the error-prone enzymes reverse transcriptase and integrase. Mostly non-functioning virions are generated. This handicap is overcome by HIV's prolific nature.

● **HIV** has ability to infect quiescent T-cells as well as Active T-cells.

● **HIV** has ability to remain latent in host cells, either in its pre-integrated state or in its integrated state. Time of latency varies: months to years. (see life cycle step 8)

HIV GENES AND PROTEINS:

● **GAG** Antigen Proteins:
Involved in packaging of virion core contents: [Capsid protein: p7.] [Core proteins: p24; others.]
● **POL** Enzyme Proteins:
Protease:
    Cleaves GAG/POL proteins from precursors.
Reverse Transcriptase:
    RNA-dependent DNA-polymerase. Also has RNAase activity to destroy RNA template.
Integrase:
    Inserts proviral DNA into host-cell genome.
● **ENV** Antigen Glycoproteins:
(Precursor gp160 gets cleaved)
  Envelope surface glycoprotein: gp120
    ▪Allows HIV attachment to host cells such as CD4 T-cells and CD4 Macrophages.
    ▪Connected to gp 41 on the virion surface.
  Envelope transmembrane glycoprotein: gp41
    ▪Allows HIV attachment to CD4(-) host cells such as glial cells and fibroblasts.
    ▪Allows HIV fusion with host cells after gp120 binds.
    ▪Enables fusion of host cells together to form syncytium wherein the virus is protected.
Note: gp120 and gp41 coding regions mutate easily and often, this enables HIV to escape host antibodies and to thwart vaccines.
● **TAT** Promoter Protein:
Transactivation of
HIV DNA reverse transcription increases HIV transcription 1000 fold.
Transactivation of
Host DNA transcription promotes transformation of proto-oncogenes into oncogenes.
● **REV** Regulation and Transport Protein:
Regulates RNA splicing.
Transports mRNA out of nucleus.
● **NEF** Negative Early Factor:
Promotes latency of HIV.
● **VIF** Virus Infectivity Factor: Anti-latency gene initiates replication, assembly, budding, maturation.
● **VPR** Transactivator.
● **VPU** Stimulates virus release.
● **LTR** Long Terminal Repeats:
Promoter and **Enhancer** regions.
5' terminus LTR: site of transcription activation and TAT binding.

Life cycle:
1. HIV gp120 attaches to CD4 portion of T-cells and Macrophages.
Note: HIV can also infect CD4 NEG cells, but the effect is unknown.

2. HIV envelope fuses with host cell membrane.

3. HIV virion core release into host cell cytoplasm

4. Uncoating of nucleocapsid enables release of GAG and POL proteins along with HIV genome.

5. The HIV enzyme Reverse transcriptase initiates creation of the double-stranded "proviral" DNA from retroviral RNA.

6. Retroviral RNA gets destroyed by viral RNase.

7. Proviral DNA enters the nucleus.

8. The HIV enzyme Integrase integrates proviral DNA randomly into host cell genome.
Note: HIV can remain latent in host cell either in the pre-integrated state or in the integrated state.

9. Integrated proviral DNA is transcribed along with host cell DNA to generate RNA by host RNA polymerase.

10. This RNA is translated into proteins by host ribosomes.

11. HIV envelope proteins get inserted in host plasma membrane.

12. HIV Capsid protein p7 begins assembly around the new HIV genomic RNA dimer, this takes place in the host cell cytoplasm.

13. HIV virion buds through the host cell plasma membrane.

14. This often causes cell lysis.

15. Protease enzyme begins its action at this point to cleave the newly translated precursor proteins into their functional components (GAG, POL). This sets the stage for maturation.

16. Maturation is the process of assembling the complex capsid. Maturation occurs only after HIV budding and host cell lysis, and only after protease has successfully completed cleavage.

Note: this is an overview of the life cycle as it is currently proposed, these details are constantly being investigated and updated.

Family:
RETROVIRUS (continued)

Genus:
Lentivirus (continued)

- **Note:** **AIDS** as defined by CDC:
Symptomatic HIV infection with
CD4 count less than 200/mm³

- **Note:** **VIRAL LOAD:**
Number of Plasma HIV RNA copies:
Typical values <20,000 copies per ml

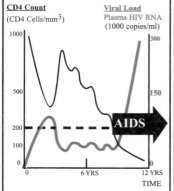

CD4 Count
(CD4 Cells/mm³)

Viral Load
Plasma HIV RNA
(1000 copies/ml)

- **Diagnosis:**
SEROLOGY:
(tests may be negative upto 6 mos).
- **ELISA:** HIV surface gp120, gp160
  Specific antibody.
- **Western blot confirmation:** HIV
  Core p24, gp41 specific antibody.
- **Indirect Immunofluorescence Assay
  (IFA)** confirmation (p24, gp41)

OTHER:
- **DNA probe, PCR amplification:**
-Proviral HIV DNA in peripheral
  mononuclear lymphocytes.
-Replicating HIV RNA in plasma,
  to assess "viral load."
- **Culture:** highly specific, but
  extremely insensitive, little value.
- **ELISA Oral secretions:**
  very effective, needs confirmation.
- **ELISA Urine:** not effective,
  no confirmation test available.
- **Rapid ELISA for serum:** results
  in 10 min., needs confirmation.
- **Home sample collection kits:**
  send to lab, needs confirmation.

SPECIES: **HIV-I**
Human Immunodeficiency Virus Type 1
Note: **HIV-2** is similar to HIV-1
But causes less severe disease.

- **Disease:**
- **Acute HIV infection:** initial presentation is rash
and fever, or asymptomatic. Serology negative.
- **Acquired Immune Deficiency Syndrome: AIDS**
Severe, prolonged, progressive drop CD4 count.
T-cell mediated immunity gets compromised.
Relentless and fatal complications begin.

- **Complications:**
- **Wasting.** chronic fatigue: can be fatal.
- **Malignancies:** Kaposi's Sarcoma, Lymphomas.
- **AIDS-related dementia:**
  HIV encephalopathy at CD4 <200.
- **Opportunistic infections:**
  CD4 >200:
    M. tuberculosis, HSV, VZV.
  CD4 <200:
    *Candida , Pneumocystis carinii pneumonia,
    Cryptococcus neoformans meningitis.*
  CD4 <100:
    *MAI infection, N. asteroides infection,
    Toxoplasma gondii CNS infection.*
  CD4 <50:
    CMV retinitis, JC virus PML.
- **Other infections:**
Bacteria: *Bartonella, T. pallidum, salmonella.*
Fungi: *C. immitis, H. capsulatum*
Protozoa: *Amebas, Cryptosporidium, Isospora.*

- **Transmission:**
- **Horizontal** via **sexual** contact:
  HIV is present in semen and vaginal secretions.
- **Horizontal** via IV drug abuse, sharing needles.
- **Horizontal** to health care worker by needle stick.
- **Iatrogenic:** Blood transfusions, organ transplants
- **Vertical** mother to child:
  transplacentally in utero;
  or post-partum via breast milk.

- **Geographic Range:** Worldwide.

- **Treatment:** Anti-retroviral medications:
- **Protease inhibitors:**
Indinavir, Nelfinavir, Ritinavir, Saquinavir, etc.
  Mechanism of action:
  (⇩viral load and ⇧ CD4 count):
  Inhibit protease enzyme;
  Prevents cleavage of protein precursor
    products of GAG and POL genes;
  This stops viral maturation;
  Stops viral spread to other cells.
- **Nucleoside Anologues:**
Zidovudine (AZT, ZDV), Lamivudine (3TC), etc
  Mechanism of action:
  Inhibition of reverse transcriptase.
  DNA synthesis chain termination.
- **Reverse Transcriptase Inhibitors (non-nucleoside)**
Delavirdine mesylate, Efavirenz, Nevirapine
  Mechanism of action:
  Inhibition of reverse transcriptase.

- **General Concepts of Management:**
- **Reduction of viral load.
- **Elevation of CD4 count.
- **Prevent/treat opportunistic infections.
- **Prophylaxis and treatments are continued for life.
- **Emotional and educational support.

- **Management**
- **HAART:** Highly Active Anti-Retroviral Therapy
  One Protease Inhibitor.
  Plus **Two Nucleoside Anologues,**
  Or Plus **One Nucleoside Anologue and
    One Reverse Transcriptase Inhibitor.**
- *M. tuberculosis* prophylaxis: **Isoniazid** (INH).
- At **CD4=500:**
  AZT plus Indinavir.
  Or **AZT**, plus **3TC**, plus **Indinavir.**
- Upon AZT failure: add or switch to **ddI** or **ddC.**
- At **CD4=200:**
  PCP prophylaxis: **TMP-SMZ.**
- At **CD4=100:**
  MAI prophylaxis: **Rifabutin.**
  Toxoplasma prophylaxis: **TMP-SMZ.**
- At **CD4=50:**
  CMV retinitis treatment.
- **HIV in Pregnancy:**
  Delivery by cesarean section;
  AZT for mother **AND** for newborn;
  No breast feeding.

- **Vaccine:** No effective vaccine against HIV.
- **Helpful vaccines:**
  Hib for *H. influenzae;*
  Pneumovax for *S. pneumoniae;*
  Influenza virus vaccine.
- Avoid live-organism vaccines except MMR.

- **Prevention:**
Avoid risky sexual contact; use condoms.
Health care workers use universal precautions.

Chapter 18
PRIONS (Proteinaceous Infectious Particles)

SPECIAL FACTS:

PRIONS:

Non-DNA
Non-RNA
Protein particles:

● Prions cause chronic, latent, slowly progressive, and consistently fatal infections of the CNS. Often called: **Slow Infections** or **Transmissible Neurodegenerative Diseases**

● CNS pathological changes: **"Spongiform" Encephalopathy** Non-inflammatory Swiss cheese-like parenchymal vacuoles.

● Prions resist destruction by agents which destroy nucleic acids, but are destroyed by agents which destroy proteins.

● Prions infect neurons, then spread through the CNS by axonal transport, and replicate by some unknown means. Little is known about Prions.

● The normal human **PrP gene** codes for normal protein designated **PrPc**. Prion protein is similar to this, but Prion protein, designated **PrPsc**, is not a gene-product of the human PrP gene.

● Disease:
CREUTZFELDT-JAKOB DISEASE [CJD]
▪ Rare disease, usually begins in middle age.
▪ Manifest by variable neurological symptoms, **myoclonus**, and rapid progressive **dementia**.
▪ Seizures or cranial nerve involvement is rare.
▪ Rapidly fatal within months.

● Transmission:
▪ **Spontaneous mutation**; idiopathic.
▪ **Horizontal** to health-care workers.
▪ **Iatrogenic** infection occurs due to contaminated surgical instruments; to contaminated corneal transplants; or to contaminated cadaver-derived human hormones.
▪ **Familial**-autosomal dominant inheritance occurs.

● Warnings:
▪ **Health care workers** may be at risk of infection while handling neural tissue and CSF, especially during neurosurgery, during autopsy, or during work with brains of cadavers.
▪ **Universal precautions** are required.
▪ **Instrument sterilization** requires minimum of one hour of autoclaving at 132°C or one hour of immersion in 1N Na OH.

● Diagnosis:
▪ CT scan, MRI and CSF may be normal.
▪ **EEG** is usually abnormal.
▪ **Brain biopsy:** spongiform, no inflammation.
▪ **Immunostaining** of brain reveals **PrPsc protein** infectious particle.

● Treatment: None, always fatal.

● Disease:
KURU
▪ Found in one tribal group of Papua-New Guinea.
▪ Characterized by cerebellar ataxia, intentional tremors, myoclonic jerks, and choreoathetoid movements.
▪ Fatal within months-years.

● Transmission:
▪ **Horizontal** via cannibalistic ingestion of infected human brains and by handling of infected brains.
▪ Limited to Papua-New Guinea.

● Diagnosis:
▪ CT scan, MRI and CSF may be normal.
▪ **EEG** is usually abnormal.
▪ **Brain biopsy:** spongiform, no inflammation.
▪ **Immunostaining** of brain reveals **PrPsc protein** infectious particle.

● Treatment: None, always fatal.

● Diseases:
FAMILIAL PRION DISEASES
  ▪ Familial Fatal Insomnia
  ▪ Gerstmann-Straussler-Scheinker Syndrome
  ▪ Familial Creutzfeldt-Jakob Disease

● Diagnosis:
▪ CT scan, MRI and CSF may be normal.
▪ **EEG** is usually abnormal.
▪ **Brain biopsy:** spongiform, no inflammation.
▪ **Immunostaining** of brain reveals **PrPsc protein** infectious particle.

● Treatment: None, always fatal.

Chapter 19
VIRUS CROSS REFERENCE

BUDS FROM NUCLEUS
Herpesviruses

DNA VIRUS REPLICATION IN CYTOPLASM
Poxvirus

SMALLEST VIRUS
Parvovirus

LARGEST VIRUS
Poxvirus

"INFECTIOUS" VIRUSES
[SS+ RNA genome]
[Encode RNA polymerase]
  Picornaviruses
  Caliciviruses
  Togaviruses
  Flaviviruses
  Coronaviruses

DIPLOID RNA
Retroviruses

RNA VIRUSES WHICH REPLICATE IN NUCLEUS
Orthomyxoviruses
Retroviruses

NO ECLIPSE PERIOD
Reoviruses

ARBOVIRUSES (vector-borne)
Togaviruses (except Rubivirus)
Flaviviruses (except Hepatitis C)
Reovirus coltivirus
Bunyaviruses

SLOW VIRUS INFECTIONS
JC virus: PML
Measles virus: SSPE
Retroviruses:
HTLV-1:
   T-cell Leukemia/Lymphoma
   Tropical Spastic Paraparesis
HTLV-2:
   Hairy Cell Leukemia
HIV: AIDS

PRION SLOW INFECTIONS
Creutzfeldt-Jakob Disease
Kuru
Familial Fatal Insomnia
Gerstmann-Straussler-Scheinker
                    Syndrome

HEPATITIS VIRUSES

Picornavirus Hepatitis A
        Acute Hepatitis

Hepadnavirus Hepatitis B
Sexually-transmitted hepatitis
        Acute Hepatitis
        Chronic Hepatitis
        Carrier State Hepatitis
        Fulminant Hepatitis

Flavivirus Hepatitis C
Blood-transfusion hepatitis
        Acute Hepatitis
        Chronic Hepatitis
        Carrier State Hepatitis

Defective virus Hepatitis D
[Requires HBV infection]
        Acute Hepatitis
        Chronic Hepatitis
        Carrier State Hepatitis
        Fulminant Hepatitis

Calicivirus Hepatitis E
        Acute Hepatitis

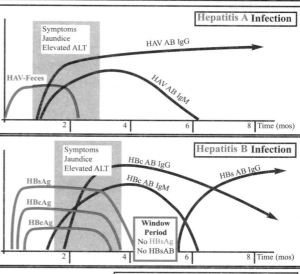

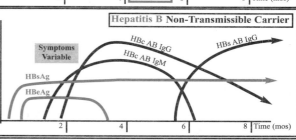

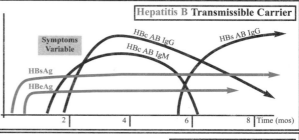

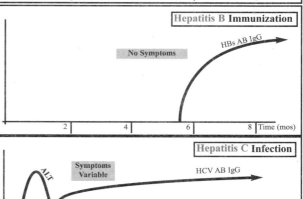

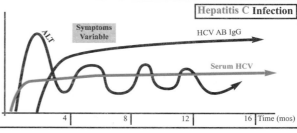

Chapter 20

FUNGI

Mycotic Disease (Mycosis)

> **FUNGUS:** Eukaryotic; Cell wall of chitin; Cell membrane of ergosterol.
> **Yeast:** Fungal single cell phase.
> **Mold (mycelial):** Fungal multicellular filamentous colony phase.
> **Dimorphic:** when a fungal species can exist in yeast phase or mold phase depending on environmental conditions.

Category:
CUTANEOUS FUNGI
Route of Infection:
Contact or Trauma

Organisms:

Dermatophytes:
Epidermophyton spp
Microsporum spp
Trichophyton spp
- Tinea
  (ring worm)

Superficials:
Exophiala werneckii
- Tinea Nigra
  (brown spots)
Malassezia furfur
[Dimorphic]
- Pityriasis Versicolor
  (hypopigmentation)
Piedraia hortae
- Black Piedra
  (black nodules on scalp hair roots)
Trichosporon cutaneum
- White Piedra
  (yellow nodules on axilla, beard, groin hair shafts)

Category:
SUBCUTANEOUS FUNGI
Route of Infection:
Trauma

Organisms:

Sporothrix schenckii
[Dimorphic]
- Ulcerative lymphatic tracts
- From thorns

Cladosporium spp
Fonsecaea spp
Phialophora spp
- Chromomycosis
  (wart-like granulomas of feet, legs)

Madurella spp
Pseudallescheria spp
- Mycetoma
  (abscesses and sinus tracts of feet)

Category:
SYSTEMIC FUNGI
Route of Infection:
Respiratory

Organisms:

Blastomyces dermatitidis
[Dimorphic]
- Pulmonary infection
- Granulomatous ulcers of skin and bone

Coccidioides immitis
[Dimorphic]
- Pulmonary infection
- Erythema Nodosum
  "Valley fever"
  "desert rheumatism"

Histoplasma capsulatum
[Dimorphic]
- Pityriasis Versicolor
  (hypopigmentation)

Paracoccidioides brasiliensis
[Dimorphic]
- Pulmonary infection

Category:
OPPORTUNISTIC FUNGI
Route of Infection:
Colonization during immunocompromised state

Organisms:

Aspergillus fumigatus
Aspergillus flavus
- Fungus balls in lungs
- Chronic sinusitis
- Allergic Asthma
- *Aspergillus flavus* produces Aflatoxin

Candida albicans
- Oral thrush
- Diaper rash
- Vaginitis
- Disseminated disease

Cryptococcus neoformans
- CNS infection, meningitis (grows well in CSF)

Mucormycosis:
Absidia spp
Mucor spp
Rhizopus spp
- Paranasal sinus necrosis
- Especially in Diabetics

CUTANEOUS FUNGI

SUBCUTANEOUS FUNGI

DERMATOPHYTES:

Epidermophyton spp
Microsporum spp
Trichophyton spp

- Diseases: **Tinea: "Ring worm," annular rash.**
  - **Tinea capitis:** scalp, hair-shaft infection.
    - Mostly in children, highly contagious.
  - **Tinea barbae:** beard infection.
  - **Tinea corporis:** body infection.
  - **Tinea cruris:** "jock -itch"
  - **Tinea pedis:** "athlete's foot"
  - **Onychomycosis:** finger/toe nail infection.
- Transmission: **Horizontal** via direct contact; when warm and damp Dermatophytes are nurtured by **keratin in skin.**
  - *Microsporum* are found on **dogs** and **cats.**
- Diagnosis:
  - Skin/hair/nail scrapings preserved in 10%KOH examined to see **mold form septated hypae.**
  - Scrapings may be cultured on Sabouraud agar.
  - Wood's Lamp: green fluorescence of *Microsporum.*
- Treatment:
  - **Topical antifungals.**
  - **Griseofulvin** (oral) for Tinea Capitis and Onychomycosis.
  - **Keep skin cool and dry.**

Exophiala werneckii

- Disease: **Tinea Nigra: brown spots on palms and soles.**
- Transmission: infection arises due to direct contact.
  - *Exophiala* is found in **soil.**
- Diagnosis: Skin scrapings/microscopy show mold hyphae.
- Treatment:
  - **Topical keratolytic agent.**
  - **Topical Salicylic acid.**

Malassezia furfur

Formerly *Pityrosporum ovale* and *Pityrosporum orbiculare*)
- Disease: **Pityriasis Versicolor (Tinea versicolor):**
  Non-itchy, depigmenting lesions: shoulders, chest, back, upper arms.
- Transmission: Usually exist as commensal yeast on human scalps. Disease arises when the yeast phase fungi transform into the mold phase fungi with hyphae. Cause of transformation is unknown.
- Diagnosis:
  Skin scrapings preserved in 10%KOH: microscopy shows round yeast forms present along with short hyphal mold forms.
- **Note: DIMORPHIC** (yeast and mold forms occur).
- Treatment:
  - **Topical azole antifungal cream.**
  - **Oral Ketoconazole.**
  - **Often relapses.**

Piedraia hortae

- Disease: **Black Piedra: black nodules on scalp hair roots.**
- Transmission: Horizontal via direct contact.
- Diagnosis: Skin scrapings/microscopy show mold hyphae.
- Treatment: Topical Salicylic acid.

Trichosporon cutaneum

- Disease: **White Piedra:**
  Yellow nodules on axilla, beard and groin hair shafts.
- Transmission: Horizontal via direct contact; sexual contact
- Diagnosis: Skin scrapings/ microscopy show mold hyphae.
- Treatment: Oral Ketoconazole. Relapse is expected.

Sporothrix schenckii

- Disease: **Sporotrichosis:**
  Painless nodules form along lymphatic channels.
  These nodules sometimes ulcerate.
- Transmission: via direct contact: infection arises in **scratches** or puncture wounds while **gardening**; especially by rose bush **thorns,** wood splinters, hay, straw, or mosses.
- Diagnosis:
  - Skin tissue specimen preserved in 10%KOH examined to see **"cigar-shaped" budding yeast.**
  - Skin tissue specimen may be cultured on Sabouraud agar, to grow the **mold form** which has characteristic hyphae with **"daisy" cluster of conidia.**
- **Note: DIMORPHIC** (yeast and mold forms occur).
- Treatment: Oral Potassium Iodide
- Prevention: Wear protective clothing while gardening.

Cladosporium spp
Fonsecaea spp
Phialophora spp

- Disease: **Chromomycosis:**
  Papular, verrucous, sometimes pedunculated or **cauliflower-like** growths due to chronic infection of subcutaneous tissues. These growths develop slowly over years and show **central clearing** as they spread. No ulcerations and no sinus tract formations occur. Feet and legs are the most common sites of infection.
- Transmission: via direct contact: infection arises due to puncture wound while working with rotting wood or soil.
- Diagnosis: Skin scrapings preserved in 10%KOH examined to see **brown "copper penny" fungi in Macros.**
- Treatment: Surgical excision.

Madurella spp
Pseudallescheria spp

- Disease: **Fungal Mycetoma (Eumycetoma):**
  Abscess formation of subcutaneous tissues and bones with pus-like discharge from multiple **sinus tracts** which form along lymphatic channels mostly on **feet,** sometimes on hands or elsewhere. The pus contains varied-colored granules.
- Transmission: via direct contact: infection arises due to puncture wound or trauma while walking with unprotected feet on soil.
- Diagnosis: Microscopy of pus shows **mold hyphae** and the characteristic **species-specific colored granules.**
- Treatment: Combination of Dapsone, TMP-SMZ, and Surgery.
- Prevention: Wear shoes.

SYSTEMIC FUNGI

Blastomyces dermatitidis

- Diseases: **Blastomycosis:**
  Initial mild **pulmonary** infection spreads via **hematogenous** route to manifest as **verrucous and ulcerative skin lesions**.
- Transmission: via **inhalation** of the **mold conidia** from dust-clouds at construction sites or crop-dust during harvesting on farms.
  Most common in Mississippi river valley, mid-west and south USA; occurs worldwide.
- **Note:** this is **not contagious**, no horizontal transmission.
- Diagnosis:
  - Skin tissue specimen or sputum preserved in 10%KOH:
    Multi-nucleated yeast undergo single broad-based budding.
  - Skin tissue specimen may be cultured on Sabouraud agar, grows **mold form: septated branching hyphae, microconidia**.
- **Note: DIMORPHIC** (yeast and mold forms occur).
- Treatment: Itraconazole.

Coccidioides immitis

- Diseases: **Coccidioidomycosis:**
  - **Influenza-like pulmonary infection** with fever, cough.
  - **Erythema Nodosum with Arthralgia:**
    "Valley Fever" and "Desert rheumatism" (west USA)
    usually resolves spontaneously.
  - **Pneumonia and disseminated disease**. Can be fatal.
    May disseminate to bone, joints, skin or meninges.
    Disseminated disease is common in AIDS patients
    and pregnant women during 3rd trimester.
- Transmission: via **inhalation** of the **mold arthrospores** from soil.
  Most common in warm climates of the USA, Central America, and South America.
- **Note:** this is **not contagious**, no horizontal transmission.
- Diagnosis:
  - **Lung biopsy**, other tissue specimen, sputum preserved in 10%KOH, stained with lactophenol cotton blue: see **yeast "spherules"** which are round pouches that contain endospores, no budding.
  - **Specimen may be cultured on Sabouraud agar**, to grow the **mold form: septated branching hyphae with arthrospores**.
    Warning: culture-grown spores are infectious to lab personnel.
  - **Serology:** IgM and IgG antibodies to mold phase antigens; or complement-fixing antibody titer (CF test).
  - **Skin test** (turns NEG in chronic disease due to anergy.)
  - **Chest X-Ray:** calcifications, granulomas.
- **Note: DIMORPHIC** (yeast and mold forms occur).
- Treatment:
  - Amphotericin B.
  - Fluconazole for meningitis.

Histoplasma capsulatum

- Disease: **Histoplasmosis:**
  Similar to tuberculosis; pneumonia, granulomas, caseating necrosis may heal to form **"coin lesion"** (focal calcification).
  Chronic disease may lead to **cavitation** and **dissemination** in blood. Can be **fatal**.
- Transmission: via **inhalation of the mold conidia** from moist **soil**, **bird droppings**, and **bat droppings**.
  Mostly in central/eastern USA; occurs worldwide.
- Diagnosis:
  - **Lung biopsy** tissue specimen or sputum preserved in 10%KOH, stained with **silver or Giemsa stain**: see **oval yeast** which undergo budding within Macros.
  - **Specimen may be cultured on Sabouraud agar**, to grow the **mold form: septated branching hyphae with microconidia and turberculated macroconidia**.
  Warning: culture-grown spores are infectious to lab personnel.
  - **Serology:** complement-fixating antibody titer (CF test).
  - **DTH skin test** (turns NEG in chronic disease due to anergy)
  - **Antigen Detection:** urine antigen, serum antigen.
  - **Chest X-Ray:** calcifications, granulomas.
- **Note: DIMORPHIC** (yeast and mold forms occur).
- Treatment: Itraconazole or Amphotericin B.

Paracoccidioides brasiliensis

- Disease:
  Pulmonary infection similar to tuberculosis; remains sub-clinical or dormant; progresses upon diminished immunity.
  Oral mucosal lesions also occur.
- Transmission: via **inhalation of mold spores** from soil.
  Mostly in rural Central and South America.
- Diagnosis:
  - **Lung biopsy** tissue specimen or sputum preserved in 10%KOH, reveals yeast which undergo multiple budding.
  - **Sputum may be cultured on Sabouraud agar** to grow **mold**.
  - **Serology** can be used to follow the disease.
- **Note: DIMORPHIC** (yeast and mold forms occur).
- Treatment: Itraconazole.

OPPORTUNISTIC FUNGI

Aspergillus fumigatus
Aspergillus flavus

- Diseases: Aspergillosis:
- **Aspergilloma:**
   "Fungus balls in lung" (fungus balls = groups of mold hyphae):
   In patients with pre-existing lung disease (old tuberculosis cavity).
   Causes hemoptysis; can be fatal.
- **Chronic sinusitis** of paranasal sinuses; "fungus balls" in sinuses.
- **Allergic Asthma** from mold spores.
- *A. flavus* produces **Aflatoxin** on nuts and grains.
   Aflatoxin is toxic and carcinogenic.
- Transmission: inhalation of mold spores by **immunocompromised**
   host. Ubiquitous in nature, in soil and in decaying vegetation.
- Diagnosis:
   - **Lung biopsy** tissue specimen or sputum preserved in 10%KOH:
     Mold form: septated branching hyphae with spores.
   - Specimen may be cultured on Sabouraud agar.
   - **Chest X-Ray:** shows air pockets and evidence of fungus balls.
- **Note:** *Aspergillus* has mold form only, even as they invade tissues.
- Treatment:
   - Surgery for fungus balls.
   - Amphotericin B.

Candida albicans

- Diseases: **Candidiasis:**
- **Oral Thrush:** focal white patches on oral mucosa and tongue;
   they bleed when scraped off.
- **Cutaneous Candidiasis:** blotchy red, itchy rash which spreads
   and may occur anywhere. **"Diaper Rash"** in infants.
- **Onychomycosis and Paronychia:** infection of finger/toe nails
   and nail folds; from chronic wet hands; washing dishes, etc.
- **Vaginitis:** common infection of women. May be asymptomatic
   or yield a curd-like discharge and cause pruritus of vulva.
- **Chronic Mucocutaneous Candidiasis:** disseminated disease
   may lead to chronic infections anywhere such as skin,
   heart (endocarditis), lungs, CNS (meningitis), bone, etc.
- Transmission: *Candida albicans* is normal commensal of human GI
   tract and female genital tract. Infection arises from destruction of
   other host commensals (as occurs during use of some antibiotics),
   or from immunocompromised state of the host.
   Usually, candidiasis infections are not contagious.
- Diagnosis:
- **Tissue biopsy** preserved in 10%KOH: budding **yeast, pseudohyphi**.
- **Germ tubes**, unique to *C. albicans*, may be seen extending from
   round yeast forms; found in **serum** during disseminated disease.
- Specimens may be **cultured** on Sabouraud agar to grow yeast which
   have **chlamydospores** (unique to *C. albicans*) and **blastospores**.
- **Skin test:** POS in most people
   NEG in immunocompromised patients to indicate **anergy**.
- Treatment:
   - Clotrimazole: oral lozenge.
   - Nystatin: oral, topical or suppository.
   - Amphotericin B for disseminated disease.

Cryptococcus neoformans

- Diseases: **Cryptococcosis:**
- **Pulmonary infection:** may be mild or severe and fatal.
- **Meningitis:** *C. neoformans* disseminates rapidly from pulmonary
   infection then thrives in CSF. Meninges are diffusely infected,
   and infection spreads rapidly to brain parenchyma.
   Complications: Cranial nerve palsies, blindness, hydrocephalus, and
   cerebral edema. Can be fatal, relapse is common, persistence
   of neurological deficits is common. Incurable in **AIDS** patients.
- Transmission: Cryptococcus is ubiquitous in nature. Infection arises
   in **immunocompromised** patients due to **inhalation** of **yeast** from
   soil or from **pigeon droppings**.
- Diagnosis:
- **CSF** specimen preserved in 10%KOH: stained with **India Ink**:
   Encapsulated yeast which undergo budding.
- Tissue specimens may be stained with Mayer's mucicarmine stain:
   The **large capsule**, unique to Cryptococcus, will appear **pink**.
- **Serology** to detect the capsular antigen.
- **Urease test:** isolates show positve urease test within 15 min.
- Treatment:
   - Amphotericin B plus Flucytosine.

Absidia spp
Mucor spp
Rhizopus spp

- Disease: **Mucormycosis:**
(old terms: Phycomycosis or Zygomycosis):
Fungi **invade blood vessel walls:** cause tissue necrosis; especially in
paranasal sinuses, brain, lungs, and GI tract. Can be fatal.
- Transmission: these fungi are ubiquitous in nature, especially as
bread molds. Infection is rare and arises due to immunocompromised
situations, especially in **diabetic** patients.
- Diagnosis: Tissue preserved in 10%KOH:
   Mold: non-septate hyphae, branch at right angles, sporangium.
- Treatment:
   - Surgery.
   - Amphotericin B.

Chapter 21

FUNGI CROSS REFERENCE

INTRACELLULAR
Cladosporium spp
Fonsecaea spp
Phialophora spp
Histoplasma capsulatum

INDIA INK STAIN
Cryptococcus neoformans

CHLAMYDOSPORES
Candida albicans

GERM TUBES
Candida albicans

DIMORPHIC
Malassezia furfur
Sporothrix schenckii
Blastomyces dermatitidis
Coccidioides immitis
Histoplasma capsulatum
Paracoccidioides brasiliensis

MOLD ONLY
Dermatophytes
   Epidermophyton spp
    Microsporum spp
    Trichophyton spp
Aspergillus fumigatus
Absidia spp
Mucor spp
Rhizopus spp

YEAST ONLY
Cryptococcus neoformans
Candida albicans

NON-SEPTATED HYPHI
Absidia spp
Mucor spp
Rhizopus spp

PSEUDO-HYPHI
Candida albicans

TOXIN PRODUCING
Aspergillus flavus (aflatoxin)

FOOTBALL-SHAPE CONIDIA
Microsporum spp

DAISY-SHAPED CONIDIA
Sporothrix schenckii

CIGAR-SHAPED YEAST
Sporothrix schenckii

MULTINUCLEATED YEAST
Blastomyces dermatitidis

SHERULE YEAST
Coccidioides immitis

MULTIPLE-BUDDING YEAST
Paracoccidioides brasiliensis

ENCAPSULED YEAST
Cryptococcus neoformans

ANIMAL-RELATED
Microsporum spp
   (cats, dogs)
Histoplasma capsulatum
   (birds, bats)
Cryptococcus neoformans
   (birds)

SKIN TESTS
Coccidioides immitis
Histoplasma capsulatum
Candida albicans

<u>NOTE:</u>
1. These light microscope color plates represent typical specimens (not ideal specimens) as encountered in clinical practice.
2. All of the color plates on this page are magnified to equal high power to allow meaningful comparison of relative sizes.

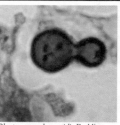

Blastomyces dermatidis Budding.
Tissue Biopsy (GMS stain)

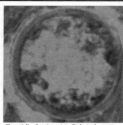

Coccidiodes immitis Spherule.
Tissue Biopsy (GMS stain)

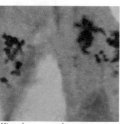

Histoplasma capsulatum
Tissue Biopsy (GMS stain)

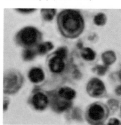

Candida albicans
Tissue Biopsy (GMS stain)

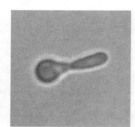

Candida albicans Germ Tube.
Incubated in serum for 3 hours.

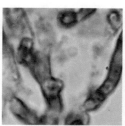

Aspergillus fumigatus
Tissue Biopsy (GMS stain)

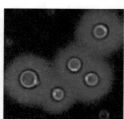

Cryptococcus neoformans Capsules.
CSF (India Ink stain)

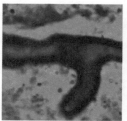

Mucor spp., Rhizopus spp.
Tissue Biopsy (GMS stain)

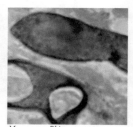

Mucor spp., Rhizopus spp.
Tissue Biopsy (GMS stain)

Chapter 22
PARASITES

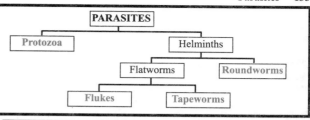

PROTOZOA:

PNEUMOCYSTIS:
Pneumocystis carinii
   Pneumonia

AMEBAS:
Entamoeba hystolytica
   Dysentery
Naegleria fowleri
   Meningoencephalitis
Acanthamoeba spp
   Meningoencephalitis
   Keratitis

FLAGELLATES:
Giardia lamblia
   Diarrhea
Trichomonas vaginalis
   Vaginal discharge
Leishmania donovani
   Kala-azar
Leishmania spp
   Oriental sore
Trypanosoma cruzi
   Chagas
Trypanosoma spp
   African sleeping sickness

SPOROZOANS:
Cryptosporidium spp
   Diarrhea
Isospora spp
   Diarrhea
Toxoplasma gondii
   Encephalitis
Plasmodium spp:
   Malaria
       P. falciparum
       P. malariae
       P. ovale
       P. vivax
Babesia spp
       Malaria-like

HELMINTH
FLAT WORM (Platyhelminth)
FLUKE: Trematoda

SCHISTOSOMIASIS:
Schistosoma haematobium
Schistosoma japonicum
Schistosoma mansoni

LIVER FLUKE:
Clonorchis sinensis

LUNG FLUKE:
Paragonimus westermani

HELMINTH
FLAT WORM (Platyhelminth)
TAPE WORM: Cestoda

PORK TAPEWORM
   and Cysticercosis:
Taenia solium

BEEF TAPEWORM:
Taenia saginata

FISH TAPEWORM:
Diphyllobothrium latum

HYDATID CYSTS:
Echinococcus granulosus
Echinococcus multilocularis

HELMINTH

ROUNDWORM:Nemetoda

INTESTINAL NEMATODES:
[Human Intermediary Host]:
Ancylostoma duodenale
   Hook worm
Necator americanus
   Hook worm
Strongyloides stercoralis
   Thread worm
Ascaris lumbricoides
   Largest nematode
Enterobius vermicularis
   Pin worm
Trichuris trichiura
   Whip worm

EXTRAINTESTINAL LARVAE
[Humans as Dead-End Host]:
Ancylostoma caninum
   Cutaneous Larva Migrans
Toxocara canis
   Visceral Larva Migrans
Trichinella spiralis
   Trichinosis

TISSUE NEMATODES:
[Vector-Borne Larvae]:
Dirofilaria immitis
   Dog heart worm
   Lung lesion
Loa loa
   Eye worm
Onchocerca volvulus
   River Blindness
Wuchereria bancrofti
   Filariasis
   Elephantiasis
Brugia spp
   Filariasis
   Elephantiasis

[Non-Vector Larvae]:
Dracunculus medinensis
   Guinea worm

PROTOZOA

PROTOZOA FEATURES:
- <u>Unicellular</u>.
- <u>Cyst</u>:
Non-motile, encapsulated, transmission stage of life cycle.
- <u>Trophozoite</u>:
Motile, feeding, multiplying stage of life cycle.

PNEUMOCYSTIS

<u>Note</u>: Can be classified as yeast phase of fungus.

Pneumocystis carinii

- <u>Disease</u>: **Interstitial pneumonia**
  P. carinii Pneumonia is known as "PCP":
  Also called "Plasma Cell Pneumonia."
  Occurs in **immunocompromised** patients.
  Common in **AIDS** patients with **CD4 count < 200.**
  Highly fatal in AIDS.
- <u>Transmission</u>: via inhalation of *P. carinii* cysts.
  Cysts and trophozoites cause interstitial inflamation.
  P. carinii is ubiquitous in nature.
  <u>Note</u>: PCP is probably not contagious.
- <u>Diagnosis</u>:
  Bronchoscopy biopsy: silver stain shows cysts.
- <u>Treatment and prophylaxis</u>: TMP-SMZ.

AMEBAS

Entamoeba hystolytica

- <u>Diseases</u>: **Amebiasis:**
  - **Dysentery** with bloody diarrhea:
    Invades colon to cause **"tear-drop ulcer."**
    No PMNs respond, no inflammation.
  - **Liver abscesses**
- <u>Transmission</u>: Entamoeba Cysts; **fecal-oral** route.
  Cysts mature in small intestine **lumen** to become
  Trophozoites which invade colon and liver.
- <u>Diagnosis</u>:
  - **Cysts** found in solid stool. Serology confirmation.
  - **Trophozoites** found in diarrhea, they ingest RBCs.
  - Ultrasound for liver abscess.
- <u>Treatment</u>:
  - **Diloxanide fuoate** for luminal infection.
  - **Iodoquinol** in pregnancy for luminal.
  - **Metronidazole** for tissue invasion of colon, liver.

Naegleria fowleri
Acanthamoeba spp

- <u>Diseases</u>: **Meningoencephalitis; Keratitis**
- <u>Transmission</u>:
  - **Meningoencephalitis** via swimming in warm fresh
    water as the trophozoites enter nasal mucosa then
    pass cribriform plate. Southern USA.
    <u>Note</u>: Acanthamoeba meningoencephalitis occurs
    only in **immunocompromised** patients.
  - **Keratitis**, most often by Acanthamoeba, occurs
    mostly in healthy **contact lens** users.
- <u>Treatment</u>:
  - **Amphotericin B** for CNS infection.
  - **Propamidine isethionate** for keratitis.

FLAGELLATES

Giardia lamblia

- <u>Disease</u>:
  Persistent Foul-smelling diarrhea, no fever.
- <u>Transmission</u>:
  Fecal-oral route: Cysts in contaminated water get
  ingested; undergo excystation in doudenum to
  become **trophozoites** that attach to intestinal wall.
  - Horizontal transmission:
    Common among children and homosexuals.
  - Zoonotic transmission:
    Common in hikers who drink stream water.
- <u>Diagnosis</u>: **Stool sample:**
  - **Cysts or trophozoites** with **Trichrome stain**.
  - Stool antigen detection kits are available.
- <u>Treatment</u>: **Metronidazole**
- <u>Prevention</u>: Boil or Filter the water.

Leishmania donovani Kala-azar (visceral)

- <u>Vector</u>: **Sand-fly**.
- <u>Treatment</u>: **Stibogluconate**.

Leishmania spp Oriental Sore (cutaneous)

- <u>Vector</u>: **Sand-fly**.
- <u>Treatment</u>: **Stibogluconate**.

Trichomonas vaginalis

- **Vaginitis:** Green, foul-smelling vaginal discharge.
- **Sexually-Transmitted Disease**.
- <u>Diagnosis</u> by wet-mount of discharge: trophozoites.
- <u>Treatment</u>: Metronidazole for patient and partner.

Trypanosoma cruzi

- **Chagas Disease:** *T. cruzi* invade cardiac myocytes
  to cause arrhythmias; also invade nerve plexus of
  GI tract to cause **mega-colon** and mega-esophagus.
- <u>Vector</u>: **Reduviid Bug**.
- <u>Treatment</u>: **Nifurtimox**.

Trypanosoma spp

- **African sleeping sickness:**
  Fever, demyelinating **encephalitis**, coma, death.
- Ability to alter surface antigens.
- <u>Vector</u>: **Tsetse-fly**.
- <u>Treatment</u>: **Suramin**.

PROTOZOA

SPOROZOANS

Cryptosporidium spp
Isospora spp

- Disease: **Diarrhea in immunocompromised.**
Note: *Cryptosporidium* and *Isospora* stool sample smear shows **oocysts** in **Modified Acid Fast Stain.**

Toxoplasma gondii

- Diseases: **Toxoplasmosis:**
  - **Encephalitis** in immunocompromised, especially **AIDS.** Neurological signs, **multiple mass lesions,** usually in basal ganglia. May **relapse** even after effective treatment, can be **fatal.**
  - **Congenital Toxoplasmosis:** child spontaneously aborted; stillborn; born with encephalitis; or born mentally retarded.
- Life Cycle:
  Oocysts = shed in feces, get ingested
  Tachyzoites=invasive intracellular trophozoite.
  Tissue cysts = persist in tissues for life.
- Transmission:
  - **Zoonotic transmission** occurs via ingestion of:
    Oocysts in food contaminated by cat feces, or
    Tissue cysts in under-cooked meats (lamb, pork).
  - **Vertical transmission:** transplacentally when mother gets primary infection during pregnancy.
- Diagnosis: (~34% AIDS patients have Toxo.)
      (But only ~6% have CNS Lymphoma.)
  - **CT scan:** (MRI, MRS, SPECT also helpful.)
  -Non-contrast: hypodense, usually multiple lesions.
      (Lymphoma is usually hyperdense, and single.)
  -Contrast: ring-enhances, usually multiple lesions.
      (Lymphoma ring-enhances, but usually single.)
  - **Congenital: CT scan** shows focal calcifications.
  - **Serology** of newborn will show high IgM titer.
- Treatment: **Pyrimethamine plus sulfadiazine.**
- Prevention:
  - Avoid cats, especially if HIV or pregnant.
  - Cook food well.

Babesia spp

- Disease: **Malaria-like** symptoms.
- Transmission: **Vector-borne via Tick bite.**
  Northeast USA, California, Europe.
- Diagnosis: Peripheral smear shows **trophozoites** within RBC's in **pairs,** resemble *P. falciparum,* and in **tetrads ("maltese cross"). Giemsa stain.**
- Treatment: **Quinine plus Clindamycin.**

Plasmodium spp: *P. falciparum*
                             P. malariae
                             P. ovale (rare)
                             P. vivax

- Disease: **Malaria:**
- Symptoms: Cycle of Fever/chills:
      Every 48 hrs for *vivax, ovale.*
      Every 72 hrs for *malariae.*
      Irregularly for *falciparum.*
  "Black-Water Fever" hemaglobinuria occurs due to severe *falciparum* hemolytic anemia.
- Life Cycle:
  - **Asexual cycle in Humans:**
    1° tissue phase: mosquito "injects" **sporozoites** which go to liver and mature into tissue **schizonts.**
    Blood phase: liver tissue schizonts burst; release **merozoites** into blood to infect RBCs (and to become **trophozoites**). These then mature into blood **schizonts** which burst to release more **merozoites** which infect more RBCs, etc.
  Note: Bursting RBCs corresponds to cycle of fever.
    2° tissue phase: *ovale* and *vivax* can remain latent in the liver as **hypnozoites** for months and then reactivate; this explains relapses.
  - **Sexual cycle in Mosquitoes:**
    Some **gametocytes** develop in RBCs; then get released when the RBCs burst; then get ingested by mosquitoes during a bite; then merge to form **zygotes.** The zygotes mature then divide into **sporozoites** which go to the mosquito salivary glands, to be injected.
- Transmission:
  - **Vector-borne** via **mosquito** bite.
  - **Vertical** transplacental in utero.
  - **Iatrogenic** due to blood transfusion.
- **Note:** People with Sickle cell gene or Thalassemia are resistant to malaria.
- Diagnosis:
  - **Peripheral smear:** RBCs contain:
    falciparum: small ring form trophozoites.
        "Banana" shape gametocyte (rare).
    malariae: large, single, band trophozoite.
        "Daisy" shape schizont.
    ovale: large, single ring trophozoite; in
        big oval shape RBC; Schuffner dots.
    vivax: large, single ring trophozoite; in
        reticulocytes; Schuffner dots.
        Schizonts with many merozoites.
  - **Labs:** ↓hemoglobin; ↓hematocrit.
- Treatment: (problematic due to resistant strains.)
  - **Chloroquine:** blood phase, and prophylaxis.
  - **Mefloquine:** in chloroquine-resistant areas.
  - **Primaquine:** tissue phase, and 2° hypnozoites.
  - **Antifolates** for chloroquine resistant strains.
  - **Antibiotics** for chloroquine-antifolate resistance.
  - **IV Quinine** for acute life-threatening attack.
- Prevention:
  - Mosquito netting, and topical repellents.
  - Insecticides, destruction of mosquito habitat
  - Prophylactic medication before, during, and after travel to endemic area.

FLUKES

FLUKE FEATURES:
- Adhesive suckers.
- Short, flat body.
- Blind gut.

SHISTOSOMIASIS

Schistosoma haematobium

- Disease:
  Infection of **veins of the bladder** and sometimes of esophagus: tissue destruction by **eggs**.
- Life cycle:
  Snails→ Human (urine)→ Snails.
- Transmission: via *S. haematobium* **cercariae** penetrating skin while swimming in fresh water. Found in **south-east Asia**.
- Diagnosis:
  - Eosinophilia;
  - **Urine sample:** ovum with terminal spine.
- Treatment: Praziquantel.

Schistosoma japonicum

- Disease:
  Infection of the *veins* **of the liver** and sometimes esophagus: tissue destruction by **eggs**.
- Life cycle:
  Snails→ Human (urine)→ Snails.
- Transmission: via *S. japonicum* **cercariae** penetrating skin while swimming in fresh water. Mostly found in **south-east Asia**.
- Diagnosis:
  - Eosinophilia;
  - **Stool sample:** characteristic ovum.
- Treatment: Praziquantel.

Schistosoma mansoni

- Disease:
  Infection of the **veins of the liver** and sometimes esophagus: tissue destruction by **eggs**.
- Life cycle:
  Snails→ Human (urine)→ Snails.
- Transmission: via *S. mansoni* **cercariae** penetrating the skin while swimming in fresh water. Found in **south-east Asia**.
- Diagnosis:
  - Eosinophilia;
  - **Stool sample:** ovum with large lateral spine.
- Treatment: **Praziquantel.**

- **Note:** **"Swimmer's itch"**
  Is caused by non-human-infecting Schistosomas.

LIVER FLUKE

Clonorchis sinensis Oriental Liver Fluke

- Disease:
  Infection of the **bile ducts** leads to **cholangitis** and sometimes **cholangiocarcinoma**.
- Life cycle:
  Snail→ Fish(scales)→ Human (feces)→ Snail.
- Transmission: via ingestion of **encysted larvae** present on raw or undercooked fresh-water **fish**. Found in **south-east Asia**.
- Diagnosis:
  - Eosinophilia;
  - **Stool sample:** characteristic ovum with operculum
- Treatment: **Praziquantel.**

LUNG FLUKE

Paragonimus westermani

- Disease:
  Infection begins in **small intestines** then penetrates through diaphragm to **lung parenchyma**.
- Life cycle:
  Snail→ Crab→ Human (feces)→ Snail.
- Transmission: via ingestion of **encysted larvae** present on raw or undercooked **crab**. Found in **south-east Asia**.
- Diagnosis:
  - Eosinophilia;
  - **Stool sample:** characteristic ovum with operculum
- Treatment: **Praziquantel.**

TAPE WORMS

TAPEWORM FEATURES:
- **Scolex = attachment head:** (suckers, hooks, sucking grooves)
- **Long, flat** body.
- **Proglottids =** Multiple segments. Older ones become gravid.
- **No gut:** Nutrients absorbed through tapeworm skin.

PORK TAPEWORM

Taenia solium **INTESTINAL TAPEWORM**
LARVAL CYSTS→Worms
- Disease: Larval cysts (cysticerci) attach with hooks into the mucosa of **small intestines**. The worm then matures in intestinal lumen (15 foot length). The worm actively absorb nutrients from host.
- Symptoms: anorexia and diarrhea.
- Life cycle:
  Pigs→ Human (feces)→ Pigs.
- Transmission: ingestion of **larval cysts** (cysticerci) present in raw or undercooked **pork**. Found in **Mexico, Ecuador, India, Asia.**
- Diagnosis: **Eosinophilia;** Stool sample: gravid proglottids/eggs
- Treatment: **Praziquantel** or **Niclosamide** kills the worm, but does not kill the eggs; **Laxatives** used to remove the dead worm and eggs.

BEEF TAPEWORM

Taenia saginata **INTESTINAL TAPEWORM**
LARVAL CYSTS→Worms
- Disease: Larval cysts (cysticerci) attach with their suckers onto the mucosa of **small intestines**. Worm matures in the intestinal lumen (30 foot length). The worm actively absorb nutrients from host.
- Symptoms: anorexia and diarrhea.
- Life cycle:
  Cattle→ Human (feces)→ Cattle.
- Transmission: ingestion of Larval cysts (cysticerci) present in raw or undercooked **beef**. Found in **Central and South America, Africa.**
- Diagnosis: **Eosinophilia;** Stool sample: characteristic gravid proglottids/eggs.
- Treatment: **Praziquantel** or **Niclosamide** kill the worm, but does not kill the eggs. **Laxatives** used to remove the dead worm and eggs.

FISH TAPEWORM

Diphyllobothrium latum
INTESTINAL TAPEWORM
LARVAE→Worms
- Disease: Larval cysts (cysticerci) attach with their sucking groove onto mucosa of **small intestines**. The worm actively absorb nutrients from host.
- Symptoms: **Megaloblastic Anemia:** *D. latum* takes up **vitamin B12**. Also anorexia and diarrhea.
- Life cycle:
  Copepod→Fish(flesh)→Human(feces)→Copepod
- Transmission: via ingestion of **larvae** present in raw or undercooked **fresh-water fish**. Found in **North America, Europe, Japan.**
- Diagnosis: **Eosinophilia;** Stool sample: characteristic operculated eggs.
- Treatment: **Praziquantel** or **Niclosamide.**

Pork Tapeworm Cysts

Taenia solium **CYSTICERCOSIS**
EGGS→Larval Cysts
- Disease: CNS cysticercosis: brain lesion caused by single or multiple larval cysts (cysticerci).
- Symptoms: **Seizures**, focal neurological deficits. Cysts may be found elsewhere: muscles, periorbital.
- Life cycle: **Pigs→ Human (feces)→ Pigs.**
  ↓
  Humans (dead-end host)
- Horizontal transmission: via ingesting **eggs** or **proglottids** present in human feces, the eggs hatch into larvae which break through the intestinal wall, travel via bloodstream to the brain or elsewhere. Found in **Mexico, Ecuador, India, Asia.**
- Diagnosis: **Eosinophilia;** CT/MRI: calcifications (dead cysts); ring enhancement (live cysts)
- Treatment: **Antiepileptics** for seizures; **Praziquantel** or **Albendazole** to kill larval cysts. **Steroids** for inflammation that arises as larvae die.
- **Note:** Most often **only** anti-seizure meds are given because cysts will eventually die on their own. Brain inflammation by killing the cysts can be deadly.

Dog Tapeworm Cysts

Echinococcus granulosus (Dog Tapeworm)
- Disease: **HYDATID CYST** (Unilocular) Infection of liver, lungs, or brain: single, large, fluid-filled cyst containing thousands scoleces.
- Symptoms: related to infection site, mass effect.
- Life cycle: **Sheep→ Dog (feces)→ Sheep.**
  ↓
  Humans (dead-end host)
- Transmission: via ingesting **eggs** present in dog feces, the eggs hatch, break through intestinal wall, travel via the bloodstream to liver and elsewhere. Found worldwide **where sheep live among dogs.**
- Diagnosis: **Eosinophilia;** serology, radiology.
- Treatment: Surgery; careful not to disrupt the cyst and spread the infectious contents; this can cause new infection (sometimes multilocular).

Fox Tapeworm Cysts

Echinococcus multilocularis
- Disease: **HYDATID CYST** (Multilocular) Liver: multiple fluid-filled cysts contain scoleces.
- Symptoms: Jaundice.
- Life cycle: **Rodents→ Fox (feces)→ Rodents.**
  ↓
  Humans (dead-end host)
- Transmission: via ingesting **eggs** in **fox feces**, the eggs hatch, break through the intestinal wall, travel via bloodstream to the liver. Found worldwide **where foxes live.**
- Diagnosis: **Eosinophilia;** serology, radiology.
- Treatment: Surgery; careful not to disrupt the cyst and spread the infectious contents; this can cause new infection.

ROUND WORMS

ROUNDWORM FEATURES:
- **Round**, of varying lengths.
- **Non-segmented**.
- **Mouth, gut and anus**.

EXTRAINTESTINAL LARVAE
Human Dead End Host — PENETRATE SKIN

Ancylostoma caninum
(Dog Hookworm)
CUTANEOUS LARVAE MIGRANS
- Symptoms: Dog Hookworm larvae penetrate skin and "creep" around to cause painful, itchy rash.
- Treatment: topical Thiabendazole.

EXTRAINTESTINAL LARVAE
Human Dead End Host — INGESTED

Toxocara canis
(Dog Ascarid)
VISCERAL or OCULAR LARVAE MIGRANS
- Symptoms: Hepatomegaly, blindness.
- Transmission: Dog Ascarid eggs: ingested, become larvae, travel and die in various organs:
- Treatment: No effective treatment. Steroids for ocular disese.

Trichinella spiralis
(Pig or Bear)
TRICHINOSIS
- Symptoms: Fever, myositis, periorbital edema.
- Transmission: Ingest larval cysts in undercooked pig (pork) or bear. Larvae travel via blood to encyst in striated muscles ("nurse cells"). First in Ocular muscles. Myocarditis can be fatal. Occurs worldwide, all climates.
- Diagnosis: Muscle biopsy; **Eosinophilia**.
- Treatment: No effective treatment. Steroids for symptomatic relief.

INTESTINAL NEMATODES
Human Intermediary Host - PENETRATE SKIN

Ancylostoma duodenale Old-world Hook worm
Necator americanus Americas Hook worm
- Symptoms: pneumonitis, intestinal upset, **anemia**.
- Transmission: **Larvae** in soil penetrate **bare feet**: Travel via blood to lungs; then to trachea; then get swallowed. They attach to intestinal wall, mature, and suck blood.
- Diagnosis: **Eosinophilia**; stool sample: **eggs**.
- Treatment: **Mebendazole**.

Strongyloides stercoralis Thread worm
- Symptoms: abdominal pain, peri-anal pruritus. Can be fatal in immunocompromised patients.
- Transmission: **Larvae** in soil penetrate **bare feet**: Travel via blood to lungs; then to trachea; then swallowed. They burrow into intestinal wall, mature, and lay eggs.
- Autoinfection: eggs in feces, some turn into larvae to infect colon: Larvae penetrate colon wall, travel via blood to lungs, then to trachea, then swallowed, then burrow into intestinal wall; may disseminate.
- Skin infection: Larvae that arrive at anus may burrow into peri-anal skin to cause itchy rash.
- Diagnosis: **Eosinophilia**; stool sample: **Larvae**.
- Treatment: **Thiabendazole**.

INTESTINAL NEMATODES
Human Intermediary Host - INGESTED

Ascaris lumbricoides
Largest intestinal nematode.
Most common cause helminth infection worldwide
- Symptoms: pneumonitis, anorexia, and sometimes intestinal obstruction.
- Transmission: fecal-oral: ingested eggs hatch into larvae which penetrate intestinal wall, travel via blood to lungs, then to trachea, then swallowed, then back to intestinal lumen where they mature but they do not attach.
- Diagnosis: **Eosinophilia**; stool sample: **eggs**.
- Treatment: **Mebendazole**, or **Pyrantel pamoate**.

Enterobius vermicularis Pin worm
Most common cause helminth infection in USA.
- Symptoms: peri-**anal pruritus**, bed-wetting.
- Transmission: oral route: ingested eggs hatch into larvae which mature and reside in colon. After mating, female pinworms travel to anus (usually at night) to lay eggs. This accounts for the itchy anus, and for the presence of infective eggs in the environment. Common in **children**.
- Diagnosis: **Eosinophilia**; stool sample: no eggs; **"tape test"** to collect eggs from peri-anal skin.
- Treatment: **Mebendazole**, or **Pyrantel pamoate**.

Trichuris trichiura Whip worm
- Transmission: Ingest eggs, become larvae, travel to cecum.
- Diagnosis: No eosinophilia; stool sample: eggs.
- Treatment: **Mebendazole**.

TISSUE NEMATODES
Vector-Borne Larvae

Dirofilaria immitis
(Dog heart worm) **Lung lesion**
- Symptoms: lung nodule forms as worm dies.
- Vector: mosquito deposits larvae; worldwide
- Treatment: self-limited.

Loa loa Eye worm
- Symptoms: worm crawls across eyeball.
- Vector: **biting fly** deposit larvae; Africa.
- Treatment: **Diethylcarbamazine** (DEC), Surgery.

Onchocerca volvulus River Blindness
- Symptoms: skin nodules, itchy **"leopard" rash**. **Blindness** results due to worms that travel through the skin to the eye to cause scarring of cornea.
- Vector: **black fly** deposits larvae; tropical.
- Treatment: **Ivermectin**.

Wuchereria bancrofti Filariasis, Elephantiasis
Brugia spp Filariasis, Elephantiasis
- Symptoms: obstruction of lymphatic vessels: Filariasis indicates acute, recurrent symptoms; but Elephantiasis indicates chronic obstruction, edema. Microfilariae circulate in host blood only **at night**. They remain in liver and lungs during the day.
- Vector: **mosquito** deposits larvae; tropical.
- Treatment: **Diethylcarbamazine** (DEC).

TISSUE NEMATODES
Non-Vector-Borne Larvae

Dracunculus medinensis Guinea worm
- Symptoms: skin nodules; skin ulcers.
- Transmission: via ingestion of infected **copepods** (in drinking water); **larvae** get released from the copepod; the larvae break through intestinal wall, and travel to skin. **Tropical**.
- Treatment:
  - Pretreat with **Metronidazole**.
  - Slowly wind the worm onto a stick while pulling it out of the skin.

Chapter 23

PARASITE CROSS REFERENCE

INTRACELLULAR
Leishmania donovani
Trypanosoma cruzi
Cryptosporidium spp
Isospora spp
Toxoplasma gondii
Plasmodium spp
Babesia spp

TEMPERATURE TROPISM
Leishmania spp

Modified ACID-FAST STAIN
Cryptosporidium spp
Isospora spp

MEGALOBLASTIC ANEMIA
Diphyllobothrium latum

INFECT THROUGH SKIN
Schistosoma spp
Ancylostoma spp
Necator americanus
Strongyloides stercoralis

SWIMMING-RELATED
Naegleria fowleri
Acanthamoeba spp
Schistosoma spp

HUMAN DEAD-END HOST
Echinococcus spp
Ancylostoma caninum
Toxocara canis
Trichinella spiralis
Dirofilaria immitis

SNAIL-RELATED
All Flukes

SEAFOOD-RELATED
Clonorchis sinensis
  (fish scales)
Paragonimus westermani
  (crab)
Diphyllobothrium latum
  (fish flesh)

COPEPOD-RELATED
Diphyllobothrium latum
Dracunculus medinensis

CAT-RELATED
Toxoplasma gondii

DOG-RELATED
Echinococcus granulosus
Ancylostoma caninum
Toxocara canis
Dirofilaria immitis

INHALATION ROUTE
Pneumocystis carinii

VECTOR-BORNE
Leishmania spp (sand fly)
Trypanosoma cruzi (reduviid bug)
Trypanosoma spp (Tsetse fly)
Plasmodium spp (mosquito)
Babesia (tick)
Dirofilaria immitis (mosquito)
Loa loa (fly)
Onchocerca volvulus (black fly)
Wuchereria bancrofti (mosquito)
Brugia spp (mosquito)

NOTE:
1. These light microscope color plates represent typical specimens (not ideal specimens) as encountered in clinical practice.
2. All of the color plates on this page are magnified to equal high power to allow meaningful comparison of relative sizes.

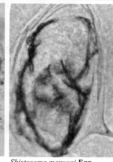
Shistosoma haematobium **Egg** Feces

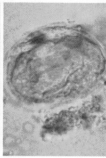
Shistosomajaponicum **Egg** Feces

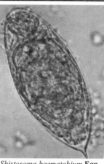
Shistosoma mansoni **Egg** Feces

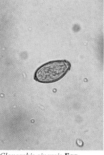
Clonorchis sinensis **Egg** Feces

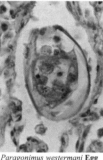
Paragonimus westermani **Egg** Lung biopsy

Taenia solium **Egg** Feces

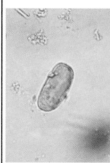
Ancylostoma duodenale **Egg** Feces

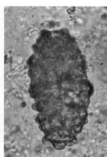
Ascaris lumbricoides **Infertile Egg** Feces

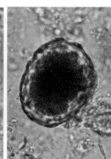
Ascaris lumbricoides **Fertile Egg** Feces

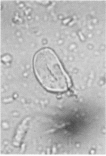
Enterobius vermicularis **Egg** Feces

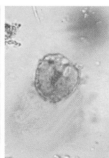
Enterobius vermicularis **Advanced Egg** Feces

Trichuris trichiura **Egg** Feces

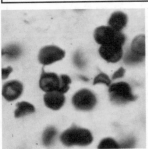

Pneumocystis carinii
Lung biopsy (GMS stain)

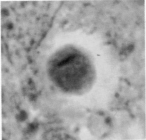

Entamoeba hystolytica **Cyst**
with Chromatoid Bar Body
Feces (Iron Hematoxylin stain)

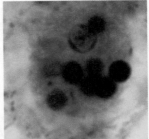

Entamoeba hystolytica
Trophozoite has ingested RBCs
Feces (Iron Hematoxylin stain)

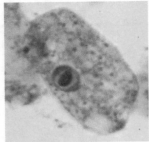

Acanthamoeba spp
Culture (Trichrome stain)

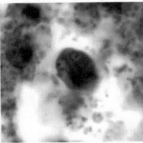

Giargia lamblia **Cyst**
Feces (Iron Hematoxylin stain)

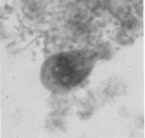

Giargia lamblia **Trophozoite**
Feces (Trichrome stain)

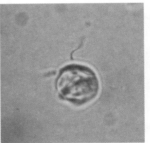

Trichomonas vaginalis
Vaginal wet mount

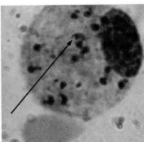

Leishmania donovani
Inside Macrophage
Bone marrow aspirate (Giemsa)

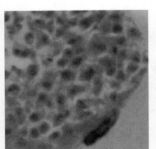

Trypanosoma cruzi **Kinetoplasts**
Heart biopsy (H&E stain)

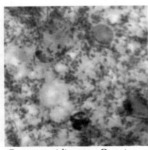

Cryptosporidium spp **Oocytes**
Feces (Modified Acid Fast stain)

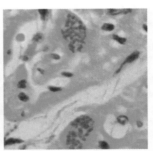

Toxoplasma gondii **Cysts**
Tissue biopsy (H&E stain)
Medium power view

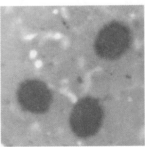

Toxoplasma gondii **Trophozoite**
Tissue biopsy (H&E stain)

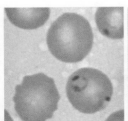

Plasmodium falciparum
Blood smear (Giemsa)

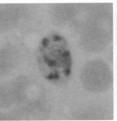

Plasmodium malariae
Blood smear (Giemsa)

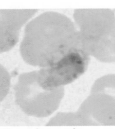

Plasmodium ovale
Blood smear (Giemsa)

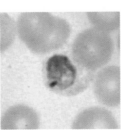

Plasmodium vivax
Blood smear (Giemsa)

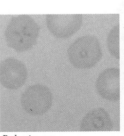

Babesia spp
Blood smear (Giemsa)

Chapter 24
GENERAL CROSS REFERENCE

NORMAL FLORA COMMENSALS
SKIN:
Staphylococcus spp
Streptococcus spp
Propionibacterium acnes
NOSE:
Staphylococcus aureus
MOUTH/THROAT:
Streptococcus Viridans Group
Non-gonococcal Neisseria spp
Non-Typeable Haemophilus
Candida
TEETH/GINGIVA:
Group D Streptococcus
Anaerobes:
 Peptostreptococcus
 Lactobacillus spp
 Actinomyces israelii
 Fusobacterium spp
 Prevotella spp
STOMACH:
Some Gram POS Bacteria
INTESTINES:
#1 *Bacteroides fragilis*
other anaerobes
Enteric E. coli
Enterococcus spp
VAGINA:
Lactobacillus spp
Gardnerella vaginalis
Group B Streptococcus
E. coli
Candida

CAUSES OF MENINGITIS:
ASEPTIC (VIRAL)
#1: Picorna Enteroviruses
 Echo virus
 Coxsackie viruses
 Polio virus
#2: Mumps virus
#3: Herpes Simplex virus 1
#4: Lymphocyticchoriomeningitisvirus
BACTERIAL
#1: *Haemophilus influenzae*
 (especially children)
#2: *Neisseria meningitidis*
#3: *Streptococcus pneumoniae*
#4: *Listeria monocytogenes*
NEONATAL
#1: *Group B Streptococcus*
#2: *E. coli*
#3: *Listeria monocytogenes*
IMMUNOCOMPROMISED
#1: *Streptococcus pneumoniae*
#2: *Listeria monocytogenes*
ADULTS/ELDERLY
#1: *Streptococcus pneumoniae*
HEAD TRAUMA/SURGERY
#1: *Staphylococcus aureus*
CHRONIC MENINGITIS
Mycobacterium tuberculosis
Treponema pallidum
Borrelia burgdorferi
Cryptococcus neoformans

MENINGITIS CSF FINDINGS:
VIRAL (ASEPTIC)
 Normal color
 Normal pressure
 ↑Proteins
 ↑Lymphocytes
 Slight ↓Glucose
(Herpes causes blood in CSF)
BACTERIAL
 Cloudy color
 ↑Pressure
 ↑Proteins
 ↑PMN leukocytes
 ↓↓↓Glucose
TUBERCULOUS
 Cloudy color
 ↑Pressure
 ↑Proteins
 ↑Lymphocytes
 ↓↓Glucose
CRYPTOCOCCUS
 Same CSF as tuberculosis
 India ink stain of CSF
SYPHILIS
 VRDL test of CSF
LYME DISEASE
 ↑Proteins
 ↑↑↑Lymphocytes
 Normal Glucose

NUCHAL SIGNS:
Nuchal rigidity (neck stiffness)
Brudzinski sign
Kernig sign

MENINGITIS TREATMENT:
VIRAL (ASEPTIC):
Symptomatic treatment only
BACTERIA:
Haemophilus influenzae
 Cefotaxime,
 Ceftriaxone or
 Chloramphenicol
Neisseria meningitidis
 Penicillin G
Streptococcus pneumoniae
 Penicillin G
NEONATAL BACTERIA:
Ampicillin plus Gentamicin
MENINGITIS PROPHYLAXIS:
1. *Group B Streptococcus*
 In Pregnant mother carriers:
 Ampicillin Intrapartum IV
 (Erythromycin in penicillin allergy)
2. *H. influenzae, N. meningitidis*
 Rifampin for contacts
MENINGITIS PREVENTION:
1. Mumps virus vaccine
2. *H. influenzae* type b vaccine
 (very effective)
3. *N. meningitidis* vaccine
 (moderately effective)
4. *S. pneumoniae* vaccine
 (moderately effective)

PNEUMONIA:
COMMUNITY ACQUIRED:
 Productive cough:
 Lobar pneumonia
 Bronchopneumonia
#1. *Streptococcus pneumoniae*
 (rusty sputum)
#2. *Haemophilus influenzae*
#3. *Staphylococcus aureus*
ATYPICAL Community acquired:
 Dry, non-productive cough:
 Interstitial pneumonia:
#1. *Mycoplasma pneumoniae*
 (especially teenagers)
#2. *Chlamydia pneumoniae*
#3. *Coxiella burnetii*
#4. Viral:
 Influenza A and B
 Adenovirus 3, 4, 7 (military)
 RSV (infants)
#5. *Legionella pneumophilia*
 (humidifiers, etc.)
IMMUNOCOMPROMISED:
[COPD, Diabetes, Alcoholism]:
Klebsiella pneumoniae
 (currant jelly sputum)
Pseudomonas aeruginosa
IN AIDS:
Pneumocystis carinii protozoa
IN CYSTIC FIBROSIS:
Pseudomonas aeruginosa
Post Viral URI Pneumonia:
Staphylococcus aureus

INFECTIVE ENDOCARDITIS:
SUB-ACUTE ENDOCARDITIS:
 Chronic infection.
 Fatal in 3-6 months.
 Infects defective heart valves.
 Hematological spread.
 Especially after dental work.
 Left heart valves most common:
 mitral and/or aortic,
 valvular vegetations.
SUB-ACUTE ORGANISMS:
#1. *Streptococcus Viridans Group*
#2. *Streptococcus Group D*
#3. *Enterococcus spp*
#4. *Staphylococcus epidermidis*
#5. *Salmonella spp*
ACUTE ENDOCARDITIS:
 Fulminant infection.
 Fatal in days to weeks.
 Infects healthy heart valves or
 defective heart valves.
 Left heart valves most common:
 mitral and/or aortic,
 valvular vegetations.
ACUTE ORGANISMS:
#1. *Staphylococcus aureus*
#2. *Streptococcus pneumoniae*
#3. *Coxiella burnetii*
INFECTIVE ENDOCARDITIS
IN IV DRUG ABUSERS:
 Right heart valves common:
 especially tricuspid,
 valvular vegetations.
DRUG ABUSER ORGANISMS:
#1. *Staphylococcus aureus*
#2. *Pseudomonas aeruginosa*
#3. *Candida spp*
#4. *Serratia marcescens*

"CULTURE NEGATIVE"
INFECTIVE ENDOCARDITIS:
reasons why blood cultures show no
growth during infective endocarditis:
#1. Prior treatment with antibiotics
#2. Organisms:
 Coxiella burnetii
 Brucella spp
 Chlamydia spp
 Fungi
 HACEK organisms:
 Haemophilus spp
 Actinobacillus spp
 Cardiobacterium spp
 Eikenella spp
 Kingella spp

INFECTIVE MYOCARDITIS:
May be rapidly fatal within hours.
ORGANISMS:
#1. Coxsackie viruses
#2. Other Picornaviruses
#3. *Corynebacterium diphtheriae*
#4. *Trypanosoma cruzi protozoa*
 (Chagas disease)

ACUTE RHEUMATIC FEVER:
 Pancarditis (affects all layers).
 Auto-immune-mediated sequelae.
 Follows pharyngitis infection by
 Group A Streptococcus
RHEUMATIC HEART DISEASE
 Cardiac valve deformities:
 Chronic and progressive sequelae
 (develops over years to decades)
 from the auto-immune-mediated
 post-pharyngeal infection by
 Group A Streptococcus

CANCER ASSOCIATIONS:
Streptococcus Group D
 (Colon cancer)
Helicobacter pylori
 (Gastric carcinoma)
HPV-16, HPV-18
 (Cervical carcinoma)
HBV, HCV, HDV
 (Hepatocellular carcinoma)
EBV
 (Burkett Lymphoma)
 (Nasopharyngeal carcinoma)
HTLV-1
 (T-cell Leukemia/Lymphoma)
HTLV-2
 (Hairy Cell Leukemia)
HIV
 (Kaposi sarcoma)
 (CNS Lymphoma)
Clonorchis sinensis fluke
 (Cholangiocarcinoma)

GENERAL CROSS REFERENCE

URINARY TRACT INFECTION:
(10^5 bacteria/ml urine)
Ascending route is most common
(via the urethra).
Common in women (short urethra)
CYSTITIS (bladder or lower UTI)
Most common UTI, no fever.
PYELONEPHRITIS
(kidney or upper UTI)
Fever, back tenderness.
UTI ORGANISMS:
#1. *Uropathogenic E. coli* (95%)
#2. Proteus mirabilis
others   Enterobacter cloacae
        Serratia marcescens
        Klebsiella pneumoniae
        Pseudomonas aeruginosa
        Staph. saprophyticus
        Enterococcus spp.
HEMORRHAGIC CYSTITIS:
    Adenovirus 11, 21
KIDNEY STONES:
(Nephrolithiasis, Urolithiasis)
(Struvite stones: triple phosphate =
    ammonium magnesium phosphate)
(Renal calculi: Staghorn calculi).
#1. *Proteus mirabilis*
Others: *Proteus vulgaris*
         Morganella morganii

SEPSIS:
#1. *Staphylococcus spp*
#2. Streptococcus spp
NOSOCOMIAL BACTEREMIA:
#1. *Uropathogenic E. coli*
#2. *Klebsiella pneumoniae*
#3. *Pseudomonas aerginosa*
#4. *Enterobacter spp*
Other: *Yersinia enterocolitica*
      (in multiple blood transfusions)
      Providencia rettgeri
      (in nursing home with catheter)

#1 CAUSATIVE ORGANISMS:
CELLULITIS:
#1. *Group A Streptococcus*
Other: *Pasteurella multocida*
      (from cat/dog bite)
OTITIS MEDIA:
#1. *Streptococcus pneumoniae*
Others: *Nontypeable H. influenzae*
      Moraxella catarrhalis
SINUSITIS:
#1. *Streptococcus pneumoniae*
#2. *Nontypeable H. influenzae*
EPIGLOTTITIS:
#1. *Haemophilus influenzae type b*
    (must intubate immediately)
PERITONITIS:
#1. *Bacteroides fragilis*
OSTEOMYELITIS:
#1. *Staphylococcus aureus*
Note: *Salmonella spp* is common in
patients with Sickle cell anemia.
INFECTIOUS ARTHRITIS:
#1. *Staphylococcus aureus*
Note: *Neisseria gonorrhoeae* causes
monarticular infectious arthritis in
sexually active young women.
Note: *Serratia marcescens* common
from intra-articular injections.

Sexually Transmitted Diseases
STDs:
#1. *Chlamydia trachomatis*
BACTERIA:
Neisseria gonorrhoeae
    (urethritis)
Treponema pallidum
    (painless chancre)
    (1°, 2°, 3° syphilis)
Chlamydia trachomatis
    (urethritis)
    (lymphogranuloma venereum)
Haemophilus ducreyi
    (painful chancroid)
Calymmatobacterium granulomatis
    (Donovanosis)
    (granuloma inguinale)
Gardnerella vaginalis
(wet mount: epithelial "clue cells")
    ("bacterial vaginosis")
    (foul-odor discharge)
VIRUSES:
HPV (condyloma acuminata)
HBV (hepatitis)
HSV-2 (herpes genitalis)
CMV (Mononucleosis)
EBV (Mononucleosis)
Molluscum contagiosum virus
    (Poxvirus papule)
HTLV-1,-2 (malignancy)
HIV (AIDS)
FUNGI:
Candida albicans (yeast)
PARASITES:
Trichomonas vaginalis
    (foul-odor discharge)
OTHER:
Phthirus pubis (Crab lice)
Sarcoptes scabiei (Scabies)

NEONATAL INFECTIONS:
#1. *Group B Streptococcus*
#2. *E. coli*
ROUTES OF VERTICAL
TRANSMISSION:
    Transplacental in utero.
    Ascending in utero.
    Passage through vagina at birth.
    Breast feeding.
"TORCH" ORGANISMS:
    [Congenital neonatal infections]
    [Transplacental vertical infection]
Toxoplasma gondii protozoa
Other:
    Group B Streptococcus
      (not transplacental)
    Listeria monocytogenes
    E. coli (not transplacental)
    Treponema pallidum
    Parvo B19
    HIV
Rubella virus
CMV
HSV (non-transplacental)
FROM BREAST FEEDING:
HBV
HTLV-1, HTLV-2
HIV
NEONATAL EYE INFECTIONS:
Neisseria gonorrhoeae
Chlamydia trachomatis

LIVE VACCINES
(ATTENUATED):
BACTERIA:
    Francisella tularensis
    Mycobacterium (BCG)
VIRUSES:
    Adenovirus 4, 7
    VZV
    Poxvirus (small pox)
    Poliovirus (OPV)
    Rubella (MMR)
    Yellow Fever virus
    Mumps (MMR)
    Measles (MMR)

DEAD VACCINES
(INACTIVATED):
BACTERIA:
Streptococcus pneumoniae
Neisseria meningitidis
Bordetella pertussis (DTwP)
Haemophilus influenzae b (Hib)
Vibrio cholera
Bacillus anthracis
Yersinia pestis
Rickettsia prowazeckii
Borrelia burgdorferi
VIRUSES:
HBV
HAV
Poliovirus (IPV)
Japanese Encephalitis virus
Rabies (HDCV, RVA)
Influenza A and B

TOXOIDS:
Corynebacterium diphtheriae (DPT)
Clostridium tetani (DPT)
Bordetella pertussis (DTaP, DTwP)

VACCINES FOR ANIMALS:
Brucella spp
Leptospira interrogans
Toga encephalitis viruses
    Eastern equine
    Western equine
    Venezuela

PSEUDOAPPENDICITIS:
    Salmonella spp
    Campylobacter jejuni
    Yersinia enterocolitica

REITER SYNDROME:
Post-infectious autoimmune mediated
arthritis; HLA-B27 genotype
    Salmonella spp
    Shigella spp
    Campylobacter spp
    Yersinia enterocolitica

REYE SYNDROME:
Post-viral-infection sequelae seen in
children using aspirin during infection
    #1. Influenza B
    #2. Influenza A
    #3. VZV

NOMENCLATURE
CLARIFICATIONS:
"Coagulase Neg Staphylococcus" =
Non *S.aureus* Staphylococci.

MRSA = "Methicillin-Resistant-
Staphylococus-aureus.

VRE =
Vancomycin-Resistant-Enterococcus.

"Beta-hemolytic Streptococcus" =
Group A Strep. (GAS) and
Group B strep. (GBS).

Enterococcus is a distinct genus,
not part of *Streptococcus.*

Pneumococcus =
Streptococcus pneumoniae.

Gonococcus =
Neisseria gonorrhoeae.

Meningococcus =
Neisseria meningitidis.

"Diphtheroids" =
All non-*C. diphtheria Corynebacteria.*

Moraxella catarrhalis is new name
formerly *Branhamella catarrhalis.*

Bartonella is the new genus name for
formerly *Rochalimaea.*

Non-typeable *H. influenzae* =
Non-type b strains of *H. influenzae.*

AFB refers to **Acid-Fast Bacteria.**

Acid-fast stain =
Ziehl-Neelsen or Kinyoun stain.

Modified Acid-fast = AFB stain but
without alcohol, sometimes still called
Acid-fast.

MAI and MAC = Mycobacterium-
Avium-Intracellulare Complex.

Non-tuberculous or Atypical
Mycobacterium = those strains which
do not cause Tuberculosis.

Non A non B hepatitis =
HCV or HDV and sometimes HEV.

Abbreviations used throughout the book:

a.k.a.= Also known as
AB= antibody
AFB= Acid-Fast Bacteria.
Ag= antigen
ALT= Alanine aminotransferase
APC= antigen presenting cell
BM= basement membrane
CDC= Center for Disease Control
CNS= Central nervous system
COPD= Chronic obstructive pulmonary dis
CSF= Cerebral spinal fluid
DIC= Disseminated intravascular coagulation
DPT= Diphtheria Pertussis Tetanus vaccine (also known as. **DTaP** and **DTwP**).
e.g.= Example
GAS= Group A Streptococcus
GI= Gastrointestinal
HTN= hypertension
ICU= intensive care unit
IUD= Intrauterine device
IV= intravenous
LFT= liver function test
Lymphos= lymphocytes
Macros= macrophages
MMR= Measles Mumps Rubella vaccine
Monos= Monocytes
MRSA= Methicillin-Resistant S.-aureus
NEG= negative
PID= pelvic inflammatory disease
PMN= polymorphonuclear neutrophil
POS= positive
RBC= red blood cell
RES= reticuloendothelial system
RUQ= right upper quadrant
Spp= all or several of the species, collectively, within a given genus.
STD= sexually transmitted disease
TB= tuberculosis
URI= upper respiratory infection
UTI= urinary tract infection
WBC= white blood cells